Neuroscience in the Courtroom

What Every Lawyer Should Know about the Mind and the Brain

William R. Uttal

Lawyers & Judges Publishing Company, Inc.

Tucson, Arizona

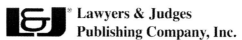 **Lawyers & Judges
Publishing Company, Inc.**
P.O. Box 30040 • Tucson, AZ 85751-0040
(800) 209-7109 • FAX (800) 330-8795
e-mail: sales@lawyersandjudges.com
www.lawyersandjudges.com

Library of Congress Cataloging-in-Publication Data

Uttal, William R.
 Neuroscience in the courtroom : what every lawyer should know about the mind and the brain
/ William R. Uttal.
    p. cm.
Includes bibliographical references and index.
ISBN-13: 978-1-933264-38-7 (softcover : alk. paper)
ISBN-10: 1-933264-38-1 (softcover : alk. paper)
1. Neurosciences. 2. Forensic neurology. I. Title.
RC343.U88 2008
612.8--dc22
                          2008033738

ISBN 13: 978-1-933264-38-7
ISBN 10: 1-933264-38-1
Printed in the United States of America
10 9 8 7 6 5 4 3 2 1

Other Books by William R. Uttal

- Real Time Computers: Techniques and Applications in the Psychological Sciences
- Generative Computer Assisted Instruction (with Miriam Rogers, Ramelle Hieronymus, and Timothy Pasich)
- Sensory Coding: Selected Readings (Editor)
- The Psychobiology of Sensory Coding
- Cellular Neurophysiology and Integration: An Interpretive Introduction
- An Autocorrelation Theory of Form Detection
- The Psychobiology of Mind
- A Taxonomy of Visual Processes
- Visual Form Detection in 3-Dimensional Space
- Foundations of Psychobiology (with Daniel N. Robinson)
- The Detection of Nonplanar Surfaces in Visual Space
- The Perception of Dotted Forms
- On Seeing Forms
- The Swimmer: An Integrated Computational Model of a Perceptual-Motor System (With Gary Bradshaw, Sriram Dayanand, Robb Lovell, Thomas Shepherd, Ramakrishna Kakarala, Kurt Skifsted, and Greg Tupper)
- Toward A New Behaviorism: The Case Against Perceptual Reductionism
- Computational Modeling of Vision: The Role of Combination (With Ramakrishna Kakarala, Sriram Dayanand, Thomas Shepherd, Jaggi Kalki, Charles Lunskis Jr., and Ning Liu)
- The War between Mentalism and Behaviorism: On the Accessibility of Mental Processes
- The New Phrenology: On the Localization of Cognitive Processes in the Brain
- A Behaviorist Looks at Form Recognition
- Psychomythics: Sources of Artifacts and Misrepresentations in Scientific Cognitive neuroscience
- Dualism: The Original Sin of Cognitivism
- Neural Theories of Mind: Why the Mind-Brain Problem May Never Be Solved
- Human Factors in the Courtroom: Mythology versus Science
- The Immeasurable Mind: The Real Science of Psychology
- Time, Space, and Number in Physics and Psychology
- Distributed Neural Systems: Beyond the New Phrenology

For Mitchan

Contents

Acknowledgments xi

Introduction xiii

Chapter 1: What is the Mind? 1
1.1 Introduction...1
1.2 A Short History of the Mind 7
1.3 What are the Major Challenges to Mind Reading in the Courtroom?.........15
    A. Inaccessibility 16
    B. Irreducibility and Modularity..19
    C. Complexity..20
    D. Stochastic Nature of Mind 20
    E. Explanation and Description 23
Endnotes..24

Chapter 2: What is the Brain?...27
2.1 Introduction...27
2.2 A Short History of the Brain 28
2.3 Theories of How the Mind is Produced by the Brain 34
2.4 Brain Imaging Methods 40
    A. Positron Emission Tomography...42
    B. Functional Magnetic Resonance Imaging (fMRI) 44
2.5 The Analysis of fMRI Data..48
2.6 On Variability and Reliability 55
Endnotes..61

Chapter 3: Brain Images and the Detection of Deception............63
3.1 Introduction...64
3.2 A History of Lie Detection 66
3.3 A Meta-Review of the Empirical Literature Supposedly Supporting the
    Use of Brain Imaging as a Lie Detector 78
    A. Spence, Farrow, Herford, Wilkinson, Zheng, and Woodruff (2001)......81
    B. Langleben, Schroeder, Maldjian, Gur, McDonald, Ragland, O'Brien,
        and Childres (2002) 82
    C. Lee, Liu, Tan, Chan, Mahankali, Feng, Hou, Fox, and Gao (2002) 82

D. Ganis, Kosslyn, Stose, Thompson, and Yurgelun-Todd (2003) 83
E. Spence, Hunter, Farrow, Green, Leung, Hughes, and Ganesan (2004)..84
F. Kozel, Revell, Loberbaum, Shastri, Elhai, Horner, Smith, Nahas,
    Bohning, and George (2004) 84
G. Kozel, Padgett, and George (2004)..85
H. Kozel, Johnson, Mu, Grenesko, Laken, and George (2005)...................86
I. Langleben, Loughhead, Bilker, Rupare, Childress, Busch, and Gur
    (2005) 87
J. Davatzikos, Ruparel, Fan, Shen, Acharyya, Loughhead, Gur,
    Langleben (2005)...88
K. Phan, Magalhaes, Ziemlewicz, Fitzgerald, Green, and Smith (2005) ...89
L. Lee, Liu, Chan, Ng, Fox, and Gao (2005)..89
M. Nunez, Casey, Egner, Hare, Hirsch (2005) 90
N. Abe, Suzuki, Tsukiura, Mori, Yamaguchi, Itoh, and Fujii (2006) 91
O. Grezes, Berthoz, and Passingham (2006) 91
P. Mohamed, Faro, Gordon, Platek, Ahmed, and Williams (2006) 92
3.4 A Summary of the Sixteen Experiments on Brain Images and Lie
    Detection...93
    A. Which Areas are Identified as the Point of Maximum Activity? 94
    B. What Areas, Other than Maximum Peaks, Are Involved? 97
    C. Some Inescapable Conclusions 100
3.5 Evaluation of the Use of Brain Images as Lie Detectors 102
    A. There is No Single Place or Group of Places that Has Been Empirically
       Associated with Deception or Any Other Mental Process 104
    B. Brain Images Do Not Measure Mental Activity Any More Directly
       Than Does the Polygraph 105
    C. Lying or Deception is an Ill-Defined Process Probably Composed of
       Many Different Mental Processes 107
    D. Validity of the Measures 108
    E. Practical Problems 109
3.6 Interim Conclusions 114
Endnotes..118

Chapter 4: The Brain and the Control of Aggression 121
4.1 Introduction..121
4.2 Who are the Neuropsychologists? 126
    A. Neuropsychologists...127
    B. Forensic Neuropsychologists 128
    C. Cognitive Neuroscientists (Physiological Psychologists)...................128
    D. Psychiatrists (Biological and Functional)..128
    E. Neurologists 129
4.3 What is Neuropsychology? 130
    A. Case Studies 131

4.4 The Problems of Neuropsychological Test Reliability and Validation 134
    A. Neuropsychological Tests 134
    B. Reliability 136
    C. Validity 138
4.5 Classic Physiological Psychology and Definitions of Aggression...........141
4.6 A Traditional History of Brain Mechanisms of Aggression and
    Violence 146
4.7 The Modern Empirical Literature on Aggression 150
    A. The Limbic System 153
    B. The Papez Circuit..163
4.8 Human Aggression and Brain Mechanisms 165
4.9 Interim Conclusions..168
Endnotes..171

Chapter 5: The Neuroscience of Cognitive Dysfunction 175
5.1 Introduction...175
5.2 Some Caveats...179
    A. Prematurity and a Lack of Robust Replication.................................179
    B. Legal Culpability in the Face of Neuroscientific Findings 180
    C. Variability...181
    D. The Multifactorial Nature of Behavior...182
    E. Differing Standards and Criteria 183
    F. Linguistic Confusions...184
5.3 Some Plausible Relations of Mental Dysfunction and Neuroscience........185
    A. Cognitive Deficits Attributable to Brain Deficits: The Agnosias,
       Aphasias, Amnesias, and Apraxias..186
    B. Consciousness and Coma States 208
    C. Brain Death 215
5.4 When "Neuroscience" is not Neuroscience 222
    A. Mental Illness 223
    B. Other Behavioral Mysteries Lacking a Neuroscientific Foundation....232
5.5 Interim Conclusions 239
Endnotes..242

Chapter 6: Some Concluding and Summarizing Comments....................247
6.1 Introduction...247
6.2 What is the Current State of Cognitive Neuroscience Theory?.................252
6.3 Ethics..253

Bibliography 257

About the Author 279

Index...281

Acknowledgments

It is to my wife, May, Michiye, Mitchan, or Mom, as she is variously known, that I once again dedicate this new work. Without her support and wisdom, nothing would have happened. My love is matched only by my appreciation for all of the things she has done to make it possible for me to continue my work.

Others have also provided other kinds of support. Among those to whom I am most grateful is my friend and colleague Professor Patricia Couvillon of the University of Hawaii. Pat has made it possible for me to spend the last six productive summers at the University of Hawaii.

I am also grateful, perhaps more than they can appreciate, to my colleagues in our little Metaphysical Society. Peter Killeen, David Hestenes, Warren Egmond, and Mike McBeath opened a door of critical comradeship that has been terribly important to me. Our discussions and controversies, our agreements and disagreements, the freedom to brag and to complain a bit about both accomplishments and failures, were especially important to me.

Finally, I note that I have enjoyed the hospitality and material support of the Industrial Engineering department at Arizona State University for a decade since my retirement in 1999. Deans and chairs have come and gone, but the institutional commitment to provide me with a hospitable work environment has contributed greatly to my continued productivity.

Introduction

Eventually even the most arcane and esoteric science comes into contact with ordinary human affairs. Thus it is that scientific studies of the brain have developed to a point that they are increasingly influential in one of the most practical and worldly of human arenas—the judicial process. What had previously been matters of interest to only philosophers and an interdisciplinary science called cognitive neuroscience now seems to have developed to the point at which it may have a direct role to play in courtroom proceedings. As this convergence of the arcane and the mundane develops, it places an enormous burden on members of both of the involved communities, cognitive neuroscientists as well as legal professionals, to understand the culture and knowledge of the other.

There is no question that modus operandi of scientists and lawyers differ in many ways. Science, ideally, is evaluated in terms of evidence and formal proofs derived from observations of natural laws; jurisprudence is a much more arbitrary profession in which disputation and advocacy of ambiguous human generated traditions, folkways, and agreed upon societal regulations often take the place of physical evidence and fact. To the lawyer, appearance, emotion, prejudice, and impression may have more force than even the most robust scientific fact especially when the ultimate decisions should be based on what are purely scientific criteria. This leads, all-too-often, to what is clearly junk or pseudoscience playing an inordinately influential role in the courtroom. It also can lead to misuse of what is generally accepted as good science with the inevitable result of miscarried justice.

The situation is exacerbated by the fact that the educational backgrounds of neuroscientists and attorneys are very different. Each has been trained to use different tools and even, it may be argued, to think in different ways. It is quite likely that some of the most fundamental assumptions underlying the thought processes of the two respective professions differ to such a degree that not only are there different reservoirs of factual information, but the very logical processes on which they depend may differ. What may be immediately comprehended by an attorney may be incomprehensible to neuroscientists and vice versa.

Furthermore, what science knows (and does not know) is sometimes completely misunderstood by members of the legal profession. Like many other laypersons, lawyers and judges often overestimate the real progress that has been made by cognitive neuroscientists and are oblivious to much of the constraints and limits of the scientific method. Nowhere is this misunderstanding more prevalent than with regard to recent developments in cognitive neuroscience, the science dedicated to explaining relationships between mental processes and the brain. In the last decade in particular, wonderful new developments in studying the brain have suggested to some that we are on the verge of amazing new break-throughs in understanding how the mind-brain system works. However dramatic the results produced by these new methods may appear to be, it has to be ac-knowledged that there is still an unbridged gap between what we know about brain function and what we know about mental processes. Despite the popular media's continual and extravagant misinterpretation of what we know about how the brain produces the mind, there are still many technical, conceptual, and em-pirical misunderstandings about what the modern fields of experimental psychol-ogy and cognitive neuroscience have actually accomplished and what they have to say to each other.

This statement must be understood in the context that there is no residual scientific doubt that it is the brain that, in principle, explains everything about the mind. In practice, however, achieving neural explanations of the mind is still an unfulfilled quest. Should it ever be accomplished, however, most scientists agree that a brain theory of the mind would be complete and require no other explana-tory (e.g., supernatural) mechanisms. What and how we think is purely a matter of what the brain is doing.

Among the most important prevailing misunderstandings about the mind-brain relationship that might have some relevance to our courtroom proceedings are the following:

1. The aspect of our life that we refer to as the mind, consciousness, sen-tience, or a host of other terms is not directly accessible. There is no way to measure what a person is thinking by any mechanical, electronic, or brain imaging procedure. At best, we have some modest correlations between measures of brain activity and what a person is thinking. At worst, we draw inferences based on underdetermined data. That is, nei-ther brain nor behavioral response tells us enough to determine what is really going on in a person's mind. No experimental technique or intro-spective report has yet been invented that can bridge the gap and provide access to a person's thoughts. Although a major goal in jurisprudence has always been to understand a person's state of mind, including such aspects as their motives and competency, in fact such judgments about a person's true mental state are always uncertain and arbitrary. The best

we can do is to observe a person's behavior, tie it to past performance, and use it, to a limited degree, to predict the likelihood of similar behavior in the future. However, psychologist's and psychiatrist's predictions of specific future behavior are almost always tainted by uncertainty, vagueness, low accuracy, and ultimately testimonial controversy.

2. Despite the hype, especially in recent years with the emergence of methods fully capable of examining the anatomic and physiological aspects of the brain such as PET (Positron Emissions Tomography) and fMRI (functional Magnetic Resonance Imaging), the problem of how the brain makes the mind remains recalcitrant and possibly unsolvable. Neural theories of the mind abound at all levels of neural activity (single neuron, fields, neural networks, and distributed systems of neural modules); however, each has major difficulties associated with data sampling, the loss of critical information during data pooling, or the sheer intractability of the analytic problem, respectively.

3. This does not mean that there has not been enormous progress in both psychology and neuroscience; only that the gap between the two fields has not yet been bridged. We actually know far less about the mind-brain relationship than is generally appreciated by the lay public. The general argument I make here is that there is no neuroscience of the mind in the formal sense of what a good science should offer.

4. Despite the long-term history of attempts to localize modules or components of the mind in particular regions of the brain, most high level cognitive processes appear to activate most if not all of the brain. The search for a brain locus or a particular response specifically associated with deception (or any other mental activity) is, therefore, not likely to be fulfilled. The popular as well as the professional assumption that components of the mind are localized in specific places of the brain remains one of the great unresolved issues in mind-brain research activity. Currently this centerpiece hypothesis of modern cognitive neuroscience is being severely challenged.

5. A particular goal of jurisprudence is to find objective measures of deception. Despite the excitement surrounding brain imaging, a detailed examination of the empirical research on "lie detection" shows that it is inconsistent and unsupportive of the idea that there is a brain signal (or place) specific to lying.

6. Neuropsychology, the subfield of cognitive neuroscience that deals with the relation between brain injuries or disease, on the one hand, and behavior, on the other, has a very poor record of definitively establishing these relations. The brain is a highly adaptive and flexible organ; many

regions can take over functions from others and many are redundant; i.e., multiple regions may simultaneously, and perhaps even independently, control mental activity or behavioral responses. Furthermore, individual variability in brain structure tends to make any particular association ungeneralizable from person to person.

7. Neuropsychologists' judgments of the effect of brain lesions or malformations on behavior, therefore, are as tainted by uncertainty, vagueness, low accuracy, and ultimately controversy as are those of their behaviorally oriented psychological and psychiatric colleagues. Although such opinions are usually presented with a seductive veneer of colorful pictures of brain anatomy and physiology, in fact, the associations drawn may be as misleading as those based on behavior alone. The complexity of the mind-brain problem and the primitive stage of our knowledge about the role of the brain in generating a general, much less a specific, understanding of the relationship between the mind and the brain accounts for the uncertainty in this field.

8. Therefore, the attribution of criminal misbehavior or cognitive dysfunction to specific brain injuries is probably inappropriate. The science supporting the association of specific brain regions with abnormal behavior is inconsistent and largely based on highly variable and often anecdotal evidence. The primitive state of the field of neuropsychology (along with a considerable portion of related research in cognitive neuroscience) accounts for discrepancies between "experts" and the varied legal history of admissibility of this kind of evidence.

9. Mental illness remains a puzzling and largely unexplained field. Aberrant behavior is not only poorly defined but its causes and treatment, even if they work, remain obscure and poorly understood.

10. Finally, the ethical issues involved in applying cognitive neuroscientific evidence in the courtroom are extensive.

All these assertions can be summed up quite simply. At the present time, the link between brain activity and our minds is only poorly understood by cognitive neuroscientists. It is probably not too much of an exaggeration to conclude by saying that virtually nothing is known about how the brain produce mind. Much of what is offered in the proceedings in our courtrooms, therefore, does not meet the standards set by the *Frye* or *Daubert* criteria. The remainder of this book is aimed at adding substance to these preview statements.

Chapter 1

What is the Mind?

Synopsis
1.1 Introduction
1.2 A Short History of the Mind
1.3 What are the Major Challenges to Mind Reading in the Courtroom?
    A. Inaccessibility
    B. Irreducibility and Modularity
    C. Complexity
    D. Stochastic Nature of Mind
    E. Explanation and Description
Endnotes

MYTH: It is possible to know a person's thoughts.
TRUTH: A person's mind is private and inaccessible.

1.1 Introduction

The legal world, perhaps more than any other aspect of our society, is constantly challenged to determine the contents of someone's mind. From ancient until modern times, the participants in the theater of the courtroom have sought by trials of one kind or another to determine what a person's thoughts were when they committed a crime or asked for adjudication of the meaning of a contract. Physical evidence, examinations and cross-examinations, behavior, and even electronic instruments have all been used to delve deeply into the thoughts of witnesses and defendants alike.

A popular and prevailing view is that there exist methods and devices that can "read the mind" and that we can determine from the resulting evidence what a person is thinking or was thinking. Indeed, it is an unwritten assumption of the legal system that we may draw conclusions about the motives and intents of a defendant from these probes into a person's mental processes. A major thesis of this book, however, is that lawyers, judges, and investigators of all kinds cannot read the minds of plaintiffs and defendants using any of these behavioral or physiological tools. A related premise is that no psychologist or neuroscientist can do so either with any degree of validity. A third is that no machine sensitive

1

to objective measures of autonomic or brain activity can break this barrier. This book is intended to support these arguments by examining the scientific database available from many years of relevant scientific activity.

The purpose of this introductory chapter is to support these theses by highlighting the fact that the mind and our thoughts, contrary to popular opinion, are private and inaccessible to any form of inquiry, whether it is cross-examination, brain imaging, or psychological tests in either "controlled" laboratory or interview situations. Part of the argument I make here is that it is only the behavior (broadly defined to include verbal utterances) of an individual that can be measured and any attempts to infer mental processes from either behavior or brain image are beset by many difficulties and obstacles.

To understand this point of view, it is necessary to consider what the nature of mind is and what the difficulties in accessing its contents are. To accomplish this, it is necessary to detail the nature of the obstacles that confront legal "mind readers." Among the most important preliminaries is that we understand exactly what the mind is and the nature of modern theories of mind. To understand the current state, we must also peer back into the history of the mind, for our past and present views of its nature have a direct impact on today's judicial proceedings.

Indeed, of all of the questions that have perplexed humanity from the dawn of consciousness, none has been as often asked and none remains as thoroughly unanswered as the great conundrum—what is the mind? Although modern scientific psychology has been mainly committed to the study of the mind since its nineteenth century beginnings, an enormous body of research has brought us no closer to an answer to this perplexing question than any of our predecessors. Science still does not even have a good appreciation of the general meaning of the mind beyond the commonsense and personal one that each of us enjoys individually. Where direct measurement and precise definition are to be desired, we have only speculation, analogy, and indirect inference.

After all of the centuries in which theologians, philosophers, and psychologists have sought a crisp definition of mind, it is still the case that all that can really be said is that each of us is individually aware of the nature of our personal mental activity and, by an act of extrapolation and analogy, we assume that this same level of sentience also characterizes others with whom we converse.[1] Thus, it is nothing more than a common sense agreement that my conversants share with me the same level of awareness and mental function I enjoy that makes human discourse possible. Beyond that, the many attempts by scholars of all kinds to define the mind have been and continue to be fruitless and uninformative. I still think the best we can do is to establish certain properties of it.

I now reiterate something I have repeatedly (Uttal, 1978; 2004) introduced as a basis for discussion, fully appreciating how incomplete this effort must necessarily be. In the terminology of philosophy, these are essentially the unprovable, but generally accepted, ontological axioms on which study and research in the field of psychology must be based. These assertions, however, say nothing about the fundamental nature of the mind nor do they provide us with a system of measurement that would permit the mind to be quantified either in scientific research laboratories or in courtrooms.

1. Mind is an individual and not a community process. A meeting of the minds is a literary metaphor, not a scientific one. Minds cannot communicate directly, only through the medium of mutually observed behavior and indirect inference.

2. Direct, unequivocal interpersonal communication of primary mental states, processes, or actions is not possible. All such communication is mediated by behavioral responses, be they verbal, endocrine, or postural. An inference about the nature of mind from interpersonally observable behavior is, at best, a treacherous and noisy path to knowledge. This indirectness has plagued psychology and all of its predecessors since the emergence of our concern with individual self-awareness.

3. Although there is no question that the activity of the brain is responsible for the process we call mind, there is no measurement of brain activity that has been rigorously identified with the content of our thoughts. It is, for many reasons, impossible to know what a person is thinking, from any measure of brain activity.

4. Any insights we have of what is going on in another's "mind" are, therefore, indirect and, for all purposes, unverifiable. The two main reasons for this opacity are:
   A) The fact that many quite different mechanisms could produce the same overt behavior (the "one outcome to many possible mechanisms" problem). Behavior, therefore, underdetermines which of many possible and plausible explanations is the correct one.
   B) Extraordinarily complex and nonlinear systems like the mind-brain are particularly recalcitrant to analysis into meaningful sets of components.

5. Mind is best considered to be a function or a process rather than an organ, object, stuff, or thing. When we characterize it as such a quasi-material object, the idea is stimulated that the thing can be broken up into components, parts, or modules—an idea that is at least unproven and probably incorrect. Yet, modularity of mind and brain are the core premises of much of current and past neuropsy-

chology, a questionable subfield of cognitive neuroscience often invoked in legal proceedings. The modular premise, however, is almost certainly fallacious and raises serious doubts concerning the applicability of the findings of brain disease and injury to the determination of behavior.

6. The word "mind" is very closely related in purported definition to other terms from other domains of study including "consciousness," "awareness," "soul," and the "true ego."[2] Therefore, natural and supernatural explanations sometimes become erroneously intertwined. Even though mind is fundamentally inaccessible and cannot be quantitatively measured, it is not a supernatural phenomenon. It is a real process of the brain reflecting real physical (i.e., neural) actions, albeit highly complex ones.[3] (Abstracted and extended from Uttal, 1978, 207-208.)

Unfortunately, these general properties of mind do not denote it specifically; much worse, they do not provide the basis for empirical research on an entity that is orders of magnitude more elusive than an ivory billed woodpecker. While the woodpecker could conceivably appear after years of invisibility, there is little serious hope that the neural basis of the mind will be revealed to us at any conceivable point in the future. The problems and difficulties inherent in this task are in principle so challenging that all such hopes are unlikely to be fulfilled.

Philosophers such as Wittgenstein (1953), Strawson (1954), Wisdom (1956), and Searle (1992) have all, along with many of their predecessors, struggled with this inability to define mind for generations without resolution. The usual argument supporting the accessibility of the mind is that because of our private experience of mind and the commonality of behavior, a reasonable analogy suggests that others also must have the same degree of sentience including self awareness, consciousness, and decisiveness that I sense in myself. However, reasoning by analogy is fraught with illogical steps and fallacious conclusions. Shorter (1967) concisely spelled out the frailties of such an argument. He noted that reasoning by analogy "does not establish its conclusion with an adequate degree of certainty" (p. 7). The problem is further compounded by the fact that there is no way to confirm or deny the conclusion (i.e., that others have minds); there is, in practical fact, no Turing test[4] to determine whether one is speaking to a person or an automaton.

The difficulty that one encounters when inferring something about the minds of others from their behavior was made crystal clear in the well-known, but studiously ignored, admonition of William James (1890) when he alluded to the "psychologist's fallacy":

> The great snare of the psychologist is the *confusion of his own stand-point with that of the mental fact* about which he is making his report. I shall hereafter call this 'psychologist's fallacy' *par excellence*. (p. 196)

This advice to psychologists extrapolates to all other humans when we attempt to draw conclusions about the minds of others. All too often and in all too many contexts we tend to assume that our fellow humans are thinking in the same way we do. James' advice is especially appropriate to psychologists, jurists, criminal investigators or anyone seeking to read other minds.

In this context, there is another relatively new area of psychology that goes under the rubric of "theory of mind" that is at least tangentially related to theories of the mind. That is, children, adults, and presumably to a certain degree, animals, are assumed by some psychologists to attribute mental states to others; that is to develop a "theory of the mind of others" which is useful in conducting our activities. Although it seems reasonable and plausible that we do this to some limited degree, it is impossible to test this idea directly and long leaps of logic and assumption stand between observed behavior and the actual mental awareness of another mind. A theory of the mind, therefore, is nothing more than an elaborate version of arguing by analogy.

This version of a "theory of mind" was originally called to modern attention in the work of Premack and Woodruff (1978) when they asked the rhetorical question—does the chimpanzee have a theory of mind? That is, does the behavior of this ape indicate that they are aware that mental processes (of which they are presumably aware in themselves) exist in others of their kind? This a novel use of the term "mind" but it doubly falls victim to the psychologist's fallacy (which itself arises out of our inability to access mental states). Although James' admonition speaks to how the psychologist may or may not be able to read the mind, the "theory of mind" concept requires that the psychologist read the mind of an entity that in turn is supposed to be reading the mind of another.

There are many barriers that keep us from knowing the details of how our minds work. Later in this chapter, I identify some of these barriers, but for the moment, I hope my readers will accept the fact that mind is terribly difficult to define in any strict scientific or operational manner and impossible to directly measure. If these propositions are true, the entire effort to ascribe underlying mental motives, intent, choice, or veracity to behavior is at risk; yet, these are exactly the goals of many judicial proceedings. It is all too easy to feign or imitate an emotional or cognitive process contrary to what one actually is experiencing. Lying comes in so many guises that it is hard to imagine how one would ever be able to detect deception, intentional or unintentional.

Certainly, as one reviews the brief history of the concept of mind, it becomes very clear that the lack of precise definition and its fundamental inaccessibility has led to a prodigious and diverse number of imaginative, sometimes even fantastic, interpretations and theories of the exact nature of mental processes. Indeed, it may not be too farfetched to suggest that inadequate definition of the word "mind" is the most basic source of many of the judicial disputations as well as the advocacy (as opposed to evidentiary) nature of our courtrooms. Unlike the laboratory, where reliable empirical evidence is the gold standard, many legal cases are based on unconfirmable and unchallengeable speculation about the mental state of a defendant prior to the commission of a crime, what it is now, or what it is likely to be in the future.

Another indication of a persisting inability to define mind is that we constantly add new words (e.g., intelligence, psyche, attention, consciousness, cognition, etc.) to designate it without adding any new meaning. From the traditional concept of "soul" to the most modern formulations of "consciousness," a vast number of neologisms have been proffered, each with its own historical baggage of underlying assumptions and connotations rather than precise denotations. Each new word leads more or less directly to a particular perspective on the nature of mind. For example, once accepted as a premise, dualist notions of mind lead, quite logically, to the religious concept of an afterlife. From there it is an equally reasonable step to a heaven or hell as a repository for this immortal entity and thence to the other accouterments of religious ritual. On the other hand, a materialistic physicalism in which mind is but a process of the brain leads, equally logically and inevitably, to the idea that mental processes cease with death of the physical body. On a more immediate level, the nature of our concept of mind can structure the strategies that we use to pursue a courtroom case.

This book will add other arguments for the ineffability and inscrutability of mind and the frailty of the large number of different efforts to define it. Although there is much noise and hubbub, in the final analysis, it is difficult to argue against the unavoidable conclusion that no definition of the mind can be shown to have any claim on validity (or even of clarity) over any other. Each is unprovable and none has any special access to the truth. Psychologists, in particular, have a plethora of competing theories of underlying mental activities that are difficult to distinguish. One reason for this difficulty is that some of the criteria for theory validity useful in the physical sciences may not be useful when one attempts to explain the mind. For example, Ockham's razor, the principle of parsimony, is often used as a guide to distinguish between competing theories in physics. This works in a relatively simple mechanical world; however, in the brain with its enormous complexity and undeniable redundancy, simplicity need not play the same role and may actually be misleading in the sense that it champions trivial over more elaborate and truthful explanations.

Thus, our conception of what the mind is in psychology is beset with a number of serious challenges, some of which may be insurmountable. The impenetrable mind remains recalcitrant to measurement, analysis, and explanation by all of our current scientific strategies; all we can ever measure is behavior. We must conclude, furthermore, at the outset of this discussion that there is at present no compelling definition of the mind and none foreseeable in the future. It is into this vacuum that our judicial system is thrust when juries and judges seek to read the minds of the participants in a civil or criminal proceeding. To further understand the reasons for this continuing perplexity, I now consider what the mind has meant to various people throughout history.

1.2 A Short History of the Mind

Questions about the nature of the mind have occupied proto-psychologists, philosophers, theologians, physiologists, psychologists, and legal authorities for millennia. The number of different points of view is beyond count. No history of any reasonable length, certainly not one as abbreviated as the present one is intended to be, can begin to trace the course of how the mind has been conceptualized over the course of human history. For that matter, there must have been prehistoric folk psychologists who began to wonder about their past thoughts (i.e., memories), their current awareness of the world around them, their dreams, as well as their future anticipations, hopes, and expectations.

However, when and where these questions began to be asked will never be known. Unlike our bones, ideas do not fossilize. There is, in short, no such thing as "archeo-psychology." Even behavior has to be inferred from the material artifacts and we can never be completely certain that some unfamiliar device served the behavioral function that its shape might have at first suggested. Ritual objects are even less likely to leave traces of the thoughts associated with them than are utilitarian objects, the practical use of which is sometimes more obvious.

Other interpretations of ambiguous observations do not have the force of experiential fact. For example, speculation runs rampant in paleoanthropological circles about the possible ritual meaning of a few grains of pollen found in middle Paleolithic internments. For these practical reasons, we cannot now definitively answer such questions as when did the mind appear as a topic of concern or even more profoundly, when did sentience and self-awareness arise in our evolutionary history?[5]

It is only with the invention of writing that the content of thoughts began to be recorded. Even then, the differences that existed between cultures and cultural stages mitigated the value of even this indirect entrée to the thoughts of other times and other societies. Thoughts do not translate directly to the written word; the meaning of a thought can be obfuscated and distorted by the limits of writing to communicate ideas. This is not a difficulty that has been ameliorated over the years despite our age-old efforts to make our language ever more precise. Many modern court battles are waged over the actual meaning of an ambiguously written contract. Much of the pleasure of reading a book is to be found in the freedom to attach specific meaning to ambiguous expressions.

Be that as it may be, it is with the remnants of the earliest Sumerian and Egyptian writing that any serious history of the mind must begin. Clearly, however, at that momentous point in the story, there was already a long prehistory in which people sought to understand the significance of their own consciousness, its impermanence, and communication of its contents to their fellow beings as well as their relationships to their material worlds. We know little of these preliterate times, only that the contents of the written literature obviously did not spring from nothing. By the time of the Sumerian empire and the Old Kingdom of Egypt, elaborate mythologies and legal proscriptions had evolved from unknown precursors.

What we do know is that almost all of these early civilizations had highly developed religious dualisms[6] in which the soul was supposed to continue on in some kind of afterlife. The Egyptian model was particularly elaborate and much of the cultural and material effort was expended on the concept of a multipartite soul consisting of the "ka," the animating life force; the "ba," the deceased personality; the "akh" the postmortem combination of the "ka" and the "ba"; the "set" the shadow or shade of a person"; and, finally, the person's name. Preserving the body so that these aspects of the person's soul could be reunited with the body at some future time was carried to the extreme by the Egyptian culture and, combined with the elaborate written record that was left, provided us with the most elaborate historical insight into what the soul cum mind meant to ancient people.

Many other societies had similar ideas about mental processes, if not the particularly complex supernatural structure that the Egyptians venerated. Until the revolution of scientific thinking in classic Greece, the prevailing view was that the mind was a manifestation of a separate kind of reality (than that of the body) that persisted beyond death. Suffice it to say that the mind was considered to be an aspect of an immortal soul that did not follow the natural laws of the material world. My interpretation (Uttal, 2004) was that, at its most fundamental level, it was the fear of death and the desire to perpetuate one's personality that led to the development of the extraphysical and supernatural nature of the mind, thence to all of modern religions, and ultimately to many of the problems that vex our courtrooms and psychological research activities today.

Many consider the first naturalist, nontheological ruminations about the nature of the mind to be a gift of the earliest Greek natural philosophers. The great

Thales of Miletus (634-546 BCE) is often given the honor of being the first scientist; it was he who, quite possibly, first altered thinking about mind and soul
from what were the preexisting supernatural and dualistic explanations to the
more naturalist and monist[7] ideas that prevail today.

As it became ever clearer to the ancients that the problem of understanding the mind was going to be enormously difficult, philosophical speculation
proliferated. Plato (428-327 BCE) and Aristotle (384-322 BCE), the two giants
of classic Greek philosophy, had differing views of the nature of mind. Plato
was the epitome of the soul-body dualists; he argued that soul (i.e., the mind)
survived the body. His book, the *Phaedo*, argues strongly for the immortal nature
of mind.

In this regard, Plato's essentially dualistic point of view was lagging behind
some of the evolving ideas of mind that were emerging in pre-Christian times.
On the other hand, Aristotle's great book, *De Anima*, treated the mind cum soul
as the embodied or actualized "form" of the potential afforded by the body.[8]
Although there is still much ambiguity about the specific intent of some of his
language, Aristotle was clearly moving in the same naturalist direction pioneered
by Thales two and a half centuries earlier when he (Thales) proposed that the
soul could not be separated from the body. Where Plato was clearly a dualist, Aristotle was at the very least a proto-monist. This was to be the basic controversy
of succeeding centuries—was the mind a transitory natural phenomenon or was
it a persistent supernatural entity that survived the decay of the material body?

In the centuries following the classic Greek philosophers, concepts of the
mind evolved substantially from primitive religious ideas and dualist Greek (i.e.,
Platonic) concepts of the mind. Perhaps the most influential intellectual foundation of the rise of Christianity was the felt need for an afterlife (the persistence of
the mind-soul after death), something that had been of little interest to the Hel-
lenistic Hebrews. Times were so tough under the Roman occupation of the first
century before Christ that only the hope of "something better" ahead both in the
short term (a posthumous heaven for the just) and in the long term (the ultimate
resurrection of the body) made life bearable. When these beliefs were offered
by a small Jewish offshoot cult led by a Judean carpenter, it was the key to the
emergence of what are today's two largest religions, Christianity and Islam.

Following the time of Christ in which the foundation ideas of the new religion were canonized in the New Testament, the next important step was the
curiously modern psychology proffered by St. Augustine of Hippo (354-430),
in such monumental books as his *Confessions*. Augustine did much to bring together the ideas of the classic Greek philosophers, especially a form of Neo-
Platonism and the newly empowered Christian religion. He rejuvenated, if not
invented, introspection as a means of understanding the soul and on that basis,

he thought, to achieve knowledge of God. Furthermore, in a very modern vein, he distinguished between different classes of mental activity including rational and logical thought, perception (i.e., the role of the senses), and memory. He also was one of the first to spell out some of the still currently accepted functions of the mind such as recall and thinking, and anticipated modern ideas with regard to the psychology of time. Perhaps most relevant to modern jurisprudence was his interpretation of the role of free will, an issue that continues to perplex legal historians and ethicists today.

In many ways, Augustine, in the light of his times, was a very modern psychologist incorporating not only Greek rationalism and the search for understanding into his philosophy but also seeking to answer fundamental questions about the nature of the individual's relation to God. His views of the rational mind were to dominate for at least another millennium, and their vestiges can be detected well into our times.

St. Thomas Aquinas (1225?-1274) followed much in Augustine's footsteps making his greatest contribution in his book *Summa Theologiae*. His goal, like that of his famous predecessor, was to find some semblance of accommodation between the naturalist position and the theological one. This resulted in a philosophy that has come to be called natural theology.[9] It was in this context of reason and rationality that Aquinas tried to frame his view of Christianity and in particular the nature of the soul.

The human soul was identified by him with the term "ego" which was to be understood as an individual process characterized by consciousness and freedom of choice. Aquinas believed that the very fact that we were conscious was evidence of both the mind's existence and its permanence, thus providing a foundation for the promised afterlife. Many scholars believe the greatest non-theological influence on Aquinas was Aristotle rather than Plato; however, his belief in an afterlife suggests the opposite.

The respective views of Augustine and Aquinas typified the changes in thinking about the mind that occurred in the years between classic times and the Renaissance. In the west, at least, virtually all concern with the nature of the mind or soul was embedded in attempts to justify the increasingly dominant religion—Christianity. Of course, other views were being expressed by scholars in other parts of the world. However, where the issue was explicitly faced, it was framed in the context of philosophical speculation characterized by a dualistic view of the mind as something separable from the material body and persistent after physical death.

It is, of course, extremely difficult to identify a critical break point between these views of the soul and the beginning of the modern idea that the mind was a natural process. However, the views of one scholar-priest do stand out. William of Ockham (1288?-1348?) was one of the first to be categorized as a nominalist, i.e., that words and concepts, especially universals, have no independent existence other than as names or designators of that which they name. Opposed to nominalism was a peculiar kind of Platonic dualism in which the most abstract concepts (e.g., the mind) could have their own independent reality.

Ockham's nominalism led to a different kind of thinking in which objects had a reality only in terms of their being experienced and perceived. (This point of view ultimately resulted in the idealism of Bishop George Berkeley, 1685-1753.) Among the most important outcomes of nominalism was the effort to reduce the number of "real" entities necessary to account for our observations. The similarity of this idea and the one for which William is best remembered—Ockham's Razor—seems clear. The names of an entity, since they have no independent existence, can all too easily be invented and then repeatedly reinvented and one should not multiply these entities or their names beyond necessity. Modern psychology should heed this centuries-old admonition!

Although William was a Franciscan monk, his "razor" was a highly modern idea that suggests that supernatural explanations, including those of his religion, might be superfluous. This kind of thinking could and did get him into trouble with the then-dominant ecclesiastical authorities, but it also provided the basis for modern science's equivalent—the "principle of parsimony."

William of Ockham's nominalism can be thought of as a proto-materialism to the extent that it rejected possible unperceived entities and minimized the role of intervening supernatural explanations. He, thus, set the stage for what were specifically materialist theories of the mind in the centuries to come. Although dualistic ideas still predominated, they were not only religiously based; they were also conceived of as two different forms of natural reality.

During the Renaissance Andreas Vesalius (1514-1564) and Leonardo da Vinci (1452-1519) both added remarkable insights into how the nervous system worked. By this time there was an increasingly wide spread appreciation that the brain and the mind were more than just "closely related." Each of these scientists (let us welcome Leonardo to the ranks) had their own view of the nature of the mind. In general, it was incorporated into the naturalistic theme pioneered by Thales and Aristotle in classic times. These totally materialist theories, based as they were on the anatomy of the brain, often mistook what the essential parts of the brain were (Leonardo still believed that the fluids in the ventricles of the brain were the essence of the mind-soul). However, by this time the idea that the brain was the seat of the mind was nearly universally accepted by natural philosophers if not by theologians. Thales' ancient natural materialism was a major theme of the nature of the mind from that time on. This idea was strengthened by a continuing series of observations about the neuroanatomy and neurophysiology of the brain, a topic to which I return in Chapter 2 for a more detailed consideration.

However, it still was not to be the dominant theme. Supernatural and dualist ideas exerted and continue to exert an enormous influence on the concept of the mind for the same reason they always have—continuing assertions that the mind was something quite different than the body. Herein lay the solution to the most fundamental human fear—how can my precious consciousness, the essence of *ME*, not continue to exist although there is no denying that my body ceases to function and decay after a pitifully short number of years? The dualist answer to this age-old question was that the things—the mind and the brain—represent two different kinds of reality.

The person who formulated the idea of the natural basis of mind as a function of the brain most specifically was René Descartes (1596-1650). Despite his own personal religious convictions, Descartes proposed one of the first theories of the mind in which theological ideas were absent from psychobiological discussions.[10] To Descartes, the mind was half of a substance dualism in which the body and the mind were considered to be different kinds of reality. This new approach incorporated older ideas about the immortal soul or mind that could persist without a body. Unfortunately, Descartes contributed greatly to the current strategy of thinking of the mind as an aggregation of modular parts that could be independently studied like the components of a machine. This was a minor, although as we see later a very influential, flaw considering his other important contributions to psychology, mathematics, and physiology.

Thales mechanistic and monistic view of the mind as a process of the brain or body eventually appeared once again in John Locke's (1632-1704) book *An Essay Concerning Human Understanding*. This masterwork established the foundation for the empiricist theories that were to follow, theories that said that we knew nothing until we experienced it and that the mind was nothing but the accumulation and integration of these experiences. This empiricism set the stage for the heavy emphasis on learning that was to guide and stimulate psychology's study of mental activity in the centuries to come.

Locke, however, was as equivocal as his predecessors about the nature of the soul. He argued that it was not possible to resolve whether the individual's views on an afterlife and resurrection were valid or not. Most of Locke's writing sensibly avoided efforts to define the mind; instead he seems to have generally assumed that it was neither a process of the body requiring its own kind of reality nor a result of the hand of God. To him, it was just a process of the material body. This monistic perspective is the essence of the modern naturalist view and brings us to the conceptual and ideological point at which modern psychology emerges in the form of laboratory-oriented experimental and physiological psychology, approaches that were brought to fruition by such psychologists as Wilhelm Wundt (1832–1920) and by such neurophysiologists as Luigi Galvani (1737-1798).

Throughout its history, the contemporary theory of mind has always been profoundly influenced by the metaphor provided by whatever technology was available. Fluids, clocks, and more recently computers have provided metaphors and sometimes specific theories. The most important recent influence was the invention of the programmable digital computer; it provided the impetus for the emergence of what is now known as cognitive psychology, arguably the most pervasive theory of mind in modern times. Cognitive psychology is a mentalism that assumes that the mind is accessible by inference from our observations of behavior or by introspection. The contending school is behaviorism. The former was initially championed by such influential psychologists as William James (1842–1910) and the latter by the equally significant John B. Watson (1878–1958).

Comparative discussions of the manifold schools of modern psychology can be found in such texts as the one by Marx and Hillix (1973). Therein are detailed the debates and controversies distinguishing the various schools and systems of psychological thinking that dominated the twentieth century. Each system takes a stance on the ability of the mind to be investigated; each accepts or rejects the modern mentalist tenet that we can infer something about underlying mental processes and events by either introspection or experimental observation of behavior.[11] At present, the debate over the mind's accessibility is relatively quiescent. Behaviorists and cognitivists have retreated to their respective philosophical redoubts and rarely confront each other. Considering the centrality of the issue, this is unfortunate.

This all too brief telegraphic presentation of the history of the mind omits discussion of a host of other philosophers, theologians, proto-psychologists, neuroscientists, and psychologists who contributed other points of view and ideas. Many of the ideas about the mind turned out to be only historical curiosities; others profoundly influenced the way we think about the ways we think. Sometimes this is very explicit and sometimes it is presented in a cryptic and poorly appreciated, but influential, manner. For readers who would like a much more complete history of the ancestors of scientific psychology and the emerging modern view of the mind, I direct them to three excellent sources, all of which have been helpful to me in writing this section. They are D. B. Klein's (1970) *A History of Scientific Psychology*; T.H. Leahey's (1997) *A History of Psychology;* and D. N. Robinson's (1998) brilliantly commented reader *The Mind*.

It may be worthwhile to distill the main points from this brief history to clarify how the concept of the mind has changed over the years and where the debates continue. This transformation is not complete and many people still trust ideas that were popular millennia ago. However, among my colleagues in the field of scientific psychology, I believe that certain facts are clear:

1. Consideration of the nature of the mind has been a major preoc-
    cupation for millennia.
2. Early concerns with the desire to maintain the essence of one's per-
    sonality and consciousness after death led to dualist beliefs that
    still indirectly influence our laboratories and our courtrooms. (See
    Uttal, 2004.)
3. This led to the emergence, in turn, of ideas of supernatural (i.e.,
    unobservable) events, of primitive beliefs in beings and objects
    that controlled our fates, and ultimately to increasingly formal re-
    ligions.
4. In the seventh century BCE, a new world view—naturalism—be-
    gan to emerge in ancient Greece.
5. Naturalist concepts of the mind were originally instantiated in
    philosophical speculation most notably in the work of Thales and
    Aristotle.
6. New philosophies and theologies, as well as scientific discoveries,
    led some theologians to seek alternative ideas about how the hand
    of God could interact with the human mind. Although phrased in
    the language of the church, many modern ideas of the nature of
    human thought and jurisprudence emerged during the middle ages.
    Early codes of law emerged from both the need to regulate human
    societies and from theological concerns.
7. Modern materialist ideas of the mind as a function of the brain-body
    began to be expressed during and shortly after the Renaissance.
8. During the seventeenth century the idea of the mind as a mechanical
    process flowered. The foundations of a modern scientific psycholo-
    gy were laid during this time. Throughout all of these centuries, at-
    tempts were being made to define the basic mental processes. Ideas
    of perception, learning, thinking, and responding did not spring de
    novo in modern times but were built on ideas that had persisted
    from the beginning. For example, in *de Anima* Aristotle identified
    the tripartite nature of mental activity as sensation, decision, and
    response, a theme that is still reflected in modern scientific psycho-
    logical research.
9. Another persisting concept is that the mind is made of modules.
    Just as there was a powerful, albeit incorrect, impulse to initially

think dualistically, there was an equally powerful and misdirecting impulse to separate mental processes into components when psychologists study the mind. However, it must be appreciated that this may merely be a convenience helping us to finesse the inherent difficulty of dealing with what is in actuality a complex and unified system. The modern version of this component view of the mind is the idea of mental modules, an assumption that governs much of cognitive psychology.

10. The invention of the computer as a theory of mind had a profound effect on psychological thinking. Computation and brain activity share many properties. However, the analyzability of the brain is not as simple a challenge as is the reverse engineering of a computer.

11. Finally, we now live in a time in which it is still widely believed that we can infer from introspection or experimentation something about the underlying nature of the mind. This is the thesis of modern mentalism and the antithesis of modern behaviorism.

The rest of this book is aimed at evaluating the relevance of this evolving sense of what the mind is to modern jurisprudence. To begin to understand how difficult it is to "read the mind" we must answer a basic question—what are the epistemological challenges to the kind of interpretations of our thoughts that are so ardently desired and implicit in the logic of the courtroom?

1.3 What are the Major Challenges to Mind Reading in the Courtroom?

Despite the continued desire to do so in the courtroom, there are many reasons why we cannot read minds. One of the most important reasons is the lack of appreciation of the limits of empirical science. The determination of what the world is actually like is dominated by processes of exploration, observation, and experimentation. However, for any of these processes to work we must be able to measure and organize observable phenomena. The mind is not directly observable and our concepts of it are dependent on indirect and uncertain inferences from observables; that is, overt behavior and not covert mentation. Furthermore, there are severe questions about its measurability. (See, for example, the work of Michell, 1999.)

For reasons that are reasonably clear (e.g., emulating the physical sciences in the hope of producing equivalent theoretical and empirical successes), psychological scientists spend most of their effort observing behavioral phenomena, particularly in the highly formalized manner of controlled experimentation, in order to determine the relations between independent variables (stimuli) and dependent variables (responses). The technology, both instrumental and statistical for collating and summarizing data, is highly developed, perhaps most highly among psychologists because of the extraordinary complexity of the subject matter they have chosen to study. Barring the accidents of statistical sampling, random errors, sloppy design or execution, and, rarely, deliberate falsification, we can generally have confidence that the pattern of stimulus-response relations reported in a journal article is not only reliable but correct.

However, the next step is more difficult—transforming these overt behavioral observations into the covert thought processes presumed to underlay them. Such an inferential process is prone to much more serious conceptual errors than is making the original behavioral observations. Nowhere are the problems of inferring the covert from the overt more challenging than in scientific psychology. In many ways, the challenges faced in psychology are the same as in any other science; however, psychology also faces a number of special difficulties that distinguish it from, say, cosmology. This section highlights some of the especially difficult challenges that are faced when people attempt to infer the nature of mental activity from behavior. Efforts to do so are subject to all of the general obfuscations, obscurities, and uncertainties of scientific explanation in general. In addition, however, there are some especially profound obstructions, barriers, and challenges to our ability to construct satisfactory descriptions or explanations of the unobservable mind. It is the purpose of this next section to identify some of these hindrances that stand between our observations of behavior and our appreciation of what a person is really thinking. This epistemological interlude lays a general foundation for our specific concern with the difficulty of inferring mental states (reading the mind of an accused) in our legal proceedings.

A. Inaccessibility

Of all of the difficulties and challenges that psychology faces, none is more obstructive to achieving understanding than the fundamental fact that the objects of study themselves—the underlying cognitive processes and mechanisms—are not directly observable. This property is generically referred to as mental inaccessibility. Because of this inaccessibility, there are no instruments or indicators that permit either a psychologist or a juror to directly measure the state of defendant's mind. The undeniable fact is that people's real thoughts are easily obscured by intentional deception or altered memories among many other sources of uncertainty. Actors, sociopaths, and ordinary folk are able to disassociate their utterances from their true thoughts. Vested interests often serve to distort our logic so that not even the individual is aware of his or her true thoughts.

The gap between our intrapersonal privacy and interpersonal communication is profound and extreme. The mind is most likely the current state of a pattern of complex neural activity. We, as self-aware entities, do not experience the neural states directly, but can only report the overall outcome through the filter of what psychologists have called "cognitive penetration"—a phrase that refers to the ability of other mental forces than the simple "truth" to modify the contents of memory or the course of our behavior.

The gap between mental reality and how it is reported increases drastically when the complexity of the process and the costs of responding increase. In simple psychophysical experiments (e.g., testing the visual threshold of light as a function of its wavelength), there is both little complexity and little cost to reporting the presence or absence of a stimulus (a Class A observation according to Brindley, 1960). When a relative or magnitude judgment is to be made (a Class B observation according to Brindley) the likelihood of cognitive penetration is much higher. In situations in which the cost of making a "wrong" response is even higher (for example, when a jury is attempting to determine what a person was "really" thinking) cognitive penetration may have far more serious consequences.

Thus, both reasonableness and prejudice are able to modify what a person reports through the classic communication medium—introspection. This makes opaque what might have been transparent where transparency is tantamount to justice. For all scientific and judicial purposes, introspective reports are meaningless. Conscious or unconscious, intentionally or unintentionally, human thoughts are obfuscated and distorted when people are asked to reveal them. This basic fact has to be contrasted with the high degree of credulity given to the verbal reports in the courtroom.

We can identify some of the logical reasons why it is so difficult to draw conclusions about mental states from observed behavior. First, the underlying mental activity underdetermines behavior. That is, there is not enough information in the behavior to uniquely determine cognitive mechanisms and processes. There is a huge number of distinctly different ways in which any behavior can be explained; according to some theorists it is likely to be very large. Indeed, some theorists (e.g., Moore, 1956) suggest that the number is functionally, if not actually, infinite. There are many ways in which this constraint can be expressed.

- Behavioral observations do not contain enough information to specify mental processes.
- The task of inferring mental states from behavior is an example of what mathematicians refer to as an ill-posed problem that can only be solved by applying certain reasonable constraints or regularizations, that is, additional hypothetical assumptions. Some of these additional assumptions may be reasonable but some are likely to

just further becloud our understanding of what happened in a con-
tested case. Depending upon what these constraints might be, vast
numbers of equally plausible inferences may be justified.

- Behavior, therefore, represents a clear example of what scholars
have earlier referred to as the "one to many" problem. That is, because of the inadequacy of the data forthcoming from an experiment, there are innumerable possible interpretations that can be
made. Furthermore, as also shown by Moore (1956), it is not possible to carry out other experiments to reduce the possible interpretations to a unique one. Each new experiment simply multiplies
plausible possibilities.

Therefore, there is no bridging concept that links the laws of the behavioral
(stimulus) world with the mental laws of cognitive processing. Inaccessibility
may mean either that something is too far away to be directly measured (e.g., a
distant galaxy) or that it is not amenable to conventional measurement (e.g., the
mind). Physics can overcome the inaccessibility barrier because of what is called
the "Cosmological Principle," an idea built into Einstein's special relativity principle. This profoundly important physical generalization asserts that the laws of
the physical world are the same "here" or "there," no matter how distant "there"
may be.

One of the main accomplishments of psychological research has been to
identify the nonveridicalities between the laws of physics and the laws of the
mind, that is, the discrepancies between physical events and how we perceive
them. These discrepancies are exemplified by the non-uniformity of mental time
(e.g., paradoxical reversals of time) and unexpected distortions of our spatial perception (e.g., visual illusions). In other words, there is no psychological equivalent of the Cosmological Principle—the laws of the mind are not the same as
the laws of the physical world. Indeed, it seems that the mind seems to operate
by principles that tend to distort or overcome the laws of the external physical world. Psychological time, space, and number are inconstant and variable in
ways that would have driven Newton mad. Not even Einstein would have found
the laws to be systematic enough to be encompassed by his ingenious theories.

There is, therefore, no a priori way to predict the cognitive outcome of a
stimulus. The search for mental nonveridicalities has flowered into an enormous
corpus of observations in which the mind distorts, disorders, and corrupts phenomena that would otherwise follow the laws of physics. Our perceptions and
memories violate the most basic laws of sequential causality and project us into
the past as well as into the future in a way that is prohibited in the physical
world.[12] In short, both empirical observations and introspection are fundamen-

tally incapable of inferring underlying mechanisms or predicting perceptual outcomes. This point of view is spelled out in much greater detail in Uttal (2008).

B. Irreducibility and Modularity

If there is little doubt that the inaccessibility issue limits our ability to read minds, the next issue is far more contentious among psychologists. In a nutshell, the issue now confronted is whether or not the cognitive "processes and mechanisms" are separable and isolatable from each other. Thus, for example, one view (elementalism) is that we can break up a decision process into a set of subprocesses that might include, for example, "perceive," "evaluate," "choose," and "respond" or, as other examples, "think," "decide," and "learn." The contrary view—holism—would be that the mental activity is a unified process in which these components are indivisible and integral aspects or properties of an irreducible overall mental state. This is an extremely important issue; the modular assumption is ubiquitous in modern as well as older psychological theories of the nature of the mind.

The roots of the modularity hypothesis are well documented in history. For many centuries psychologists and their predecessors spoke of behavioral traits and faculties as if they were independent processes. Happiness, loyalty, perception, emotion, and even such nebulous attributes as acquisitiveness were regularly invoked when the faculties or properties of the mind were discussed.

The idea that the mind was made up of isolatable components resonated with the scientific admonitions of Rene Descartes (1596–1650). Since then there has been a widely held belief that a complex system made up of bits and pieces can only be studied scientifically by isolating each piece and studying it separately. The only caveat was that the function of all of the other components must be held constant—a very difficult to achieve property in psychological experiments. Descartes' (1649) *Discours de la méthode* offered as one of his four precepts the following advice for approaching science:

> [We should] divide each of the difficulties under examination into as many parts as possible, and as might be necessary for its adequate solution. (Chapter 2)

Psychological research, both biological and behavioral, has in the main followed this precept for practical reasons; it is very difficult to either examine or deal with the full complexity of human behavior, composed as it is of so many variables and factors. There is, therefore, a powerful tendency to break up behavior into what in retrospect can be seen actually to be quite arbitrary modules. There are too few constraints in the behavioral data to authenticate or reject one or another of what may seem to be plausible modules. Regardless of how much of a simplifying convenience the Cartesian approach may represent, there remains a powerful argument that for something like the mind in which the parts interact so strongly, we may lose sight of its true nature when we try to separate it into fictional parts.

The debate between holists and elementalists described here continues to bedevil modern scientific psychology and speaks directly to the problem of trying to understand what a person is actually thinking in practical environments like the courtroom.

C. Complexity

The next difficulty faced by anyone daring enough to attempt to read another's mind is the complex nature of the mind. A perfectly valid description of the mind is that it is nonlinear. That is, our thoughts and behaviors do not simply add together but strongly interact. Mathematical problems of this kind are notoriously difficult to solve and where approximate solutions are available they are often highly unstable depending on whatever constraints are arbitrarily applied.

On a purely psychological level, complexity is evidenced by the multifactorial nature of virtually every behavioral task. Efforts at control of what are supposed to be irrelevant factors and conditions in an experiment almost always fail. Instead, an ensemble of overt and covert influences almost always acts to confuse and distort the observations. It is very difficult to control what even the most cooperative persons are thinking by simply telling them what to think about.

Another major challenge to any one who wishes to develop a cognitive theory is that the mind is not stable in time. It changes from moment to moment and from task to task, adapting new strategies and processes on the basis of previous experience. In some contexts we refer to this as learning; in others we signify it as a kind of passive adaptation to what must be considered to be changing situations and environments. Thus, although the task may be the same, the solution conjured up during one decision-making session may not be the same as during another. Compounding this difficulty is the fact that individuals may differ, one from another, in their respective responses to what may be intended to be identical stimulus tasks.

In summary, mental processes and the neural mechanisms that account for them are extremely complex. As such, they are not amenable to the usual kind of analytic tools available to study other, simpler kinds of natural phenomena.

D. Stochastic Nature of Mind

If complexity were not enough to overwhelm our ambitious efforts to infer thoughts from behavioral responses, there are other sources of uncertainty, some identifiable and some obscure, that further impede such attempts. Behavioral data is inherently unpredictable, driven as it is by variable and random influences. No matter how well controlled an experiment may be and how well the sample of participants may have been selected, there is always a range of possible responses. We do not know, of course, if this variability results from a true indeterminativeness in human mentation or, to the contrary, if it is simply the accumulated outcome of a plethora of fundamentally deterministic factors that have not yet been identified.

Whatever its origins, response variability is particularly obvious in psychological research.[13] It is for this reason that the usual mathematical tools applied to represent and describe mental processes are statistical in nature. Conventional analytic mathematics and statistics differ in their applicability to physics and mental phenomena, respectively. Earlier (Uttal, 2008) I proposed a list of reasons why each form of mathematics had specific relevance to a particular kind of science. I briefly abstract them here.

- Conventional mathematical analyses require a level of certainty, specificity, and constancy that statistics does not. Statistics suggests general relationships; conventional mathematics demands specific ones.
- Statistics accepts and describes variability; analytic mathematics does not suffer variability gladly. Statistics always deals with response probabilities and, therefore, uncertainty. The deductive mechanisms of conventional mathematics demand certainty even though many applications and measurements may involve or at least tolerate some variation when one compares predictions and measurements in the real world.
- The meaning of a statistic depends entirely on the application; mathematics can thrive without an immediate application.[14]
- Not only is statistics inductive, but it also depends on certain assumptions that are not necessary for analytic mathematics. For example, inferential statistics assumes that a sample is an accurate representative of the original population. Furthermore, it assumes that the sample is taken from a population that is reasonably stable and does not change during the course of an experiment. Considering the adaptability of human behavior, it is possible that this is the basis for one of the great misunderstandings of psychological research—the fallacious assumption that human responses are stable from individual to individual or from sample to sample. Physics, to a much greater extent, can precisely deal with isolated events and depend on their relative stability from case to case.

- Statistics is susceptible to a variety of different types of error or biases. The sample size may be too small to permit valid inferences; the population may be impermanent or changing; or the inferences drawn may be distorted or blatantly wrong, among many others. From an epistemological point of view, the very meaning of knowledge in mathematics and statistics differs.

A host of other special problems for psychology place limits on our ability to know the thoughts of another person and are reflected in these differences. Significance testing, for example, operates at totally different levels for psychology and physics. Where a couple of standard deviation differences is sufficient to warrant publication in psychology, levels of six and seven standard deviations are required for convincing arguments in physics, especially when it comes to "proving" that a new basic particle exists.

Finally, a comment should be made of the inordinate power exerted by analogies—the only method by which we can even begin to assume that the mental processes of another person are the same as ours. Many different systems behave in the same manner and yet are based on quite different mechanisms. This is the distinction often drawn between analogies and homologies by biologists; analogies are systems that behave the same but are based on different underlying bases. An example is flight: Mammals, fish, insects, and machines all successfully fly but each of their respective abilities to fly is based on evolutionary (or engineering) developments that arise from different origins. Homologies, on the other hand, are systems that are based on similar mechanisms and evolutionary histories. Indeed, homologous structures may not perform the same function but represent divergent outcomes of a common genetic origin. What may appear to be different behavioral responses are often subsequently shown to be the result of a single underlying mental process. Similarly, behaviorally identical processes may often be accounted for by wildly different underlying mental activity.

Analogies of neural responses and psychophysical responses, of which I will have much more to say in the next chapter, are particularly seductive and yet especially prone to errors of interpretation. There is little justification in assuming that some neural observation (e.g., the time course of a neuronal response) is the cause or psychoneural equivalent of a behavioral response that exhibits a similar time course.

Thus, analogous behavior, goodness of fit, and any other criterion that one may wish to use as a basis for inferring thoughts from behavior are fraught with difficulty and uncertainty.

E. Explanation and Description

Another impediment to reading minds is the outcome of a classic misunderstanding between the respective meanings of explanation and description—the former being a term with which the latter is often confused, especially with regard to mental activity. A full explanation would involve the identification of all of the factors that account for some event or occurrence as well as the nature of their influence. It would be analytical in the sense that each of these factors could be separated and distinguished from the others and their individual nature determined, often in terms of lower level processes and mechanisms. That is, implicit in an explanation is the concept of reduction—teasing apart the events into component parts and showing how these parts work together to produce the whole. Of course, the lower level parts may themselves call out for some explanation, but that is a separate task for others with different scientific responsibilities.

Therefore, the goal of the explainer, be it a judge or a theoretical psychologist, is to demonstrate how activity (e.g., mental activity) at any one level can account for activity (e.g., behavior) at another. The most characteristic sign of a true reductive explanation is its ability to analyze the process under study into component parts and to have something to say about the interaction of those parts and how they produce the process. The property of mental parts that may make them difficult to manipulate is that they are unobservable and must be inferred from the observable behavior. Unfortunately, as we have seen, there are too few limits on the possible and the plausible parts that can be inferred and, therefore, could account for some behavior.

A description, on the other hand, is a non-analytical approach. That is, a description can fully document an individual's behavior with extreme precision and even with high degrees of predictability. It can invoke forces operating on the system without actually determining the nature of those forces, only saying something about their influence and their effects. Furthermore, a description of a behavior can be fully independent of whatever may have been the underlying mental forces and activities. A description, unlike an explanation, is formulated at the same (behavioral) level as the event itself and does not need to invoke hypothetical constructs (mental) framed in the language of some other level (physical).

One of the most basic misunderstandings in psychology as well as in other sciences is that even mathematical deductions are not explanations, but descriptions. Duhem (1906/1962) was one of the first to make this clear when he said:

> A physical theory is not an explanation. It is a system of mathematical propositions [theorems], deduced from a small number of principles [axioms], which aim to represent as simply, as completely, and as exactly as possible a set of experimental laws [observations]. (p. 7)

If this is correct, and given that most formal psychological theories are statistical (only a few are conventionally mathematical), they explain nothing; the best of them only describe. This, in a formal sense, implies that mental inferences from behavior are both formally and practically impossible.

Another way to put this is to note that mathematics is neutral with regard to underlying mechanisms. To which we must add the main thesis of this chapter—so, too, is behavior. Neither mathematics, laboratory experimentation, introspective report, behavioral observation, nor any other methodology is capable of robustly inferring mental states from behavior. To sum it all up, there is no way for one human to "read the mind" of another. The only practical conclusion for legal proceedings is the admonition to decide a case on the basis of the observed behavior and not on the basis of some possible, however plausible or implausible, hidden mental motivation, physiological deficit, or rationale. Unfortunately, with the current level of misunderstanding about what has been accomplished in the cognitive neurosciences, there are profound forces at work that make it very seductive to ignore this admonition.

Endnotes

1. Of course, there is considerable controversy regarding how well we understand the mind. Nevertheless, the absence of a consensus is the best evidence that the mind remains ill-defined and, to a certain degree, ineffable.

2. It is highly likely that it is impossible to distinguish any of these terms from each other in an operational manner. They all denote the same thing, concept, or process, however much they may differ in their respective emphases and connotations.

3. In recent years I have also become convinced that, however correct this statement may be as an ontological axiom, it is unlikely, because of the inherent complexity of the salient neural nets, that we will ever be able to identify the details of neural interconnectiveness that account for even the simplest cognitive process. Thus is our ontology separated from our epistemology.

4. The Turing Test was suggested by Alan Turing (1950) as a method of distinguishing between artificial and natural intelligence by asking a person to converse with both, through an impersonal interface such as a typewriter. If the person could not distinguish between the two, the automaton was judged to intelligent and, to a somewhat more restricted degree, conscious. Unfortunately, the Turing test cannot work since it would always be possible that the automaton was so good that it could fool the person. Indeed, it is relatively easy to program a computer to fool a person into believing a sentient

being was at the other end of the interface these days. For example, ELIZA, a computer program conceived by Weizenbaum (1996) and originally programmed by Michal Wallace, still has the capacity to fool many people.

5. Of course, this assumes that the conscious mind is a uniquely human trait. The dispute over subhuman consciousness persists and is no more likely to be resolved than is the nature of human mentation.

6. By dualism, I am referring to the concept that our minds and bodies (i.e., brains) represent two distinct kinds of realities. The major implication of this rudimentary dualism is that our souls or minds can continue to exist after the decay of the body.

7. Monism is the antithesis of dualism. It is the philosophy that assumes that the mind and body are both manifestations of a single kind of material or physical reality. Typically the former is considered to be a process of the latter.

8. Aristotle wrote that the mind was the part of the soul that "thinks and forms judgments," tasks very similar to the content of modern psychological research, but a reversal of the standard dualistic meaning of the word soul.

9. Natural theology is a point of view that argues that evidence of God is to be found in our observations of the world rather than in divine revelation. It represented to many philosophers and theologians an alternate response to the problem that few people have ever had the supernatural world revealed to them.

10. We should not, of course, overlook the fact that even the great Descartes felt it necessary to incorporate religious ideas in his writing. As it was for his predecessors, including such luminaries as Galileo and Newton, this was required by the church of their times. Whether this was just lip service to the prevailing power structure or a deep, though inconsistent, belief on their own part will always remain a mystery.

11. It is not without some value to preview at this point this author's stance on this important issue. I am a behaviorist and believe that all of the theories of the mind based on the assumption that we have access to our thoughts are impossible to either authenticate or reject.

12. It is important to emphasize that this does not mean that any supernatural forces are at work that drive these nonveridicalities. Instead, the violations of physical principles are the result of intricate processing by the very active brain-mind. Thus, the laws and forces of the mind are equally natural, just

more complex than those relatively simple ones characterizing the physical world. The problem is that the mental transformations are different than the "lawful" physical ones and there is no bridging concept to permit us to predict them based on the laws of the physical world. For example, there is no a priori means of predicting how we will see a particular illusion. Compare this to the perfectly reasonable answer to a question such as—what is the trajectory of a weight thrown from a bell tower?

13. Variability, of course, is not exclusive to psychological research. Even the most precise sciences (i.e., those in which the variability is relatively small) are subject to unknown influences affecting the outcome of measurements. Physics dotes on identifying these unknowns; psychology is overwhelmed by them.

14. To clarify this point, consider the following example. A second order differential equation of the form

$$y = x + \frac{dx}{dy} + \frac{d^2x}{dy^2}$$

can be studied, manipulated and solved independent of the specific meaning of the terms. However, each component maintains the same general meaning. For example,

$$\frac{dx}{dy}$$

always refers to a force that is proportional to the velocity or rate of change of x with respect to y. That rate of change may represent the movement of a spring, the rate of change of a population of fleas, or the decline of a photochemical; in any case, however, the course of the analysis can be impeccable and enlightening without being embedded in a meaningful context. Statistics, on the other hand, is meaningless unless embedded in a specific applied context.

Chapter 2

What is the Brain?

Synopsis
2.1 Introduction
2.2 A Short History of the Brain
2.3 Theories of How the Mind is Produced by the Brain
2.4 Brain Imaging Methods
    A. Positron Emission Tomography
    B. Functional Magnetic Resonance Imaging (fMRI)
2.5 The Analysis of fMRI Data
2.6 On Variability and Reliability
Endnotes

MYTH: We are beginning to understand how the brain makes the mind. TRUTH: The brain mechanisms underlying mental processes remain impenetrable and unknown.

2.1 Introduction

There is virtually no scientific disagreement[1] with the assertion that the brain is the organ of the body whose activities produce the phenomena of mind. The mind, however difficult it may be to define, is widely agreed to be the outcome of complex information processing associated with the brain and not with any other part of the body. However, despite the vast amount of research that has been carried out on the nervous system, most scientists and philosophers also agree that how this is accomplished remains mysterious and unknown. Somehow, sentience arises out of the actions and interactions of the myriad of neurons that make up the tissue of the brain. How this happens remains what many consider to be not only the most important problems in science but also the most intractable.

There is no question, however, that an enormous body of neuroscientific research has been successfully carried out on the anatomy and physiology of the brain. We are able to describe the electrophysiology and biochemistry of individual neurons and to track the pathways of signals from the sensory receptor regions through the logical and integrative centers of the brain to those that control motor functions in extraordinary detail. The chemistry of synaptic transmitter

27

substances, processes occurring at the most microscopic molecular levels, is well understood. However, how this all fits together into the function of the elaborate neuronal networks that ultimately become mind remains totally unknown.

In this chapter on the brain I want to accomplish several tasks. First, I want to present a brief history of our current conception of the brain. In particular, I want to emphasize a few of the classic and modern developments in our views of the role of the brain as the organ of the mind. Second, I want to review the current array of theories of how brain might make the mind. Third, I want to introduce the most modern tools, the brain imaging devices that permit us to inspect the structure and the physiological activity going on in the brain in intact human beings during mental activity. Fourth, I want to spell out what many consider the most important development in this decade—the use of meta-studies to establish that the brain is not a compartmentalized structure in which particular places encode or represent specific cognitive modules or processes. An important aspect of these meta-studies is that they document the extreme variability of the results reported from different laboratories. Indeed, this variability is so great that it belies the hope that there might ever be some objective brain image measure of what we are thinking. Variability is enhanced by the inadequate way we define mental processes as well as a number of technical problems encountered in the application of brain imaging machines.

The empirical fact of extreme variability also has a major contribution to changes in current thinking. The diversity and dispersion of the activation areas of the brain make it clear that we must move away from the conventional idea that narrowly localized brain components represent modular cognitive processes. The new concept of the operation of the brain to which we must now turn is that any cognitive process can activate almost any area of the brain and any area of the brain is likely to be activated by virtually any cognitive process.

In preview, I present a new way to look at the brain as a distributed neural system. This theory is not intended to characterize the brain as "equipotential" or homogeneous in any sense of the word; instead we must think of it as a system of many loosely interacting and poorly demarcated parts that are involved to a greater or lesser degree depending upon the nature of the thought. A further complication, as we saw in the previous chapter, is that the functions assignable to different regions of the brain are not stable; they shift from condition to condition and any effort to assign specific functions to them is "shooting at a moving target."

2.2 A Short History of the Brain

During the early days of our history and prehistory, the question of which organ of the body accounted for our mental functions was vigorously debated. Since the pulse ceased at the same time as death occurred, the heart was often taken as the seat of consciousness. This became the set piece of Egyptian theological medicine and was accepted as fact by as eminent a natural philosopher as Aristotle (384-322 BCE). Opinions to the contrary were expressed by his predecessors Alcmaeon (who lived during the early fifth century BCE) and Plato (427-347 BCE), both of whom believed that the brain was the seat of our mental activities. Although the function of the brain has always been mysterious, by the turn of the first millennium, the anatomy and, to a lesser degree, the cognitive function of the brain had been well documented by such physicians as Rufus of Ephesus who lived around the time of Christ.

As a result, by the time of Galen (130?-200?), a Greek physician working in Rome, there was little further dispute that the brain was the organ of the mind. However, a new controversy erupted concerning which part of this complex structure was the significant part. The brain could be seen on the grossest of examinations to be made up of both solid, apparently homogeneous, material as well as fluid-filled cavities. Galen accepted the prevailing theory dating from much earlier Greek times—a theory that proposed that the contents of the great cavities or ventricles in the brain were the critical parts, that they were filled with mysterious vaporous or "humoral" substances called pneuma. According to him, the particular pneuma—pneuma physicon—found in the ventricles of the brain was responsible for our perceptions and movements. The solid portions of the brain, the gray and white matters, played no significant role in mental activity in the natural philosophies of physicians of Galen's time. Indeed, as we see later, the reluctance to attribute mental functions to the solid parts of the brain persisted well into the Renaissance.

From the time of the fall of the Roman Empire until the Renaissance, relatively few studies were made of brain anatomy or function. The Catholic Church discouraged dissections and there was little intellectual activity in general throughout Europe. Avicenna or Ibn Sina (980-1037), an Arab scholar, was one of the few who was able to work on such problems outside of the restrictions imposed by the Catholic Church. The distinction between the medulla and the cerebrum of the brain, for example, is usually attributed to him. It is not clear from the literature whether or not he was referring to the brain stem in general when he used the word medulla, a word with a more restricted meaning at present. Whatever his specific meaning, Avicenna was making considerable progress in understanding the gross structure of the solid portions of the brain. However, like most of his contemporaries, he continued to attribute the source of the mind to the fluid contents of the ventricles.

The idea that the ventricles and their contents, either vapors or fluids, were the significant part of the brain with respect to its role in mental activity, as just noted, continued to be widely accepted into the Middle Ages. Galen's anatomy and mind-brain theories influenced even the great Leonardo da Vinci (1452-1519), perhaps the greatest polymath of all time. Leonardo was particularly interested in the ventricles and developed a modification of the lost wax technique used in jewelry making to demonstrate their shapes. Hot wax was injected into the ventricles, allowed to cool, and then the brain tissue was dissected away leaving a wax mold of the ventricles.

The turning point in the appreciation of which parts of the brain were the important ones regarding cognition, however, came with the work of Andreas Vesalius (1514-1564), a Belgian physician and arguably the most significant anatomist in Renaissance history. Vesalius' great book, *De Humani Corporis Fabrica* (*On the Workings of the Human Body*), is still considered to be a masterpiece of both science and art. Most germane to the present discussion, Vesalius seems to have been the first Renaissance scientist to identify the solid portions of the brain, rather than the ventricles, as the critical regions.

Nevertheless, the role of the fluid-filled ventricles as the source of our mental activities continued to be popular among a few brain scientists for many years. The absence of a good microscope and the apparent macroscopic homogeneity of the brain tissues led many scholars to assume that the solid tissues played, at best, a secondary role. These persisting "fluid" or hydraulic theories, on the other hand, were consistent with what was then the dominant contemporary theory—fluid mechanics.

Pervading all approaches to brain function at this time was the search for the "sensus communis"—the location in the brain at which all of the sensory signals were supposed to converge. The idea that there was a common place where the various senses converged to produce a unified mental experience dominated much of the thinking of this period. To many, including Leonardo, this was the site of the soul, a concept that was hardly different than what is meant by the term *mind* these days. Pevsner (2005) elaborates on the interesting story of Leonardo's contributions to neuroscience in a fascinating and highly recommended article.

Although Leonardo's studies never specifically identified the sensus communis, another of the great giants of proto-cognitive neuroscience, Rene Descartes (1596–1650), did go so far as to specify the pineal gland as the location of this elusive center. The sensus communis to him was the "common sense," the imaginative facility; in other words the place where all forms of sensory information converged to produce the awareness of our personal awareness of our own mind. Although modern science has never found a sensus communis, it is clear that the appreciation that our senses played an important role in determining our mental experiences and that their collective action played an important role in determining our behavior was an important concept that has continued to influence even the most modern scientific theories.

Descartes considered the brain to be a hydraulic system in which the nerves were considered to be tubes through which these fluids flowed to carry information to and from the brain. By the late seventeenth century, however, the hydraulic theory was on its way out and the solid portions were beginning to be accepted as the key to mental activity. Two anatomists were especially important in this transition—the Englishman Thomas Willis (1621-1675) and the Dane Nicolas Steno (1638-1686), both of whom identified the main brain structures and argued against two of Descartes' most fundamental ideas. First, they rejected the idea that the ventricular fluids played any important role in mental function. Second, they denied that the pineal gland had any special role in mentation. Willis' book *Anatomy of the Brain, with a Description of the Nerves and Their Function* (1664) and Steno's *Lecture on the Anatomy of the Brain* (1669) marked the beginnings of modern anatomies of the brain and the rejection of such outmoded concepts as the "sensus communis" as well as the primary role of the ventricular fluids. This was a paradigmatic change in neuroscientific thinking and one of the most significant milestones in the history of brain theory.

Following that critical moment in brain history, a number of major discoveries were made by a number of anatomists. Among the most important were:

- Robert Whytt (1714-1766) who discovered that reflexes were primarily controlled by spinal events.
- Georgius Prochaska (1749-1820) who suggested anew what had been a basic idea dating from the time of Plato, namely that the role of the brain was to accept sensory messages, modify them, and send appropriate responses back to the motor system.
- Charles Bell (1774-1842) and Francois Magendie's (1783-1855) demonstration that the dorsal roots of the spinal cord were sensory (i.e., conveying signals from the receptors to the brain) and the ventral roots were motor (i.e., conveying signals from the brain to the effectors).

The next step in understanding the organization of the brain, however, was not so easily resolved. The great debate, which impacts not only on modern theories of the mind-brain, but also on our courts and many other social systems, concerns the degree to which the brain is homogenous or composed of a system of relatively separate functional modules. This is the classic, yet unresolved, problem of brain localization. Is the brain homogeneous with functions distributed widely throughout the brain or is it heterogeneous with functions localized to specific places? In other words, are all parts of the brain much the same functionally or do different locations embody different mental functions? Although this may seem like an esoteric matter of little practical consequence, as we see in later chapters, the widely accepted, but increasingly dubious, solution (mental functions are localized in the brain) lies at the heart of most of the applications of neuroscience to forensics and jurisprudence.

The elevation of this controversial issue to prominence also demarcated a boundary between an earlier time when anatomy and structure were the dominant scientific issues and a later one in which physiology and function began to preoccupy students of neuroscience.

Localization theory reached its epitome in a curious pseudoscientific fad. Around the beginning of the eighteenth century, an extreme theory of cognitive localization called phrenology, although unsupported by any anatomical, physiological, or psychological evidence, was proposed by Franz Gall (1758-1928) and Johan Spurzheim (1776-1832). Their thesis was that the various properties of the mind (including such nebulous faculties as hope, acquisitiveness, and secretiveness) were associated with bumps that could be palpated on the surface of the skull. These bumps were supposed to reflect the shape of the brain beneath the skull and thereby to be related to the mental characteristics of the person. This is an extreme version of localization theory.

For years, the idea that a person's personality could be read by touching bumps on the skull was extremely popular around the world. Although the skull's bumps were eventually shown to be essentially meaningless, in historical fact, we cannot overlook the cognitive neuroscientific foundation premise of phrenology. It was one of the first, if not the first, "theories" in which specific faculties or psychological processes were associated with particular places on the brain. This is an idea that persists to this day in modern forms. Specifically it is the conceptual foundation of much of the current work done on brain imaging and cognitive neuroscience in general: approaches that also assume that different sites of activation are associated with different mental states.

There was, however, a considerable reaction to this theory of localized function at the time of Gall and Spurzheim's publications. A number of eighteenth century brain scientists, including their contemporaries such as Albrecht von Haller (1708-1777) and Pierre Flourens (1794-1867) argued strongly that the brain was a continuous (i.e., homogenous) mass of unspecialized tissue in which all of the parts were collectively activated when any thought process was executed.

This debate between localizationists and holists persists to this day. Although the locationists are currently dominating experimental strategies and theory generation, I will show later in this chapter how modern analysis techniques are beginning to question this particular current dogma. Ultimately, some compromise is likely to emerge. Indeed, the context has already shifted from a debate between extreme localization and extreme equipotentiality to one in which various intermediate degrees of distribution are proposed.

The idea that the brain acted as a whole, or nearly so, took a real beating in the later parts of the eighteenth century. Advances in surgical techniques and a few convenient wars led to the discovery of what appeared to be narrowly circumscribed regions of the brain associated with specific behavioral functions. For example, both Pierre Broca (1824-1880) and Carl Wernicke (1848-1905) discovered that there were specific regions of the brain that seemed to be more intimately related to speech disorders than other regions. Furthermore, Gustav Fritsch (1838-1891) and Edward Hitzig (1838-1907) found that stimulating regions in front of the central fissure of the brain would reliably produce motor responses. Soon after that, neuroscientists such as Herman Munk (1821-1894) plotted out visually sensitive regions of the brain.

Throughout the last century innumerable researchers have identified specific regions that seemed to be closely if not uniquely associated with particular sensory and motor functions. Indeed, what appeared to be maps of the body could be plotted both for sensory and motor functions. (See, for example, the work of Penfield and Jasper, 1954, who plotted out the so-called motor homunculus, so designated because it looked like a small picture of the human body, and of Kaaz, Nelson, Sur, and Merzenich, 1981, who plotted the multiple somatic sensory areas. Contemporaneously, Tootell, Silverman, Switkes, and DeValois, 1982, had shown that the early visual regions of the brain were retinotopic following the topology the visual field.)

At this point in our short history, the concept of a brain divided into highly specialized regions mediating specific cognitive processes was widely accepted. In recent years, however, maps showing discrete localization have been shown to be much more diffuse than initially thought. Even the sensory areas are now known to be multimodal (e.g., see Graziano, 2001). It should be noted that this is not a regression to the idea of the "sensus communis," a particular place to which all sensory information converged. Rather, it is an argument for diffuse distribution of information in which all sensory areas received all types of sensory inputs. Currently, as we see later, the localization assumption has been further contraindicated by new methods, especially those involving meta-studies of brain images. The newest data seems to argue that the response of the brain is widely distributed to even the best-controlled stimulus.

This change in our fundamental assumptions about the organization of the brain may well have an enormous impact on the way that our judicial system deals with neuroscientific measures. Specifically, if there are no well-localized signals of particular cognitive states (e.g., areas indicative of deception or deficits indicating a lack of "control" over behavior), then the entire neuropsychological concept of admitting brain images as evidence into the courtroom becomes extremely suspect. Again, the main thesis of this book must be reiterated: no measure of brain activity has yet been shown to be able to "read the mind" of a person. The correlations between objective measures such as the fMRI and cognitive processes remain too low to permit them any validity in our judicial proceedings.[2]

All of this speaks directly to the current group of theories that seek to explain how the brain produces the mind. It is the purpose of the next section to describe the variety of imaginative, although improvable, ways in which current cognitive neuroscientists have attempted to bridge the gap between observations of our behavior and recordings from the brain.

2.3 Theories of How the Mind is Produced by the Brain

One piece of evidence of the vast gulf between our knowledge of the brain and our observations of behavior can be observed in the plethora of neuroreductionist theories of the mind—theories purportedly based on observed neurophysiological activities. There is no shortage of such theories and, indeed, many neurophysiological responses can be found that correlate to a modest degree with behavioral responses and thus, with modest correlations, to mental activity. These theories invoke processes that occur at all levels of complexity and analysis ranging from global responses of the entire brain to the action of specific parts of individual neurons themselves. Unfortunately, there is little agreement among contemporary cognitive neuroscientists as to which level is the salient one since correlated activity can be found at all levels.

In an earlier work (Uttal, 2005) I classified the spectrum of neural theories into four different types:

- Brain Field Theories
- Single Neuron Theories
- Neural Network Theories
- Brain Region Theories

Each of these theoretical types, however, suffers from a fatal flaw: despite the enthusiasm of their respective proponents, none conveys the kind of detail or is supported by sufficiently compelling data to take them as being anything other than a small step beyond plausible speculation. An important point is that each of these types of mind-brain theory is based on the availability of a particular technology capable of measuring some functional aspect of the nervous system. To a degree not usually appreciated by cognitive neuroscientists, their theories are driven more by the available technologies rather than by logical and axiomatic foundations. In large part, this accounts for the diversity of and the dogmatic conviction behind the explanations that have been offered. All science should and, indeed, must operate in this way—our observational techniques are the window to reality. In this case, there is really no compelling empirical way to distinguish between the alternative neuroreductive theories. Let's look in detail at each of these theories to get an idea of why their empirical support is so limited.

1. Electrical Field Theories. Brain field theories are among the oldest simply because the instruments used to measure this kind of pooled nervous activity were among the first to be invented. The classic tool for measuring brain fields is the electroencephalograph—the EEG. This device is sensitive to signals that can be recorded from either the surface of the scalp or directly from the brain should it be exposed by trauma or the needs of surgery. The EEG was invented by Richard Caton (1842-1926) for use on animals in 1875 and first used on humans in 1925 by Hans Berger (1873-1941).

The EEG records "brain waves" of relatively low frequency (2 or 3 to 100 HZ) that are diffusely detected over much of the brain. These signals are generically described as fields because they are continuous from place to place with only gradual changes and few discontinuities as one scans the brain. EEGs were very useful in the detection of gross anatomical and functional abnormalities of the brain prior to the development of some of the brain imaging devices that appeared later in the twentieth century.

Brain fields have been shown to be correlated with some aspects of mental activity. However, they must be considered to be very "blunt" tools. These signals are the accumulation of the responses of literally billions of neurons. Thus, they throw away all of the critical and detailed information about the activity of the vast network of neurons that most likely accounts for mental processes.

2. Single Neuron Theories. At the other end of the spectrum are theories that depend upon the response of individual neurons. In this mode, the equivalent of mental function is attributed to the responses recorded from single neurons. Single neuron recording was a much later development than the EEG because of the microscopic size and the high level of technical sophistication required to record their activity. The first intracellular single neuron recordings were made by Hodgkin and Huxley (1939) from an unusually large neuron of the squid nervous system. This neuron was nearly a millimeter in diameter compared to the typical mammalian neuron which is only a few micrometers in diameter. Hodgkin and Huxley inserted a very small glass tube into the end of the large squid axon and were able to record voltages between the inside and the outside of the cell membrane. This led to monumental discoveries about the action of the neurons and the first theory of how the differential distribution of the dissolved ions (for example, Na^+, K^+, and Cl^-) in the intra- and extracellular fluids accounted for the changes in their electrical potentials when a neuron responded.

The next important step in the history of single neuron studies was the development of very fine "microelectrodes" by Graham and Gerard (1946)[3] that could be inserted through the wall of even relatively small neurons. The advantage of the microelectrode was that it was so small relative to the size of the neuron, that the membrane was able to seal around the electrode like a self-sealing tire, thus preserving the neuron's vitality for periods of time that might be as long as many hours. Considering how small the typical neuron is, this was a substantial accomplishment.

Thus, the door was opened to the study of the activity of a wide range of small neurons. Furthermore, current theories of synaptic action and neuronal conductivity, as well as those that deal with the specific molecules responsible for the activity of the individual neurons, arose from the application of this high input impedance microelectrode technology. What did not follow from this understanding of the action of individual neurons was how activity at this elegant and microscopic electrochemical level accounted for the mind.

As soon as it was discovered that individual neurons were also tracking some of the dimensions of behavior, the idea that the activities of single "pontifical" neurons were the essential codes for, in particular, sensory and motor processes, became very popular. The essence of these single cell theories was that the correlation between an individual neural response and some behavioral measure could be extrapolated to serve as an explanation of our mental activity. Although the first correlations were observed between simple sensory input and output motor processes, the idea that single cells also were able to represent much more complex cognitive processes such as intent, imagination, or learning was quickly adopted by psychologists.

The problem with single cell theories is that we really have little or no information about what is going on in all of the other places in the brain when a cognitive neuroscientist observes the activity of an isolated neuron. The strength of the Graham and Gerard technique was that it directed our attention to the activity of a single neuron while ignoring all others. However, this was also its great disadvantage—it focused attention on far too circumscribed a location (the microscopic point of the intracellular electrode) and ignored the fact that many other neurons were also responding in a meaningful way throughout the rest of the nervous system whenever a sensory, cognitive, or motor process was occurring. It was only in the rarest of experiments that any attempt was made to determine activity in other locations once a correlation between an active single neuron and a behavior was observed.

Even the most modern techniques that involve the use of multiple microelectrodes, and thus the ability to record from a number of neurons simultaneously, do not overcome this advantage cum disadvantage. At best, the activity of only a hundred neurons could be tracked simultaneously and this was a far cry from a sample of what might reasonably be expected to be involved in the creation of a thought. Nevertheless, the amount of data accumulated through such a microelectrode array could quickly overcome the ability of even the most powerful computer to analyze or even store the accumulated data.

Single neuron theories, therefore, represent wildly uncontrolled experiments in which the activities of all of the other neurons in the brain are ignored. As such, they represent a very incomplete picture of what is happening in the brain and lead to a number of untenable theories in which it was proposed that single neurons encode very complex cognitive processes by themselves. The most extreme example of such a "gnostic neuron" theory was suggested by Konorski (1967). It is not considered to be plausible these days.

3. Neural Network Theories. The next category of neural theories of the mind is based upon the premise that huge networks of interacting neurons account for the mind. Unfortunately, as just noted, it is impossible to record and analyze a sufficient number of interconnected neurons to explain how the brain might accomplish this task. Therefore the tool of choice for those pursuing this theoretical line of thought is the computer and the method is simulation. In other words, rather than attempt to do what is logistically impossible and study the simultaneous activity of the great neural networks of the brain, the properties of simulated and necessarily simplified neuronal networks are studied to see how they might produce behavior analogous to human mentation. Because the networks were programmed to emphasize dynamic processes, special attention has always been directed to how well they simulate the learning process.

The computer simulation approach depended on the development of the modern digital computer, first suggested and partially built in the late 1930s (but probably never fully tested) by John V. Atanasoff (1903–1995) and his student Clifford E. Berry (1918–1963.) Their pioneering activities are described in an excellent book by Mollenhoff (1988). Atanasoff and Berry's accomplishments, however, were originally overlooked in the rush of new computer developments subsequently required by the needs of World War II. Among the most prominent of the engineers and mathematicians to follow up on Atanasoff and Berry's work was John von Neumann (1903-1957) who developed the concept of the stored program digital computer on which all modern machines are now based. What was the first digital computer of the fully modern kind (that is, utilizing the stored program concept) is still a matter of much debate (Malcolm, 2001).

The powerful information processing capabilities of the digital computer made it possible to consider studying neural networks of modest size in a precise manner. Specifically, a major approach to theorizing how the brain might make the mind is in the form of a network of faux neurons in which the manifold interactions can be computed in practical amounts of time—"practical" being the operational term in this context. Unfortunately, neural network theories, which most probably are closer to the truth in terms of the critical processes for generating mental activity than any of the others, are typically overly simplistic toy models consisting of, at best, only a few hundred neurons that cannot be scaled up to anything approaching the level of complexity of the real brain. Beyond a few hundred, the networks become so complex that simple combinatorics raise issues of computability and mathematical intractability that prohibit solution of any realistic neuroreductive theory.[4]

The most basic combinatorial measures, such as the number of neurons and their interconnections, suggest a number of required computations that raise serious questions about the tractability of any mathematical problems generated when one attempts to simulate the mind-brain system in this manner. Indeed, combinatorial theorists have frequently argued that the mind-brain is characteristically NP-Complete—a phrase that refers to the fact that such a system represents a mathematical problem that cannot be solved in any amount of time by a computer of any conceivable power. Neuroscientists would be well advised to make the effort to understand how these mathematical principles constrain plausibility in theories of this kind.

4. Brain Region Theories. Finally, there is another theory of how the brain might make the mind that is difficult to distinguish in terms of its basic principles from those that served as the underlying assumptions of "phrenology" previously discussed. Although, the phrenological fad became a historical curiosity, the idea on which it was based—specific locations on the brain are associated with specific cognitive processes—persists in modern theory. With the development of functional brain imaging techniques such as the functional Magnetic Resonance Imaging (fMRI) and the Positron Emission Tomography (PET) devices, the emphasis changed from the bumps on the skull or electrical activity of the brain to the metabolically active regions of the brain as the purported correlates of mental activity.[5] Although the regions of interest moved from the bumps on the outside of the skull to regions on the brain itself, the fundamental assumption of localized functions continues to have an inordinate effect on mind-brain theory. Attorneys would be well advised to appreciate the limits of our knowledge of this or any other neural theory of the mind.

The basic assumption of this modern version of a traditional assumption of brain localization is that certain regions exhibited high activity when a person was instructed to "think in a particular way." However, it must be appreciated that, at best, such correlations of functional brain images with mental activity only suggest an answer to *where* in the brain a specific mental process might occur rather than *how* the brain makes the mind. They do not tell us anything about the sufficiency of a particular structure in the complex network of structures supposed to represent a particular cognitive process.

It is not at all clear, furthermore, just what would be added to our quest for a definitive theory of the mind even if the "where" question could be answered. At worst, the apparently localized responses may only be illusory. The most recent research based on meta-studies (to be described more fully later in this chapter) suggests that widely dispersed and multiple parts of the brain are activated whenever any complex cognitive process is evoked. As we see later, this runs counter to much of the neuropsychological testimony in the courtroom in which it is assumed that specific brain lesions cause (or permit) specific behaviors.

There is a further problem with brain chunk theories; even if it was determined that identified network of nodes acted together to produce mental activity, there is some mathematical thinking (Hilgetag, O'Neil, and Young, 1996) that suggests that the hierarchical order of these nodes cannot be analyzed. Because of feedback, feed forward, and feed sideways connections, the complexity of the system would prohibit conventional analysis of the role of each node and the determination of the order in which they interact.

In summary, none of the current approaches to understanding how the brain makes the mind are convincing explanations. Each is incomplete and flawed in some fundamental manner. The most likely origin of the mind is to be found in the ensemble of microscopic interactions of the vast network of individual neurons. Each of the alternative theories is handicapped by a fundamental barrier to understanding.

- Field theories by their loss of detailed information due to pooling of responses.
- Single cell theories because they ignore involved mechanisms at places other than the one at which an electrode is placed.
- "Chunk" or "neophrenological" localization theories for reasons that can be summed up as a lack of replication and an underestimation of the proportion of the brain involved in even the simplest cognitive process.
- Neural network theories because they become computationally intractable before they become complex enough to produce mind.

All of these theories share certain common attributes as well as suffering from their own specific flaws. First, all of them are correlative. Even in their most robust form, none actually shows how the seemingly magical transformation from brain matter to mental process takes place. They are simply correlations between a conveniently available measure of brain activity and some mental task. Thus, at their very best, they may answer questions of where or what in the brain may be associated with mental activity but they provide no insights into how the transformation takes place. At worst, the correlations produce an illusion of explanation without any substance.

Second, each is dependent on the availability of a particular technology. So much so, that it almost seems as if the available technology is driving the logic of theory building instead of the empirical scientific facts. Each instrument directs our attention to a particular phenomenon, which may or may not be correlated with, but is not causally related to some aspect of behavior. The EEG stimulated the field theories; microelectrodes, the single cell theory; the computer the neural network theories; and certainly the classic idea of localization has been reinforced by the emergence of the brain imaging technologies. None, other than the unachievable neural network theory, is based on a logical chain of deduction from axiomatic primitives—a hallmark of science. Each, on the other hand, may represent an epiphenomenon of brain activity unrelated to the necessary and sufficient conditions that are the true origins of the mind.

Explanations of how the brain makes the mind, therefore, remain elusive. Much more is thought to be known than actually is. If this were just an arcane theoretical enterprise, this would just be another of those disappointments that inflict an underdeveloped science. Because of the ramifications of this dearth of real understanding in such practical environments as the courtroom, however, much more serious consequences are unavoidable. This brings us to the point at which the newest and the most currently popular techniques for examining the brain must be introduced. A basic knowledge of the technical as well as the logical details of these remarkable machines is absolutely necessary for future lawyers and judges if they are to exert a proper role in jurisprudence and forensics.

2.4 Brain Imaging Methods[6]

As just discussed, the use of the electrical activity of the brain using relatively large electrodes (to produce the low frequency, widely distributed EEG) or tiny electrodes (to record the activity of single cells) largely dominated the study of brain physiology prior to the 1990s. On the anatomical side, X-rays and radioisotopes were widely used to define the structure of the brain and other organs of the body. Computer Aided Tomography—the early X-ray CAT scan capable of reconstructing the three-dimensional structure of the brain from the two-dimensional shadograms of an X-ray image—was first developed in the 1960s (by Godfrey Hounsfield and Allan Cormack; Cormack, 1963; 1964). Theoretical papers provided the foundation for Hounsfield's application of the technique in a medical setting. They jointly received the Nobel Prize in 1979 for this important work.

The word tomography, however, is now used more generally to indicate any type of three-dimensional reconstruction technique from what may be highly degraded or ambiguous information. Tomography has two tasks to perform. The first is to generate a meaningful, internal map from a series of incomplete measurements. To do so requires a complex calculation that depends upon the combination of a large amount of information ultimately ending in a two-dimensional picture or slice whose thickness is determined by the mechanical resolution capacity of the imaging system.

The second task is to combine the data depicting the two-dimensional slices into a three-dimensional, volumetric map of the internal structure. That is, a two-dimensional map is made of a slice of the brain and the information stored. Either the subject or the imaging device is then moved slightly and another slice recorded. The collection of data can then be depicted on a computer display screen in a variety of manners. For example, a plot of the entire brain may be rotated so that a slice composed of a collection of "voxels"[7] collected from a completely different plane than the one initially recorded may be displayed. For that matter, it is also possible to magnify or color the image to highlight regions of special interest or of varying magnitude. Depending on the particular measuring device, elaborate mathematical routines are required to interpret the shadows obtained by a system that is really only able to trace the course of an X-ray beam or atomic particle along a single line or that otherwise represents an ambiguous piece of data. Tomography of this kind, of course, has wide applications in many different sciences other than cognitive neuroscience.

X-ray tomography has a very important property—it is non-invasive and does not require surgery to expose some of the most important details of brain structure, for example. However, it also has substantial limitations. Three are especially disadvantageous in comparison to more modern techniques. First, it can only measure structure and tells us nothing about the functional integrity or activity of a region of the brain. Second, it requires a powerful computer and elaborate algorithms to carry out the reconstruction of the two- or three-dimensional image. Third, the repeated passage of the beam of X-rays exposes the person whose tissue is being imaged to what can be a significant dosage of this kind of ionizing radiation.

Some of these disadvantages have been progressively reduced by two new techniques that now have largely replaced X-ray tomography—positron emission tomography (PET) and functional magnetic resonance imaging (fMRI). The main advantage they enjoy is that both are able to measure the function, as well as the structure, of brain tissue. The PET technique involves the injection of radioactive substances into the body while the fMRI is quite remarkable in that it requires nothing other than the application of strong magnetic fields. Magnetic fields, although strong enough to throw heavy metal objects about, are not otherwise known to have any deleterious effects on the human body.

I now briefly discuss the PET and fMRI methods to provide an introduction to their respective technologies. Later chapters will discuss their application in legal proceedings.

A. Positron Emission Tomography

The history of the PET scanning idea is complex and many different people contributed to several of the important developments that led to its invention. Anyone interested in a detailed discussion of its history should read the article by Wagner (1998). Two milestone papers published by Ter-Pegossian, Phelps, Hoffman, and Mullani (1975) and by Phelps, Hoffman, Mullani, and Ter-Pegossian (1975) respectively document what was apparently the first application of the PET technique.

PET scans are based on the selective needs of the body to process different molecules during metabolic activity. For those of us interested in the brain, the most important metabolic process involves the oxidation of glucose as the brain carries out its functions and the subsequent depletion of its oxygen supply. As a result, the body responds by increasing oxygenated blood flow to the activated regions. Thus, the guiding assumption is that all we have to do to link cognition and brain activity is to observe regions of high oxygenated blood flow when cognitive states are varied.

This is far easier said than done, of course, but it can and has been done to quite a remarkable degree by using radioactive indicators. The trick in the PET system is to "tag" blood with a radioactive substance whose breakdown can be used as an indicator of a detectable and localizable reaction.

To understand how this happens, we must digress for a moment to consider a little nuclear physics, particularly the decay of unstable forms of radioactive oxygen.[8] The nuclei of normal, stable oxygen consists of 16 nuclear particles (8 protons and 8 neutrons) and is referred to as O^{16}. However, if a substance (for example, water — H_2O containing O^{16}) is placed in a cyclotron, the oxygen nuclei will lose one of its neutrons and become O^{15}. A PET image is generated because it is fortuitous that O^{15} is very unstable and very quickly (it has a half life of about two minutes) decays back to O^{16} by incorporating a replacement for the lost neutron. When the reaction $O^{15} > O^{16}$ occurs, a very unstable piece of sub-nuclear material — a positron (the anti-particle of an electron) is released. Positrons have a very short lifetime because they almost immediately interact with the first electron they meet and produce two photons — particles of light — as the positron and the electron annihilate each other.

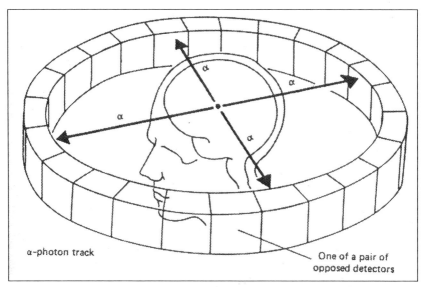

α-photon track

One of a pair of
opposed detectors

Figure 2.1 *The ring of photon detectors as they are positioned in a PET scanning imager. Opposing detectors must be simultaneously activated to detect a pair of photons marking the annihilation of a positron emitted from a radioactive tracer in a patient's body. (From Robinson and Uttal, 1983)*

This mutual annihilation and the emission of the two photons is the necessary condition for our ability to detect brain activity with a PET system. The two photons must move away from each other in exactly the opposite direction and at exactly the same speed. Therefore, if we have an array of photon detectors (such as that shown in Figure 2.1), and if a diametrically opposed pair of the detectors on the circumference are simultaneously activated we know that an $O^{15} > O^{16}$ decay occurred somewhere along the line connecting the two detectors. The more positron decays we observe, the more radioactive oxygen had been present, and the more neural activity, it may be concluded, was occurring there. Should there appear to be a locus of activity that correlated with a cognitive state, the tendency would be to assign that area the mental function that was being manipulated.

By applying appropriate tomographic mathematical algorithms, it is possible to develop a three-dimensional map of the regions of the brain that are activated, for example, by instructing the person to think about that archetypical "cow." If one accepts the assumption that particular kinds of thoughts are localized in particular parts of the brain, then associations may presumably be drawn between these brain loci and thoughts.

The PET scan device was a powerful step forward from X-ray CAT scans which could only measure structure. The two most important advantages of the PET technique were its ability to measure functional activity and its relative non-invasiveness; no surgery was necessary. However, it too suffered from several disadvantages. First, it was not completely noninvasive. Radioactive substance had to be injected into the body; although this was at a low dosage level, it was not inconsequential. Second, PET scans were slightly blurred because of a decay property of the positron—it was not immediately annihilated. Instead, the positron was able to travel a measurable distance (as much as a millimeter or two) in an unknown direction before it interacted with an electron to produce the pair of photons. This essentially added uncertainty to the exact location of the original decay of the O^{15} and thus tended to blur the final picture.

B. Functional Magnetic Resonance Imaging (fMRI)

Despite the obvious advantage of being able to record the metabolic activity of the living brain, the disadvantages just mentioned of the PET scanning technique were well overcome by another parallel development in the history of these remarkable imaging devices. In the early 1970s, Raymond Damadian (Damadian, 1971) reported his invention of a device that was sensitive to the difference between the magnetic resonances of isolated normal and tumor tissue. From his original test-tube experiments he went on to develop a whole body scanner in 1977. Although a number of other workers were later to refine the mathematical techniques required to process the signals emanating from what came to be called the Magnetic Resonance Imaging (MRI) device, it was clearly Damadian's genius that created what many consider to be the most highly developed tool for noninvasively studying the structure and functions of the body available to us today.

The next step which took MRI from the anatomic level pioneered by Damadian to the functional or physiological level (fMRI) was made by Ogawa, Lee, Kay, and Tank (1990). This group was largely responsible for inventing a device that could magnetically track functional activity instead of structure. They, thus, initiated an enormous outflow of research in which the functional aspects of the brain have been studied in the last two decades.

The fMRI as a physiological or functional tool and the MRI as an anatomic tool have few of the limitations of their predecessors. They require no injections or ionizing radiation and are theoretically unlimited in their spatial resolution, a problem that plagued both the PET and CAT scanning devices. How they work is one of the most interesting stories in modern science. I now provide an abbreviated explanation of the physics on which the device is based.

Magnetic resonance is a phenomenon attributable to the atomic physics of gases, liquids, and solids. It was first discovered by Rabi, Zacarias, Millman and

Kusch (1937). In the 1930s, it was an outgrowth of then recent developments in quantum theory which specified that the atomic nucleus can have a magnetic moment—a cumulative measure of the strength of the magnetic fields of the nuclear protons—under certain conditions. For those atoms that have an odd number of protons, there can be a measurable magnetic moment for that nucleus. However, for atoms with an even number of protons, the magnetic moments of the protons cancel each other out. Because the major constituent of our bodies is water and the atomic nucleus of Hydrogen has only one proton, many MRI measurements are largely measures of the properties of water (although not universally so as we see later).

In the usual situation with no external magnetic field applied, the orientations or directions of the magnetic moments of each proton are random. Therefore, any effort to measure their collective value would fail to detect any cumulative field. In the presence of a large magnetic field produced by a very large electromagnet surrounding the person (or specimen) under study, however, all of the protons can be forced to line up with the field oriented in the same direction as that of the large magnetic field.

A further complication of magnetized protons is that their magnetic moments are not completely stable. They tend to wobble around the direction to which they have been aligned, a process referred to as spin precession. The strength of this large magnetic field (B) and the kind of atom (α) determines the frequency (F) of wobble or precession of the magnetic field of each proton in accord with what is known as the Larmor equation:

$$F = \alpha \times B$$

Equation 2.1

The trajectory of this precession or wobble is shown in Figure 2.2. Obviously it will differ from one substance (characterized by the parameter α) to another. This difference in precession from one kind of tissue to another, therefore, is the key to distinguishing between different substances and their states deep within the body.

A basic fact of modern electromagnetic theory is that if a magnet is accelerated, oscillated, or rotated or in some other way has its trajectory changed, it will radiate a radio frequency signal whose frequency is related to the magnitude of that change. Thus, a charged proton that is wobbling or precessing will radiate a radio frequency signal with a frequency that is a direct function of the precession. If all of the magnetic moments have been aligned to the same orientation by the large magnet, this signal will be large enough to be measured by external radio frequency receivers. Given differences in α, these emitted radio frequencies will differ from tissue to tissue.

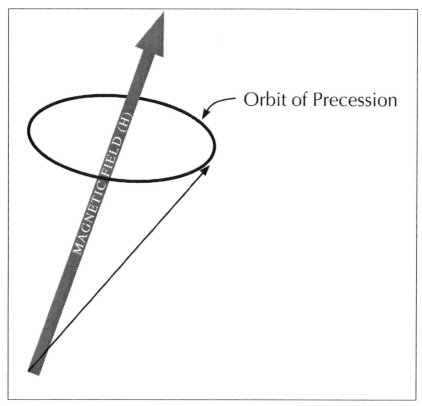

Figure 2.2 The trajectory of the precession or wobble of a proton in a strong magnetic field. This precession radiates radio signals at the frequency specified by the Larmor equation. (Drawing adapted from Mary Zhu.)

If another, but very much smaller, magnetic field (typically 1/1000th of the strength of the large magnetic field) is applied to the precessing protons by means of a small coil electromagnet usually placed inside the large magnet itself, this smaller signal will momentarily slightly misalign the magnetic moments of the protons. After the small magnet field is turned off, the protons "relax" back to the collective orientation driven by the large magnet's field. The result is that there is a momentary change in the precession of the protons that affects the radio frequency signal being radiated.

The time that it takes for the proton's magnetic field to return to its original orientation after the small magnetic field is removed is the key dependent variable in calculating the final fMRI image. Different measures of this time can be used in different ways to detect various structural or functional differences in the brain. Depending on which time measurement is used, different structures may be highlighted, activity changes noted, or chemical activity traced. For cognitive neuroscientists, it is the functional application that plays the key role in our ability to observe changes in brain activity during different mental states.

In summary, changes in the emitted radio frequency that occurs as a result of the disturbance caused by a relatively small (compared to the field exerted by the large magnet) magnetic field is the basis of a differential measurement.[9] The differences vary as a function of the nature of the tissue and its state as well as the strength of the magnetic fields. Thus, differences in the fMRI signal will occur between regions of high activity and regions of low activity.

Specifically, in the context of determining the relation between brain activity and thought, the fMRI deice is able to detect differences in the blood oxygen level dependence or BOLD.[10] Since the relative amounts of oxygenated and deoxygenated blood differ in active and inactive regions and their magnetic susceptibilities are different, the fMRI is capable of determining which brain regions are active during some cognitive process and which are inactive.

The process, of course, is under the control and analysis of powerful computer programs which take what are essentially meaningless individual measurements and reconstruct first a slice of the brain and then a full three-dimensional depiction of the brain, all without violating a person's skin or injecting a radioactive substance.

In 1993, Paul C. Lauterbur and Peter Mansfield received the Nobel Prize for work done in the 1970s in developing algorithms that convert the raw data into complete and meaningful images. An important part of their work was to show that if the magnetic field of the small coil was spatially graduated, rather than uniform, it produced the wonderful multi-dimensional pictures which are now used so extensively in many fields of biology and medicine.

In recent years, new techniques have been developed that are specialized for particular applications. Among the most important of these is Diffusion Tensor Imaging (DTI). Because of its sensitivity to water molecules, it is able to track the three-dimensional course of the myelinated nerve fibers (white matter) in the brain, tissue that is not imaged well with conventional MRI techniques. Diffusion Tensor Imaging depends on the ability to measure the slight diffusion of water molecules from predetermined points in the brain (called seeds) in particular directions. The technique requires that gradients of magnetic fields be applied in six directions. This produces complex patterns of response that have to be described as mathematical tensors. The resulting images show the course of nerve fiber tracts in the brain, thus detailing the ways in which various gray matter nuclei are interconnected. The result is extraordinarily beautiful and scientifically interesting maps of the neural tracts and has given rise to an entire new method of studying the brain—tractography.

As powerful as these technique are, there are a number of problems that emerge when we apply them to the study of the relationship between the mind and the brain. These problems will be discussed in the next section.

2.5 The Analysis of fMRI Data

Images produced by the fMRI imaging devices are both aesthetically beautiful and technologically marvelous. They have opened the door to an array of scientific studies quite unimaginable only a few decades ago. Furthermore, they have already become important, if not essential, tools in modern medical diagnosis and therapy. The amount of human suffering alleviated by these magnificent devices is comparable only to the invention of anesthesia or water purification. It is impossible to say too much about their positive aspects.

However, as beautiful and informative as these colorful images are, they are not without their limitations and they cannot be uncritically applied to all scientific or medical applications without careful scrutiny. Nowhere are these limitations more evident than in the study of the relationship between the mind and the brain, the target of cognitive neuroscience. Although some of the challenges that confront fMRI and PET studies are due to the technology of the system itself, by far the more serious ones are created by the psychological and conceptual issues arising when one attempts to measure brain correlates of mental activity.

Briefly, some of these technical problems confronting the researcher who wishes to study mental activity with the fMRI include:

- The differences between experimental and control conditions are very small. Some have argued that they may be as small as 1%. This makes the system very sensitive to noise; at best, the signal-to-noise ratios are very small. It is very easy to read marginally correlated random activity as a true signal.
- It requires a great deal of both mental and physical cooperation on the part of the subject in an fMRI to maintain bodily position and to "think" in the way that the experimenter wishes.
- Brain activity does not immediately lead to changes in the blood. Several seconds may pass before the oxygen level of an activated area begins to decline. Therefore, the fMRI is not an immediate or direct measure of either mental or brain activity.
- Artifacts of many kinds alter the responses produced by fMRI machines. Not the least of which is the noise produced by the devices when altering the required magnetic fields. This is especially true in fMRI studies of auditory mechanisms. The magnets in such systems are not quiet and impose a background, impulsive noise on the acous-

tic stimuli that are being used in an experiment on auditory sound recognition. Although there is some suggestion that this is not a serious problem (Healy, Moser, Morrow-Odom, Hal, and Fridiksson, 2007) in distinguishing between normal and aphasic patients, it remains a potential artifact in any auditory experiment.

- The beauty and the seeming face validity of the images leads to their becoming extremely potent evidence in any debate. It is now established (McCabe and Castel, 2007) that people are more likely to accept the credulity of a published report when a brain image, rather than a graph of some kind, is used to present the data. Furthermore, Roskies (2008) refers to these potent images as perpetuating an "illusion of inferential proximity" (p. 29). The point is that the attractiveness and seeming directness of these images gives them an intellectual and scientific potency that they do not entirely deserve.

- Perhaps most important is that fMRI and PET images exert a powerful force on our theory and organizing concepts. As Bookheimer (2002) noted:

> "As brain imaging data are nearly always presented in terms of focal centers of task-related activity, it is commonly assumed that all brain imaging research assumes a strict interpretation of the principles of modularity as detailed by Fodor (1983)."
> (p. 183)

The very power of these devices to see what has not been seen previously may in this way distort our view of the world as it actually is.

The major difficulty, however, as indicated in Chapter 1, is our difficulty in defining the subjective mental states and properties that we choose to compare to the objective measures provided by the brain imaging devices. The result of the amorphousness of our definitions of the mind (compared to the precision of measuring physical properties such as relaxation times in an fMRI scan) leads to a number of other related difficulties. For example, in any experiment in which the independent variable is a psychological state, it is extremely difficult to control exactly what a subject is thinking. Simple instructions such as "think about a cow" may be relatively easy to express but it is difficult to confirm that the cognitive manipulation that was expected actually happened. Even more uncertain is the cognitive result of the instruction—"do not think about a cow." Again, however easy it may be to express this instruction, it may actually lead to paradoxical results with the instructed persons unable to get the mental "cow" out of their thoughts (Wegner, Schneider, Carter, and White, 1987). The resulting ambiguity of what a person is thinking belies the necessity to crisply control what is a major requirement of any experiment—the clear-cut specification of the independent variable. No matter how precise the measurement of the dependent variable—in this case the image of the brain response—produced by the magnetic imaging system, there will always be a substantial amount of uncertainty in interpreting the functional relationships between the stimulus (the thought of a cow) and the response (the brain response image).

One result of this ambiguity and lack of control over a person's thought is that brain imaging studies typically produce very variable response patterns. This variability can be observed at several different levels even though individual responses may be relatively stable when retested for the individual. First, brain images from different people vary substantially when compared with each other. Next and even more substantially, studies carried out in different laboratories (even with what are supposed to be similar methods) are now known to produce extremely variable results. This extreme variability leads to serious questions about the validity of the measures being made. That is, the question is raised concerning whether or not the resulting brain images are actually measuring what we think they are measuring? The persisting and unresolved question—are these responses actually representations of our thought processes?—cannot be completely ignored.

Although it is sometimes argued that the brain images are direct reflections of the activity of the organ that is responsible for the mind, in empirical fact they are not quite as direct as they initially may seem. Instead, there is a chain of logical assumptions that link the observed brain responses with the correlated mental activity.

All of this work is based on a primary assumption—an axiomatic premise— that is the intellectual foundation of this entire field. *This primary assumption is that the mental states can be adequately well defined, that they can be divided up into quasi-independent cognitive modules, and that the neural mechanisms, by means of which they are encoded, are represented by relatively stable locales of the brain.* Although rarely overtly expressed, this idea (or group of ideas) is universal throughout this entire enterprise. As we shall see the empirical data does not support this hypothesis as soundly as many current cognitive neuroscience scientists would hope.

There are also a number of secondary assumptions. One of the most important is that the subtraction method, either as it is embodied in the double dissociation procedure or in some more complex statistical method, is a valid means of analyzing stimulus response relationships of this kind. That this is not so has been argued by Van Orden, Pennington, and Stone (2001) among others.

It is further assumed that the critical regions are identified by their high level of metabolic activity, as indicated by the increased depletion of oxygenated blood. To this is chained the assumption that increased mental activity forces increases in metabolic activity. Furthermore, there is an implicit assumption that different patterns of mental activity will produce distinguishably different patterns of oxygen utilization. In this context, the possibility that highly distinct details of the microscopic neuronal activity might integrate into indistinguishable global metabolic activities is generally overlooked.

To this cluster of difficulties are added many other technical and conceptual assumptions on which the final conclusion—selected regional activation by specific thoughts—is based. Obviously, the fMRI, because it comes from the brain has a certain amount of face validity. (See my earlier discussion on the ill-deserved potency of fMRI images.) Nevertheless, like any other neural correlate of mental activity, it is logically distant from the direct evidence needed to authenticate the theory it represents.

In this regard, it is not too far-fetched to suggest that the colorful images of brain activity are not actually measures of the brain mechanisms accounting for the encoding or representation of mental processes. Instead, they may be manifestations of physical processes such as the nonlinear wave mechanics of a container of variably shaped viscous material. We do know that specific patterns of activity will occur on metal plates, a phenomenon first described by Ernst Chladni (1756–1827). Similar nonlinear wave activity determined by the shape of the skull has also been used to explain the EEG (Kennedy, 1959) and as a basis for a "harmonic" theory of mental activity (Lehar, 2003). The implications of this admittedly "out-of-the–box" suggestion is that although modestly correlated with stimulus conditions, the distribution of activity in the brain measured with fMRI systems might be due to idiosyncratic anatomic and physiological events unrelated to mental activity.

Further suggestive evidence that this might be the case can be gleaned from the fact that there is much less variability in test-retest experiments carried out on a single individual using fMRI methods than on repeated experiments across groups of subjects or even across laboratories (Aron, Gluck, and Poldrack, 2006). The significance of this study is that variability appears to increase the larger and more inclusive the sample. This suggests that there are no fixed or universal properties of the imaged response. Instead, there is an increasingly high degree of idiosyncrasy due to factors other then where or how the brain is producing mental activity. If this were true, it would be difficult to find a criterion image that could be used, for example, as an indicator of deception or of any other mental state in a trial.

There are other technical issues that cloud the use of the fMRI as an objective measure of mental activity. Although there are many highly developed statistical techniques for evaluating the role of different areas of the brain in specified cognitive processes, all basic protocols require the basic idea of differencing or subtracting two responses from each other; one—the control image—produced when the specified mental state is not occurring and the other—the experimental image—produced when the subject is instructed to think about a particular event or object or to produce a desired cognitive state. The control image is then subtracted from the experimental image and the remaining brain areas of high activation are then assumed to be the regions in the brain in which the mental process is supposed to be carried out.

As simple in concept as the subtraction process is superficially, it hides a number of potential hazards to the overenthusiastic investigator. For example, the subtraction method obscures some very important facts. First, recall that the areas of activation are designated by the total amount of oxygen present in these areas' blood supply. It is not a detailed examination of the behavior of the complex network of neural interactions that most cognitive neuroscientists believe actually encode cognitive processes. Thus, two radically different patterns of detailed activity (at the neuronal network level) could produce the same integrated images. They would appear in the subtraction process to be identical but could represent diametrically opposed cognitive processes (think "cow" and "no cow"!) and vastly different neural network states.

Raz, Lieber, Soliman, Buhle, Posner, Peterson, and Posner (2004) have also criticized the subtraction method on three additional grounds.

1. The subtraction method may fail to take into account differences in posture (e.g., lying down versus standing erect) that may distort the differences obtained in control and experimental conditions.
2. Cognitive processes vary as a function of stress.
3. Cognitive factors other than those defining the control and experimental conditions may vary due to variations in wakefulness over the duration of the experiment.

Another important issue in understanding the role of the fMRI image as an indicator of mental activity is the significance of the hot spots—the narrowly demarcated regions of peak or maximum activation that are presented as evidence of localization in studies of this kind. These indicators, too, are ambiguous as well as very variable. (I return to amplify my discussion of this issue shortly.)

For the moment, however, let's just consider as basic an attribute as the spatial extent of an activated brain region. It is well appreciated in neuroscientific circles that the measured extent of the activated region is arbitrary since it depends on the criterion level of acceptability selected by the investigator. One reason for this arbitrariness is that the brain responses are not typically localized; instead they are broad regions of the brain activated to a greater or lesser degree under almost any stimulus condition.

The key fact here is that the imaged response to a particular cognitive process is rarely localized to a single peak, but is typically widely distributed across the brain. In the place of a single peak, a more likely response is a sequence of peaks and troughs of activity scattered across and throughout the entire brain.[11] Nevertheless, the criterion that dominated thinking in the years prior to the twenty-first century was to isolate the highest peak and assign to it the responsibility for the particular cognitive process being manipulated. Since there was widely distributed activity in addition to these maximum values, it was necessary to apply a threshold level of activation as a criterion for selecting the maximum peak. This is indicated by the dotted line in Figure 2.3. If the threshold was set too high, some levels of activity would be below this threshold and ignored. However much they may be ignored, some low values for activation may not represent inactive or irrelevant responses. In fact, apropos of our discussion of the subtraction process, they may represent substantially different neural network states whose cumulative activity simply summed to the same value in the control and experimental conditions respectively. The typical strategy—to pick the highest peak or peaks and to claim that these are uniquely associated with the cognitive process to the exclusion of all of the other activity—is, therefore, a recipe for misunderstanding.

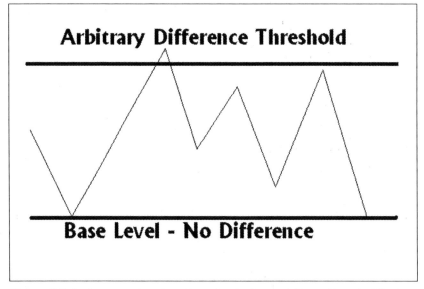

Figure 2.3 A diagram showing the effect of an arbitrary threshold on what is to be considered as a peak of "activation." If the threshold is set too high, secondary peaks may be missed. Even more serious is that apparently low levels of activation may hide massive differences of activity at the microscopic level.

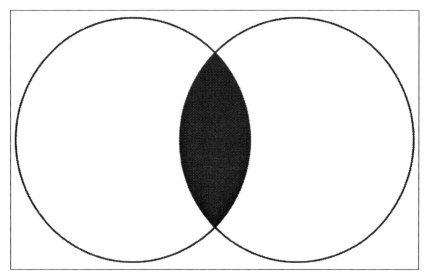

Figure 2.4 *A Venn-type diagram showing how two widely distributed responses may appear to produce a localized response by producing a fallacious region of intersection.*

Yet, this is exactly what was being done in the preponderance of studies reported in the early imaging literature; a very small number of isolated peaks was associated with a particular cognitive process. This approach, based as it is on the assumption that modular cognitive processes are localized in circumscribed regions of the brain, led many researchers to conclude (by a process that can only be described as circular reasoning) that circumscribed localization of modular cognitive processes is the characteristic organizational pattern of the mind-brain. As we shortly see, the newest meta-reviewed data do not support either the initial assumption or the final conclusion.

The extent of a peak activation can also be underestimated as a result of the statistical summation of the responses from several different individuals or groups of individuals. If three or four rather broad and indistinct areas of activation are plotted in the same space, then there will be a much smaller common area or "intersection" that falsely appears to represent a highly localized area of activation. Averaging of this kind can be depicted in the form of a Venn type diagram as shown in Figure 2.4. The common area or "intersection," which can be interpreted as a narrowly localized functional region, however, is an artifact of the cumulating or averaging process. The task for the neuroscientist (and ultimately the court) is to decide if the common response area actually defines a circumscribed brain region or is an illusion produced by the statistical summation. Given that the size of the original activated regions is arbitrary (determined by the experimenter's choice of threshold) and influenced by the estimated size of a common intersection area, there is a compelling argument that such a "peak" activation is actually much less sharply localized than has conventionally been assumed.

With this collection of conceptual challenges highlighted, we can now turn to the most serious empirical problem—variability—for anyone who still believes that the brain is composed of narrowly localized regions that represent modular cognitive processes.

2.6 On Variability and Reliability

Throughout history, virtually all scientists have agreed that the hallmark of a quality empirical result is its reliability. That is, when an experiment is repeated does it produce the same results? Nothing can more quickly demolish an observation-based hypothesis quicker than an investigator's inability to repeat an experiment and failure to show that the same (within limits) results occur in the repetition as in the original experiment. Even better, a public demonstration of the same results from an equivalent experiment carried out by another investigator would add enormous support to a claim by the original experimenter. Failure to replicate, on the other hand, can be devastating. Despite how much we may want to believe in a result because it might have some important contribution to make (e.g., test tube nuclear fusion as a potential source of boundless amounts of energy), even the most attractive and exciting ideas are quickly abandoned if the phenomenon cannot be repeatedly demonstrated and shown to be reasonably reliable.

The history of cognitive neuroscience, unfortunately, is filled with evidence of inconsistent and irreproducible findings. Much of this unreliability can be attributed to the complexity of the mind-brain system and the fact that even very slight changes in the method may produce dramatic shifts in results.

For a number of conceptual, historical, and technical reasons (some of which have already been discussed) there has been a tendency for many researchers to assume that their experiments supported extreme localization theories and that particular parts of the brain are responsible for particular cognitive processes. However, in the first decade of the twenty-first century new ways of interpreting brain image data raised serious questions about this theoretical perspective. Lurking behind the reports of isolated peaks was a lack of reliability and repeatability that largely went unnoticed in the decade of the 1990s when brain imaging first became available and then exploded into both scientific and popular awareness. This inconsistency became much clearer when a new approach involving widespread pooling of data began to be applied to brain imaging findings. This method was embodied in a strategy often used in other sciences where reliability was a question—the meta-study. The basic idea of a cognitive neuroscientific meta-study is to gather together all of the imaging experiments that explored brain responses to the same cognitive stimulus. Studies of this kind were carried out by scholars who were not usually collecting their own data, but were depending upon the published reports of others. Unlike the typical individual experimental report in which the results from *a group of individual experimental participants* are pooled to come to some conclusion, in a meta-study the results from *a group of reported studies* are pooled together to come to a conclusion.

There are two main ways that meta-studies can be carried out: meta-reviews and meta-analyses. A meta-review simply pools the data from a large group of experiments and tabulates the activation responses in the same table or plots all of these results together on the same brain map. The latter is an especially good way of showing the spatial variability of the sample of experiments. Typically, meta-reviews simply collect the locations where the individual experimenters reported activation maxima or peaks. At the very least, meta-reviews dramatically demonstrate that there is an enormous degree of variability, if not disagreement, over the brain regions to which different experimenters allocate certain psychological functions.

More complex statistical studies (meta-analyses) can also be carried out that seek to highlight some concordance or agreement between some aspects of the recorded images of responses. The goal in this case is to look at the temporal and spatial relations to extract a group of brain regions that show some evidence of working synchronously. In this approach, the statistically associated regions are plotted rather than the raw data. One of the most common forms of meta-analysis used in the past few years has been the Activation Likelihood Estimate (ALE) technique proposed by Turkeltaub, Eden, Jones, and Zeffiro (2002). This kind of meta-review is based on the probability of localization of many peak activations reported from a large group of studies. The particular example shown in Figure 2.5 is from a meta-analysis of single-word reading.

The first important meta-review of the twenty-first century was carried out by Cabeza and Nyberg (2000). They heroically consolidated the data from 275 PET and fMRI studies of a wide range of cognitive processes. Figure 2.6 displays one of the results of their review. This picture depicts the various places that investigators had reported peak activations for a traditional psychological experiment—working memory, a subset of the 275 studies reviewed by Cabeza and Nyberg. Not only does their sample show that investigators have found high levels of activity across most of the cerebral cortex, but activity was also recorded in the cerebellum, a part of the brain that has not been traditionally associated with memory other than simple forms of classical conditioning. Indeed, the only region not showing some activity in this set of experiments was the temporal lobe of the brain and this was probably a technical artifact. Prior to 2000, fMRI recordings from the temporal lobe of the brain were very difficult to obtain.

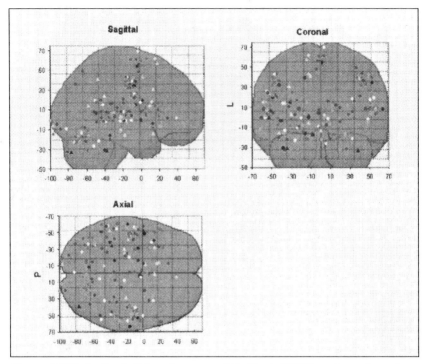

Figure 2.5 Turkeltaub, Eden, Jones, and Zeffiro's (2002) meta-review of the literature on brain images of single-word reading. This figure shows the distribution of 172 reported peaks from 11 PET studies. This three-dimensional means of plotting data assumes that the brain is transparent so that the broad distribution of responses throughout the volume of the brain can be discerned. (Reprinted from Turkeltaub, Eden, Jones, and Seffiro, 2002, with the permission of the publisher, Elsevier Science USA.)

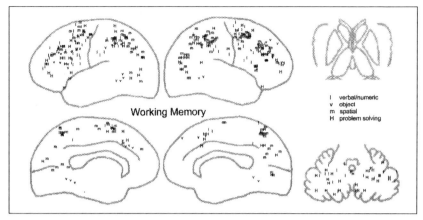

Figure 2.6 *Cabeza and Nyberg's (2000) pioneering meta-review of the literature on brain images of working memory showing the widespread responses recorded from a sample of 275 PET and fMRI studies. (Reprinted from Cabeza and Nyberg, 2000, with the permission of the publisher, MIT Press.)*

A meta-review of a more recent sample of experiments on a completely different topic has been carried out by Neuman, Lohman, Derfuss, and Von Cramon (2005). They consolidated the results of 239 activation peaks from 14 different experiments dealing with the Stroop effect, the delay introduced into the enunciation of a color name that was printed in a color other than the color named.[12] Their findings for both a meta-review and a meta-analysis are shown in Figure 2.7. The top three brain pictures show the distribution of the activation peaks reported in the 14 experiments. These activation maxima are plotted on a two-dimensional depiction of a "glass brain" to help in visualizing the three-dimensional distribution of activations throughout the brain. The bottom three pictures show the result of the more formal meta-analysis. The regions highlighted there are regions that are concurrently activated. The general point made by both sets of pictures is that widely distributed activation peaks are reported when experimental participants carry out the conditions of a particular psychological task. Whether this variability results from poorly controlled experimental conditions or reflects the true distributed biology of this cognitive process is unknown. What is crystal clear is that there is no evidence of narrow localization of the mental activity associated with the Stroop phenomenon.

Several conclusions can be drawn from these meta-reviews. First, reliability from experiment to experiment is low. Second, activation peaks are reported scattered over major portions of the brain. The idea that a specific location is activated by a specific cognitive process is severely questioned by these findings. Instead these meta-studies indicate that broadly dispersed regions of the brain are activated by relatively well-controlled stimulus situations.

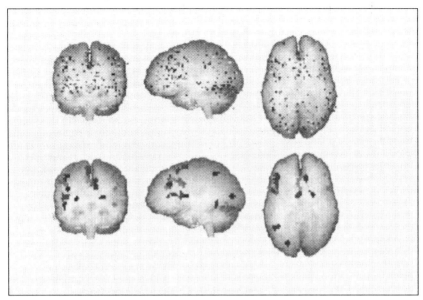

Figure 2.7 Neuman, Lohman, Derfuss, and Von Crammon's (2005) meta-review of the literature on brain images of the Stroop Effect. The location of 239 activation peaks from 16 fMRI studies are plotted again showing the broad distribution of reported responses in the upper three views. The lower three views show the results of a formal meta-analysis. Both sets demonstrate the breadth and distribution of the responses to the Stroop experiment. (Reprinted from Neuman, Lohmann, Derfuss, and Von Crammon, 2005 [Copyright 2005] with the permission of Wiley-Liss, Inc., a subsidiary of John Wiley and Sons.)

These meta-reviews do not mean that the brain is homogenous and that all its parts are equally activated when it is at work producing mental processes. Rather they set the stage for a theoretical point of view that is contrary to the foundation assumption underlying much of modern cognitive neuroscience. That traditional assumption is that "modular cognitive components are reliably localized in restricted regions of the brain." A more modern set of guiding assumptions, driven by the meta-reviews of the kind described here, can be offered:

1. Any mental act is likely to activate broad regions of the brain.
2. Any region of the brain is likely to be activated by many different mental acts.
3. Mental activity is represented by complex, widely distributed systems in the brain.

4. The brain activity that encodes or represents mental activity is highly variable from individual to individual and from experiment to experiment.

Collectively, these assumptions may be referred to as Distributed Neural
Systems Theory (DNST). There are today two different versions of DNST. The
first carries over some of the a priori assumptions of the older localization school
of thought. That is, that the distributed locations are themselves considered to be
more specific in their functions than not. This version argues that the functions of
the different nodes or centers are specific and that we can analyze their respective
functions by appropriate cognitive and brain imaging functions. The alternative
version of DNST argues, on the contrary, that there are no definable nodes, only
a system of diffuse and ill-defined regions whose function varies with the cognitive task as hand. Future research will have to resolve this brewing controversy
as well as the problem of the source of the variability.

There are, however, several possible explanations that can be considered
now for the broad distribution of brain responses and the variability that is observed between experiments. The first is that the whole approach of using brain
images is methodologically questionable. The suggestion here is that the imaging
technique is simply too blunt a tool to examine the fine detail necessary to understand how the brain makes the mind. Its general inadequacies are exacerbated
by the selection of arbitrary thresholds and the absence of good control over the
psychological states used as independent variables or stimuli.

The second explanation is that the activated area or areas that are purported
to represent a mental process may actually be extremely variable from person to
person, from experiment to experiment, and from laboratory to laboratory. Thus,
individual and group variability produce widely discrepant, although not incorrect, results. This point of view supports the conclusion that the brain itself is very
variable and no universal laws of cognitive representation are tenable—different
brains encode the same mental activity in different ways. This second explanation also suggests that it is unlikely that there is going to be a standard response
or activation site (or even a reliable pattern of sites) that can be specifically associated with a particular cognitive process. In other words, a single thought may
be represented by a wide variety of different brain mechanisms. This would not
speak well for the use of brain images in decision making in the courtroom.

The third explanation for the wide variability of the response is that there is
in fact no direct relationship between activity in a specific locale or locales for any
mental process. The responses are not just variable but are unrelated to such a cognitive state such as intentional deception or lying. What we have been assuming to
be causal relations are actually only spurious correlations. Alternatively, observed
brain activity may simply be some kind of generalized response to emotion or some
common aspect of thought that cannot be specifically associated with any particu-

lar cognitive process. In other words, the whole idea of using brain images as indicators of a specific mental process may be an excursion into pseudoscience.

In summary, there are enough suggestions in this very complex neuroscientific literature to argue that the hope that we will find specific signs of particular cognitive processes in brain images may not be a fulfillable goal. Certainly, at present there is insufficient support for the idea that PET or fMRI systems will be able to read the mind or to account for aberrant behavior to a degree that would permit us to present them as objective evidence in a courtroom. How far we are from a situation in which such measures are going to be useful in the jurisprudence and forensic domains will become clearer as I turn to potential applications of brain imaging in the courtroom in the next chapter.

Endnotes

1. Even this widely accepted assumption is disputed by a minority of cognitive neuroscientists who argue that the entire body is involved in producing the mind. Although many kinds of bodily functions obviously can affect our mental processes, it is the brain that carries out the information processing that is so mysteriously transformed into cognition. It would be logically inconsistent for neuroscientists to carry out brain research without accepting the most basic axiom—the brain is the organ of mind and its action, in principle, fully explains mental activity. Such an inconsistency would mean that the cognitive neuroscientist could never be sure of the results of an experiment because some invisible or uncontrolled factor might be perverting the findings. Any theological or philosophical notions of dualism would make the situation ever worse.

2. Typical correlation coefficients between brain images and mental states (as well as in may other kinds of widely accepted psychological experiments) are around 0.33. This is a very low value on which to base strong conclusions. Such a correlation accounts for only about 10% of the causal effects in an experiment.

3. Although Graham and Gerard did their early work on muscle fibers rather than neurons, their techniques were immediately transferred to neurons with prodigious results. The ability to record from very small single cells was clearly the major technological breakthrough in cellular neurophysiology in the second half of the twentieth century.

4. As I write these words, the popular press is touting the accomplishment of a simulated neural network supposedly comparable to "one half a mouse brain" (8000 simulated neurons). This report suggested that "biologically consistent dynamic properties" emerged. These were said to have "characteristics of thought patterns" and produced response patterns similar to the "staggered coordinated patterns seen in nature." These claims seem outlandish a priori

since it is not yet known what these patterns would be in a real brain. Much greater clarification and a complete and peer-reviewed presentation of these results must be provided before such claims can be taken seriously.

5. Brain localization has had a long history in cognitive neuroscience. Phrenology was an early version and was ultimately rejected. However, the basic idea that a specific place on the brain was associated with a particular cognitive process has had a deep and persistent influence on current thinking. Prior to the development of the brain imaging devices, the main approach was surgery or chemical deactivation or taking advantage of traumatic brain injuries. Although the techniques varied, the same underlying assumption—localized regions of the brain were associated with specific cognitive processes—has been the foundation of much of today's mind-brain theory. Fortunately, as we shortly see, modern cognitive neuroscience is moving away from this kind of localization theory.

6. A much more complete discussion of brain imaging techniques can be found in my other books (Uttal, 2001;2009).

7. A voxel is the minimum resolvable region within a three-dimensional volume as defined by three coordinates (x, y, and z). It is comparable to a pixel, the minimum resolvable region in a two-dimensional space as defined by two coordinates (x and y).

8. Although oxygen in water is often used as the trace substance, there are many other briefly radioactive materials that also can be used to trace the activity of many different parts of the body in a PET scan. Whatever is the key metabolite for the tissue of interest can be tagged and traced. The PET system is not limited to brain activity nor is it limited to oxygen.

9. This brief discussion of the fMRI process is intended to be as non-technical as I can possibly make it. Another good discussion can be found in Mattson and Simon's (1996) book.

10. The blood has different responses in a magnetic field when it is oxygenated and when it is depleted of oxygen. This difference is the basis of the ability to measure and compare brain activities under control and experimental conditions, respectively. It must be remembered however that the MRI system has many other applications involving other tissues that depend on different metabolic and physiological properties.

11. Although presented as a hypothetical at this point, in a few pages I shall demonstrate that the preponderance of empirical evidence supports this hypothesis.

12. For example, if the word "RED" is printed in blue-colored ink, it would require more time to be enunciated than if it had been printed in red-colored ink.

Chapter 3

Brain Images and the Detection of Deception

Synopsis
3.1 Introduction
3.2 A History of Lie Detection
3.3 A Meta-Review of the Empirical Literature Supposedly Supporting the Use of Brain Imaging as a Lie Detector
    A. Spence, Farrow, Herford, Wilkinson, Zheng, and Woodruff (2001)
    B. Langleben, Schroeder, Maldjian, Gur, McDonald, Ragland, O'Brien, and Childres (2002)
    C. Lee, Liu, Tan, Chan, Mahankali, Feng, Hou, Fox, and Gao (2002)
    D. Ganis, Kosslyn, Stose, Thompson, and Yurgelun-Todd (2003)
    E. Spence, Hunter, Farrow, Green, Leung, Hughes, and Ganesan (2004)
    F. Kozel, Revell, Loberbaum, Shastri, Elhai, Horner, Smith, Nahas, Bohning, and George (2004)
    G. Kozel, Padgett, and George (2004)
    H. Kozel, Johnson, Mu, Grenesko, Laken, and George (2005)
    I. Langleben, Loughhead, Bilker, Rupare, Childress, Busch, and Gur (2005)
    J. Davatzikos, Ruparel, Fan, Shen, Acharyya, Loughhead, Gur, Langleben (2005)
    K. Phan, Magalhaes, Ziemlewicz, Fitzgerald, Green, and Smith (2005)
    L. Lee, Liu, Chan, Ng, Fox, and Gao (2005)
    M. Nunez, Casey, Egner, Hare, Hirsch (2005)
    N. Abe, Suzuki, Tsukiura, Mori, Yamaguchi, Itoh, and Fujii (2006)
    O. Grezes, Berthoz, and Passingham (2006)
    P. Mohamed, Faro, Gordon, Platek, Ahmed, and Williams (2006)
3.4 A Summary of the Sixteen Experiments on Brain Images and Lie Detection
    A. Which Areas are Identified as the Point of Maximum Activity?
    B. What Areas, Other than Maximum Peaks, Are Involved?
    C. Some Inescapable Conclusions
3.5 Evaluation of the Use of Brain Images as Lie Detectors
    A. There is No Single Place or Group of Places that Has Been Empirically Associated with Deception or Any Other Mental Process
    B. Brain Images Do Not Measure Mental Activity Any More Directly Than Does the Polygraph
    C. Lying or Deception is an Ill-Defined Process Probably Composed of Many Different Mental Processes
    D. Validity of the Measures
    E. Practical Problems

3.6 Interim Conclusions
Endnotes

MYTH: There are objective measures that can detect deception.
**TRUTH: No objective method of lie detection works at a level that can sat-
isfy the *Daubert* criteria for admissibility into courtroom proceedings.**

3.1 Introduction

The development of the remarkable brain imaging devices, particularly those
that are capable of measuring functional brain activity, is one of the most important scientific developments in medical history. Their introduction into the
cognitive neuroscience field, furthermore, has revitalized mind-brain studies.
The stodgy old experiments in which the brains of experimental animals were
dissected and the resulting behavior observed seem archaic in the light of devices
such as fMRI. They offer hope that we might be on the verge of surmounting the
barriers that have existed for millennia between empirical behavioral and brain
observations and inferred mind has led some to believe that we, at long last, may
be able to objectively determine whether or not a person is lying. Unfortunately,
as this chapter shows, this hope is not likely to be fulfilled.

For reasons that are quite obvious, it has long been appreciated that behavior, particularly in the form of our utterances describing our thoughts, was a
highly undependable means of determining what a person was thinking. People
are wonderfully capable of hiding their true thoughts and emotions or simulating those emotions when called upon to do so. The skills of actors in mimicking
mental states that they do not actually experience is only a highly refined version
of the ubiquitous ability that almost everybody has to behave "properly" in the
many different roles they play in their daily lives. Further distancing our behavior from our mental states are two other factors: the vested interests that constrain
each of us to distort our memories, current thoughts, hopes, and responses on the
one hand, and the fact that we, as introspective entities, do not ourselves always
know exactly why we behave in the way we do, on the other.

As a result of our inability to access mental processes directly, there are
many problems encountered when one attempts to detect lies by what are believed to be objective measures. Not the least of these problems is that we really
have a very poor idea of what constitutes a lie. Like all other mental states, it
is very difficult to define a lie. If a person is accurately describing what they
are thinking at the moment, but it conflicts with independent evidence, is that a
lie? Is a person who is told to lie (as is the case in every experimental study of
deception) lying? In other words, must deception be intentional rather than the
result of illogic or a faded memory before it is considered to be a lie? What about

denial, delusion, or faded memory? All of these questions point to the complications of the superficially simple matter of saying whether an utterance is a lie or not. With these complications comes, as this chapter now demonstrates, a lack of experimental control and a dearth of consistent results concerning the utility of lie detector devices.

This situation is especially exacerbated in scientific studies in which deception is the intended independent variable of the experiment. Current day researchers have struggled to find some kind of a stable experimental test against which tests of lie detection procedures can be evaluated. Any evaluation of a proposed "lie detection" method must be considered within this context of poorly controlled experimental conditions and inconsistent results. As we see in this chapter, the problem of developing a robust experimental model of lying has perplexed researchers in this field for some time. Where, they ask, is the deception "fruit-fly"—the model experimental design that will allow us to study deception?

It is well that I remind my readers of some of the conclusions to which I have come in previous chapters concerning the privileged nature of our thoughts before entering into a technical discussion of the difficulties confronting efforts to find objective lie detection methods. First, despite the long history of attempts to develop techniques for reading peoples' minds, no previous technique has ever been shown to be reliable. Although many cognitive neuroscientists and psychologists loathe admitting it, there remains an uncrossed gap between our behavior and our thoughts.

Second, despite the enormous popular excitement and professional activity in which brain images have been used to supposedly measure mental activity, this approach has produced highly unreliable results. It seems likely, therefore, that brain imaging as a way of reading the mind is still an unfulfilled hope rather than an established science.

Third, we still have no plausible theory of how the brain produces the mental states we call consciousness, perception, or attention among the many other psychological activities, constructs, and processes that have been suggested to be the components of mind.

Fourth, the most common sign of some cognitive process used by cognitive neuroscientists—localized activity in a part or a few parts of the brain when certain mental states are achieved—seems to be on the verge of being rejected. Instead, as Chapter 2 has clearly demonstrated, recent meta-reviews depict enormous variability in the location of brain activations to what are thought to be the same stimulus condition. Thus, they provide compelling evidence suggesting that wide distribution is more likely to be the typical representation rather than localized responses.

Currently, therefore, there is a profound need for a reconceptualization of the problem from the "mental modules-localized brain regions" philosophy that dominated the field. We are just beginning to see the emergence of such a new point of view that hypothesizes that many parts of the brain interact in extremely complex and subtle ways to produce mental activity. A corollary of this new perspective is that these different regions perform multiple, and possibly even contradictory, functions at different times.

The purpose of this chapter is to examine the potential role that modern brain imaging devices (mainly the fMRI system) might play in a task of special current legal interest—the detection of deception in the context of the courtroom and other investigatory applications. I argue here that there are many technical, empirical, and conceptual uncertainties that raise flags about the possible use of brain images as a component of the judicial process. Most compelling of all, however, is the empirical facts that the proposed techniques just do not work!

I begin this discussion by examining the long history of efforts to determine whether or not people are truthfully describing their thoughts and recollections.

3.2 A History of Lie Detection

Determining the veracity of peoples' statements, both written and spoken, has been of concern to many societies throughout history. The most ancient writings we have, including the various secular codes (for example, that of Hammurabi) and religious texts (for example, the Old Testament) all deal with the problems encountered when the truth or falsity of a statement must be judged. Indeed, lying was considered to be such a serious offense that Hammurabi placed it at the beginning of his code of 282 laws in the form of his second and third laws.[1] Furthermore, he also proposed a "lie detection" method and, to say the least, a Draconian penalty for lying:

Law 2
If any one bring an accusation against a man, and the accused go to the river and leap into the river, if he sink in the river his accuser shall take possession of his house. But if the river prove that the accused is not guilty, and he escape unhurt, then he who had brought the accusation shall be put to death, while he who leaped into the river shall take possession of the house that had belonged to his accuser.

Law 3
If any one bring an accusation of any crime before the elders, and does not prove what he has charged, he shall, if it be a capital offense charged, be put to death.
(From the Code of Hammurabi, Ruler of Mesopotamia in the eighteenth century BCE)

The Old Testament of the Hebrews also took the act of deception very seriously. The story of the Cain and Abel peaks with an act of deception by indirection—"am I my brother's keeper?" This act, along with the fratricide itself, was to have repercussions throughout Cain's life. Lying was so serious a sin to the Hebrew people that it became one of the Ten Commandments, the code of conduct provided by what was presumably the highest authority possible. The ninth commandment[2] asserts that "You shall not bear false witness against your neighbor," clearly a prohibition against deceptive accusations and, by implication, against lying more generally construed.

The penalty for lying, however, is not quite as immediate or drastic as specified in Hammurabi's code despite the repeated admonitions throughout the Bible against intentional deception. Instead, the ninth commandment is deemed to be one of the social and religious requirements for God's blessings and, thus, one of the requirements for leading a "holy" life. To lie is to be deprived of the holy relationship with God and perhaps to be "cursed"—a penalty that could well be passed on to one's progeny. Ultimately, the penalty for breaking a commandment was the denial of a heavenly afterlife because of this particular sign of a dishonorable current life. No specific means of detecting lies, however, are proposed other than the omniscient eye of God.

Jewish traditions about lying became much more specific in the Talmudic discourses that were to follow. Some lies (for example, to save a life) were permissible but others (for example, lying to children or lying about taxes) were forbidden. Indeed, the destruction of the second temple and the resulting Diaspora of the Jewish people were attributed by some as a penalty for the paucity of honest people. False testimony in judicial proceeding was strongly condemned in the Talmud with severe penalties prescribed including such Draconian ones as "being thrown to the dogs like an animal."

The detection of deception gradually emerged from its theological background to become a major activity of judges and courts as the centuries went by. Lying was an impediment to good social order. Since defensive lying by an accused was so common, a ubiquitous goal of all societies has been to find some behavioral or other objective signal of deception.

The history of lie detection has been told by many authors including Trovillo (1939a, 1939b), Adler (2002) Grubin and Madsen (2005), Seagrave, (2003), and Adler's new book (2007). Trovillo's two papers still represent the gold standard in this field in my opinion. The newer works bring the recent history up to date.

The earliest lie detectors, of course, were other humans. We cannot know who it was who first thought that some aspect of behavior could be a sign of deception. However, one early Hindu document, the Ayur-Veda, written about 900 BCE, has been cited by Trovillo (1939a) as being at least one of the earliest to attempt to detect lying by observing behavior. The test was a means of detecting poisoners, who presumably were often placed in the situation of lying about their guilt:

> A person who gives poison may be recognized. He does not answer questions, or they are evasive answers; he speaks nonsense, rubs the great toe along the ground, and shivers; his face is discolored; he rubs the roots of the hair with his fingers, and he tries by every means to leave the house. (Quoted from p. 849 of Trovillo, 1939)

This is an interesting conglomeration of "Body English," verbal denials, and even precursors of the autonomic responses (i.e., the discolored face) that were to dominate lie detection practices throughout the twentieth century.

Behavioral indicators of deception still play an important role in some circles. Certainly juries are increasingly called upon to detect whether or not an accused is lying as described by Fisher (1997). Beyond whatever factual evidence is provided to them, juries depend to an inappropriate degree on an accused's demeanor and appearance for evaluating the credibility of proffered testimony.[3] The behavioral indicators that are believed to be associated with lying include:

- Downcast eye
- Stooped posture
- Halting speech
- And, unfortunately, race and attire

Classic Greek philosophers and physicians also have been credited with developing early means of detecting lies that anticipate the autonomic responses recorded by modern polygraphic methods. Trovillo (1939a) suggested that Erasistratus, a third century physician, was the first to use irregularities of the pulse to determine whether or not a person was telling the truth.

Rice chewing, first used by ancient East Indians was adopted as a test throughout Europe in the twelfth century. The test presumably depended on the dryness of the mouth of the deceiver; if the rice was wet after being chewed, the defendant was considered to have been telling the truth; salivation assumed to be inhibited when one is telling a lie. Although this may seem a little primitive from our modern point of view, in fact it is based on the same premise as the modern polygraph, namely that the autonomic responses of the body are altered in a specific manner when a person seeks to deceive.

However, far more intrusive and often fatal methods designed to detect deception were developed in later centuries. Truth was sought by subjecting a person to a trial[4] by ordeal or by torture. Rather than simply observing the behavior of suspected liars, the truth of statements was tested by seeing how well the accused survived some test of potential bodily damage in what might be an actual armed combat; the winner's "purity of heart and motive" were testified to by success in combat as a result of divine intervention.

Over the years, judgment of a person's veracity by ordeal included holding a hot iron in the hand or licking it, dunking in a pond, or plunging the arm into a pot of boiling water, among many other painful tests. Should the accused survive the ordeal without injury, they were considered to have told the truth, again because of divine intervention that permitted the accused to transcend the physics and chemistry of ordinary tissue damage. Obviously, many innocents were convicted of accusations because they failed the ordeal or lost the combat. As is still the case, an accusation, however weakly supported and despite a subsequent acquittal, can have a devastating effect on a person's future life. Vestiges of the ordeal can still be found in harsh or sustained examinations by contemporary authorities such as keeping the lights on at night, flooding the accused with overly loud noises, or maintaining too high or too low a temperature in a cell.

In the primitive ordeals, as just noted, the accused was supposed to be protected from injury by divine intervention if they were telling the truth. Trial by torture, however, was based on a slightly different assumption now known to be fallacious. During torture, there was no effort to avoid physical pain or damage. Instead, the prevailing opinion was that if a person was placed in a situation in which physical pain or injury was inevitable or actual, they would tell the truth, the whole truth, and nothing but the truth. Ingenious devices for inflicting pain were used throughout history, especially during the Middle Ages including the "thumb screw," the "rack," and the "iron maiden." Modern versions of these devices (including some still being used in the Iraq war) such as "water boarding," electrical shocks, or injecting pain-producing chemicals that the ancients had not envisioned are still being used to "elicit" the truth from an uncooperative conversant.

Unfortunately, we now know that people are likely to say anything, especially what the inquisitor might wish to hear, under such circumstances. Although it is obviously difficult to carry out controlled experiments on the effectiveness of torture, the general conclusion among current social scientists as well as military scholars is that it does not generally work. What torture does is to change behavior in the direction the torturer desires. However, as a practical tool for detecting whether a person is lying or not, torture falls short of success. More often, it is suspected, torture induces lying, rather than uncovering the truth.

Modern methods of lie detection are based on an entirely different assumption than that the truth can be elicited by trial, ordeal, or torture. That assumption is that there are physiological indicators over which we have little or no control, mainly mediated by the autonomic system[5], that betray a person when they are attempting to deceive. The long-term goal of modern lie detection has become one of finding an objective measure of a subjective state—that is, finding a physiological indicator. The unfulfilled hope is that lying could be measured with an appropriate "scientific" instrument with a sufficiently high level of correlation to justify courtroom admissibility. Unfortunately, no device meeting these specifications yet exists and none appears on the horizon. Fortunately, most jurisdictions do not permit the introduction of lie detection into courtroom deliberations.

Until the twenty-first century, the history of modern lie detection was the history of the polygraph, a device that was named because it mentioned several of these autonomic signals simultaneously. As Trovillo (1939a) had pointed out, even the Greeks had an idea that emotionality—an inaccessible mental (i.e., a subjective) state—could be measured with a particular autonomic signal—the pulse rate (i.e., an objective and quantitative value of the rate of the heartbeat). Changes in the pulse rate were considered to be associated with emotionally salient thoughts and emotionality was associated with lying, among other mental states. As we see later, this chain of logic does not bear scrutiny well. Unfortunately, it still remains a foundation assumption in the use of even the most modern devices that purport to detect lying.

New technologies have always spawned new means of measuring autonomic responses. Blood pressure measuring devices (sphygmomanometers) were invented in the nineteenth century; the respiratory plethysmometer was used to measure changes in the breathing rate and volume at about this same period. Subsequently, in the late nineteenth century it was discovered that there was also an electrical resistance change (the Galvanic Skin Response, the GSR, also known as the Electrodermal Response, the EDR) on the skin when a person's level of emotionality varied. Although the modern polygraph uses several, if not all of these indicators, they were actually introduced piecemeal over the years. It is interesting to note that each was used independently as a lie detector almost immediately upon their invention. The compelling fantasy that objective measures can detect deception has all-too-easily been translated into action.

The earliest history of an autonomic response's modern use as a lie detector can be traced back to the work of Cesare Lombroso (1835-1909) and his student Angelo Mosso (1846-1910). They carried out the first known studies that associated deception with blood pressure, pulse rate, and respiration using the newly developed sphygmomanometer and plethysmometer. Lombroso's (1895) classic book *L'Homme Criminel* (*The Criminal Man*) incorporated many of these seminal ideas[6] as well as his now discredited ideas about the relation between criminal behavior and physiognomy.

Although a considerable amount of basic research on autonomic responses was carried out in Europe during the nineteenth century, the autonomic response-based lie detector became popular through the work of the American psychologist Hugo Munsterberg (1863-1916) (who many have credited as being the father of American applied psychology) and his student William Marston (1893-1947).[7] Marston was not only the great popularizer of the technique but also pushed the use of the sphygmomanometer cum lie detector into the courtroom for the first time. In fact, he was the expert who introduced this test in the famous *United States v. Frye* case of 1923, the result of which was the near total banning of the autonomic lie detector (the polygraph) as admissible evidence and the establishment of the first standard—the *Frye* rule—for the admissibility of scientific evidence in most jurisdictions.[8] Although the more complex and scientifically demanding *Daubert* criteria have largely replaced the *Frye* criterion, many jurisdictions still adhere to the *Frye* standard or use none at all; few courts have rescinded the original decision to ban autonomic response-based lie detection from admissible testimony. Nevertheless, the use of the polygraph remains ubiquitous throughout industry and government.

The first apparent use of multiple indicators—blood pressure, pulse, and respiration volume—in a single device was made by Larson (1921); his device thus stimulated the creation of the word "polygraph"—an abbreviation for the multiple graphs produced by the several autonomic indicators. Many others followed over the years carrying out research and developing impressive-looking devices. Other measures, such as the GSR, have been added and subtracted from time to time. The standard modern version of the lie detector device is still the one developed by Keeler (1930).[9]

In the 1940s a number of other American investigators tried to provide a scientific foundation for autonomic lie detectors. Marcuse and Bitterman (1946), for example, advocated a "peak of tension" response measured with a Keeler polygraph to identify those with guilty knowledge. The basic idea was that an examinee would respond with elevated responses to key words that only the guilty person could know. By the next year Bitterman and Marcuse (1947) were evaluating what has come to be known as the "Control Question" procedure in which the responses were compared to relevant and irrelevant questions.

The basic idea of all of this early work that has persisted into the present was that lying would be correlated with some modification in the autonomic measures and that it was possible for a well-trained "polygraphist" to detect deception in the graphs of the several autonomic responses traced out on the polygraph. Thus, the polygraph was and still is presented as an objective measure of an otherwise inaccessible mental state. Despite its prevalence, it enjoys only the frailest scientific standing among serious researchers in the field.

Many current students of polygraphy, supporters and critics alike, consider the polygraph to actually be a three-way interaction between the polygraphist (who administers the test), the examinee, and the machine. It is likely that much of whatever success can be attributed to the machine[10] is actually accounted for by the sensitivity of the polygraphist to use subtle interpersonal cues based on their experience as interrogators. The machine, itself, is nothing more than a bit of stage setting that is especially useful when working with a naïve examinee.

The current state of the polygraphist's art is based upon three different kinds of tests for deception.

- The Directed Lying Test (DLT)
- The Control Question Test (CQT)
- The Guilty Knowledge Test (GKT)

In the DLT a base level of activity is presumed to be established by asking a person to lie and the responses compared to the responses to honest expressions. If the responses to the directed lies are more similar to some responses than to others, the ones that are similar are considered to be deceptive.

In the CQT, emotionally loaded questions that may be unrelated to deception are interspersed with neutral questions and the two sets of responses compared to questions germane to the investigation. If a response is more like the emotionally loaded control question, it is assumed to be untruthful.

In the GKT, the polygraphist looks for unusually strong responses to questions or statements concerning knowledge that only the perpetrator of a crime could have. Thus, all of the other responses (than the putatively deceptive one) serve as controls for those exhibiting guilty knowledge. For example, if a person is presented with a series of items in the form of a multiple choice test and responds especially strongly to an item that could have been known only to the perpetrator, it would be assumed that he was lying if he denied having that knowledge. Many modern students of lie detection now believe that the only one of these three methods that works to any degree is the GKT, the others having not been shown to have even minimal scientific support. Certainly, as was pointed out in the NAS report, almost all of the laboratory testing has been done with the GKT. As we see later, it is also the main method used in most of the 16 fMRI studies of deception I was able to locate and which I discuss later in this chapter.

In recent years, as new technologies have been developed for measuring other kinds of responses that might or might not be associated with lying, a variety of other kinds of lie detectors has been proposed. The following list is a partial tabulation of some of these novel efforts to develop other objective measures of the mental state we call deception. They can be divided up into two groups: those that utilize some aspect of a motor or autonomic response and those that directly measure some aspect of brain action. Along with the traditional polygraph, the first class includes:

- Voice Stress Analysis
- Facial Microexpressions
- Facial Heat Distribution

The second class includes:

- The Electroencephalogram
- The Event Related Potential
- Optical Measurements of Cerebral Blood Flow
- Brain Images such as the PET and fMRI[11]

It is the last of these proposed methods—especially the non-invasive fMRI—that has attracted the most attention and is the main target of the critical discussion to follow in this chapter. However, before I begin that discussion it is also important to understand some of the properties that distinguish these two groups.

One of the main criticisms of the first group was that they did not directly measure brain activity. All were measuring some aspect of autonomic or motor behavior that bore, at best, only an indirect relationship to the brain activity "producing" the deceptive response. At best, their effect was mediated; that is, they were only correlative, actually responding more directly to such factors as the emotions produced by the self-awareness that a person was trying to deceive than to the deception itself. All of the traditional behavioral cues to deception such as face flushing or body postures fell into this category.

Because of the widely appreciated disadvantage that the autonomic and postural cues were deemed to be indirect, a new set of measures evolved as new technologies came along. The assumption was that these new methods measured the brain's activity much more directly than did the autonomic responses. This was motivated and to a degree justified by the universal acceptance of the idea that the brain was the seat of our cognitive activities. Although as a first approximation, this was certainly true, a closer examination indicates that most of these "brain responses" are also quite distant from cognitive processes such as lying. Given the persisting degree of indirectness, brain measurements may not be that different for the two approaches.

One of the first attempts to make this crucial step from autonomic to brain responses was the use of the electroencephalograph, a continuous record of the electrical activity of the brain usually recorded from the surface of the head but occasionally from the exposed brain itself. Who first suggested this technique as a lie detector is not known but it was brought to renewed prominence by the work of Thornton (1995).

The Event Related Potential (ERP), otherwise known as the Evoked Brain Potential (EVBP), was another electrical brain signal proposed by such workers as Farwell and Donchin (1991) and Farwell and Smith (2001) as an indicator of lying. This procedure, called "brain fingerprinting" by the latter group, concentrated on the relatively small differences (between truth and lying) in the P300 wave, a positive voltage excursion that could be measured by repetitive averaging of the electrical activity of the brain. The critical part of the ERP occurs as a positive voltage excursion about 300 msec after a stimulus and, like the EEG, can be recorded over broad regions of the head.

Optical images of the distribution of blood in the brain, a noninvasive process that depends on the partial translucency of the skull to infra-red lights have also been proposed by Chance, Nioka, and Chen (2003) as a means of measuring brain activity and, thus, deception.

These processes, as well as the fMRI measure that is the main topic of this chapter, seem at first to avoid the major disadvantage of the techniques exemplified by the polygraph that depend on autonomic activity; that is, that they are, indisputably, measures of some kind of brain activity. Their measurement, therefore, is considered to be more direct than anything based on autonomic responses.

The actual situation, however, is that the brain functions measured by the imaging systems may not be any closer, in some logical sense, to the mental processes than are the autonomic ones. Unfortunately, there is no proof that the EEG or ERP actually are measures of the brain processes that are the equivalents of mental activity. For that matter, it is not even certain that they correlate with the cognitively significant neural activity of the brain as opposed to being an indirect function of its metabolism.

It can be reasonably argued that the brain images and electrical responses are as indirect as the autonomic measures. I return later in this chapter to consider this issue in more detail. For the moment keep in mind that the main hope guiding this strategy is that it will be possible to determine a useful degree of correlation between a measurable brain response and the act of deception. There is no established identity of the brain image and the mind; the brain image is no more the mind than the pulse rate. A correlation does not imply equivalence! (Yule, 1926)

Before considering the current empirical state of the relationship brain images and lying, it is important to point out that a number of studies and reviews carried out over a number of decades by the most prestigious scientific bodies have unanimously come to the same conclusion—there is no supporting evidence that justifies the admissibility of any of the standard (i.e., autonomic response based) lie detector devices into courtroom deliberations. Two important critiques of the traditional lie detection methods should have buried further use of them in investigations and judicial deliberations. That they have not is evidence of the powerful hold that the mythology of lie detection has on our collective consciousness.

The first federal government evaluation of the use of the polygraph as a lie detector was carried out by the Office of Technology Assessment (OTA) of the U.S. Congress (Anonymous, 1983). This report came to the same conclusions that are repeated again and again whenever serious scientific evaluations of the polygraph are made. In Chapter 1 of their report, the OTA noted:

> OTA concluded that no overall measure or single, simple judgment of polygraph testing validity can be established based on available scientific evidence. Validity is the extent to which polygraph testing can accurately detect truthfulness and deception.

In Chapter 7, these initial comments were expanded.

> OTA concluded that, as shown in chapter 2, polygraph testing is, in reality, a very complex process that varies widely in application. Although the polygraph instrument itself is essentially the same for all applications, the purpose of the examination, type of individual tested, examiner training, setting of the examination, and type of questions asked, among other factors, can differ substantially. The instrument cannot itself detect deception.

The report went on in Chapter 7:

> The focus of the OTA technical memorandum is not whether the polygraph test has been useful, but whether there is a scientific basis for its use. OTA concluded that, while there is some evidence for the validity of polygraph testing as an adjunct to typical criminal investigations of specific incidents, and more limited evidence when such investigations extend to incidents of unauthorized disclosure. However, there is very little research or scientific evidence to establish polygraph test validity in large-scale screening as part of unauthorized disclosure investigations, or in personnel security screening situations, whether they be pre-employment, pre-clearance, periodic or aperiodic, random, or "dragnet."

Although not rejecting the polygraph unequivocally, these paragraphs reflect the grave doubts about the utility of the approach.

The OTA report may have been among the first in drawing negative or equivocal conclusions about the polygraph and other proposed methods of lie detection, but it was not the last. Among the most prestigious subsequent negative evaluations of the entire lie detection enterprise was the one published by the National Academy of Sciences (NAS, 2003). A special committee of cognitive neuroscientific experts from a number of fields was set up to evaluate the polygraph and other methods of lie detection. The conclusions to which this group came were clear and succinct and were much more critical than the OTA report:

- Almost a century of research in scientific psychology and physiology provides little basis for the expectation that a polygraph test could have extremely high accuracy.
- The theoretical rationale for the polygraph is quite weak, especially in terms of differential fear, arousal, or other emotional states that are triggered in response to relevant or comparison questions.
- Research on the polygraph has not progressed over time in the manner of a typical scientific field. It has not accumulated knowledge or strengthened its scientific underpinnings in any significant manner.
- The inherent ambiguity of the physiological measures used in the polygraph suggest that further investments in improving polygraph technique and interpretation will bring only modest improvements in accuracy. (pp. 212 - 213)

In another summary statement, the NAS report also concluded:

In summary, we were unable to find any field experiments, field quasi-experiments, or prospective research-oriented data collection specifically designed to address polygraph validity and satisfying minimal standards of research quality. (p. 115)

Concerning the newer techniques such as the fMRI, the NAS report concluded:

Some of the potential alternatives show promise, but none has yet been shown to outperform the polygraph. None shows any promise of supplanting the polygraph for screening purposes in the near term. Our conclusions are based on basic scientific knowledge and available information about accuracy. (p. 173)[12]

Many others have joined in this wave of criticism including Lykken (1981), Iacono (2001), and Maschke and Scalabrini (2003). Among the most critical is the book by Maschke and Scalabrini who, writing under the auspices of the AntiPolygraphic organization in the fourth digital edition of their book, conclude that:

- …polygraphy, like phrenology and graphology is without scientific validity
- …our Government's reliance on unreliable polygraphy serves to protect spies, undermining – not enhancing – our national security
- …polygraph "tests" are actually interrogations
- …polygraphy depends on your polygraphist lying to and deceiving you
- …polygraphy is biased against the truthful (p. 14)

Despite an abundance of this kind of criticism and the near universal conclusion that there is no scientific basis for the use of "objective" lie detectors of the kinds described here, they continue to be used, legally and illegally, throughout the government, business, and investigative agencies. Despite what many of us believe is the overly open-minded report of the two government committees, a critical scientific outlook is that the worst deception of all is the continuing acceptance of these fraudulent techniques in our society.

The bottom line is that the polygraph has not been shown to be a valid test for deception. It is a device primarily used to terrorize naïve subjects or in the hopes that the results will be ambiguous enough to provide exculpatory evidence for someone rich enough to have their own private polygraph test. This extra-scientific kind of justification raises major questions about the ethics of their use and creates situations in which emotional reactions may lead to miscarriages of justice. The judges of the Court of Appeals of District of Columbia who ruled in the original *Frye* case should be considered heroes in the fight against this kind of pseudoscience.

Now, however, a new kind of lie detector—the fMRI brain imager—has arisen that is being as facilely accepted as the older devices were initially. It is important that we now consider the scientific merits of this new approach and attempt to place them in the context of the historic search for an objective means of evaluating the subjective state we call lying.

The general point to be made in this chapter is that application of brain imaging to lie detection is in a very primitive state of development with many technical, conceptual, and empirical difficulties. Based on the current state of research, it is likely that it will not work any better than any of its predecessors. Considering the current continuing role of the polygraph in many investigations, every effort should be made to stamp out this new pseudoscience at this early stage before it too becomes irretrievably embedded in our jurisprudence system.

To support these arguments, I now review what I believe to be most of the publications on this topic that have been published in the field since the idea was first proposed in 2000. Their intended goal was to provide an empirical basis for the use of the brain image as a lie detector. As we now see, they did not succeed in meeting this goal.

3.3 A Meta-Review of the Empirical Literature Supposedly Supporting the Use of Brain Imaging as a Lie Detector

Although there has been an explosion of popular interest in the use of brain imaging techniques in judicial forensics, the empirical research support for this idea varies from relatively thin to nonexistent. This conclusion becomes especially compelling when all of these studies are considered collectively in a meta-review. Since embarking on the research leading to this book, I have been able to find only 16 reports that deal specifically with the use of brain images as lie detectors. All were published during the period 2001 to 2006. If the results provided in these studies had been relatively stable and reliable, this would have been encouraging and provided a modicum of support for the idea that there were specific signs of brain activity that could be associated with deception. However, as we shall see the reports are not consistent or reliable; each laboratory, and indeed each experiment, paints a different picture of which areas of the brain seem to respond during lying. Where some superficial correlations between lying and brain activations occur, the matter is further complicated by the fact that the regions of the brain associated with lying are also involved in almost every other cognitive or emotional process. There is, in other words, nothing specific concerning deception in the observed activations.

Furthermore, over the course of the meta-review carried out here, it becomes clear that no single region of the brain was found to consistently indicate deception in this group of 16 studies. Instead, a diverse and broadly dispersed cluster of brain regions was reported to be activated in almost all (with one exception) of the studies reviewed here. Even worse was that none of the 16 studies identified the same localized region or pattern of regions as being associated with lying! The diversity of the observed activated regions included not only cerebral locations but also such unlikely places as the thalamus and the cerebellum. Lack of replication in any scientific field generally leads to the rejection of the presumptive hypothesis. It is remarkable, in this context, how persistent the idea of an objective fMRI measure of deception remains.

There are many reasons that account for the inconsistency in these published reports. I have already spoken of the multiple meanings and difficulty in defining a psychological construct such as the word "lie." This difficulty is exacerbated in setting up a model experimental situation in which prevarication is the independent variable. There is a broad diversity of what each investigator considers to be lying exhibited throughout this group of studies.

Therefore, the question can also be asked—how well do these laboratory tests of deception simulate lying in the real world, clouded as it is with ambiguity and human variability? The answer that the forthcoming findings shout out is—not very well!

In short, the scientific justification for using brain images as lie detectors remains questionable both with regard to their validity and reliability. Virtually all of the criticisms that have been directed at earlier devices such as the polygraph hold true for these new devices. Especially significant in this new environment is the paucity of good theoretical explanations for the phenomena. Although a complete explanation of the mechanisms underlying any phenomenon is not necessary for it to be used effectively (consider, for example, the use of aspirin or, even more exemplary, the book), some of the theoretical explanations for the effects observed when fMRI systems are used as lie detectors seem to be nothing more than ex post facto "just so stories." For example, one recurrent theme throughout this corpus of research is that lying is different than telling the truth because it requires more "mental effort" to tell a lie than to tell the truth! This post hoc and totally unverifiable hypothesis is not supported by any empirical evidence. Other explanations are based on previous assumptions of the specialized roles of brain regions, once widely accepted by cognitive neuroscientists to be axiomatic, but which are no longer considered valid. The justification for such ad hoc theories is slim and is not supported by the evidence to be considered in this section.

With this preview in hand, I now turn to a detailed examination of each of the studies suggesting that brain images may be used to detect lies. My strategy is to approach them in chronological order. To help in this analysis I now provide a map of the brain areas as designated by Brodmann (1909/1999) in Figure 3.1. Most of the experiments reviewed here use the Brodmann system as a convenient means of designating where activation occurred. The Brodmann system is widely used nowadays as a guide to localization on the brain that is more specific than such an ambiguous a phrase as the "superior fronto-lateral cortex." [13]

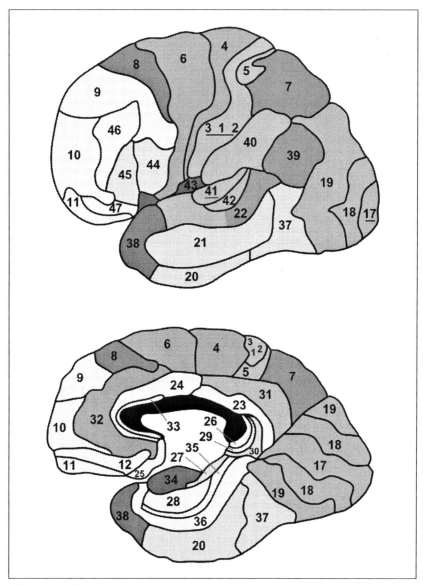

Figure 3.1 *The Brodmann system of designating the location of various regions on the brain. (Used with the permission of Professor Mark Dubin, Department of Molecular, Cellular, and Developmental Biology, University of Colorado.)*

It is very important, however, to appreciate that the Brodmann areas were defined on the basis of cytoachitectonic criteria; that is, on the basis of anatomic differences among the shapes of the constituent neurons. The boundaries between the areas are not congruent with known functional attributes nor are they sharply or unambiguously demarcated one from another. Furthermore, there is a substantial amount of variability of the sulci and gyri of the surface of the brain. Therefore, the Brodmann system must also be considered to be inexact. It is however, the best we have. What the Brodmann classification system does do is provide a convenient means of comparing which regions were activated in the different reports now to be considered. Its most important attribute, however, is that it is the localization system most used by researchers in this field.

One final introductory comment is also appropriate in this context. All of the studies reviewed here involve some kind of a subtraction process. In general a reference or control pattern of activations produced by some cognitively neutral state is subtracted from a condition in which a particular mental process is required. In the case of these deception studies, this is usually executed by subtracting the brain image acquired when a person is telling the truth from one in which the person is lying. The subtraction process, however, is extremely susceptible to a number of artifacts and incorrect interpretations. By itself it is one of the major sources of error and variability in this field of research. I return later to consider the full implications of the flawed subtraction method.

In the following abstracts of the 16 articles, I ignore some of the behavioral experiments that were carried on in conjunction with the fMRI examinations and concentrate on the specific regions of activation reported by each study as they sought objective measures of deception.

A. Spence, Farrow, Herford, Wilkinson, Zheng, and Woodruff (2001)

Spence and his colleagues were apparently the first to suggest using fMRI images as lie detectors. Their pioneering study used a relatively small sample of subjects (10) and found that a single, but bilateral, area—the ventrobasal prefrontal cortices (BA 47)[14]—was more highly activated and had longer response times when their subjects were lying than when they were telling the truth. They used two different protocols, one in which test questions were presented visually and one in which they were presented over earphones. The subject was instructed to tell the truth or lie depending on the color of the "yes" or "no" signals on a computer display. Their procedure was essentially a directed lying test (DLT).

Although Spence and his colleagues designate BA 47 as the main region differentiating a lie from the truth their figures show "significantly greater neuronal response[s]" in a number of other area ranging from the occipital lobe to other frontal areas. These dispersed responses occurred whether or not a visual or an auditory display was used. Their decision to identify a single area as a sign of lying was apparently based on the assumption that the maximum region of activation was the sole locus for the representation of a mental process such as deception. All of the other studies reviewed in this meta-review reported multiple areas of activation.

B. Langleben, Schroeder, Maldjian, Gur, McDonald, Ragland, O'Brien, and Childres (2002)

Langleben and his colleagues approached the problem from a different point of view than had Spence and his colleagues. Rather than using a directed lying test, they used a version of the guilty knowledge test (GKT) in which their subjects (18) lied or told the truth concerning whether or not they had a particular playing card in their pocket. Their results indicated that activation differences between truths and falsehoods could be observed in a wide area that extended over the following regions:

- Anterior cingulate (BA 24 and 32)
- Right superior frontal (BA 6 and 8)
- Superior frontal (BA 8)

Additionally, a somewhat smaller secondary area consisting of the following regions also increased in activity when a subject was lying:

- Left postcentral (BA 1, 2, 3, and 40)
- Left pre- and post central (BA 3, 4, and 6)
- Left precentral (BA area 6)

C. Lee, Liu, Tan, Chan, Mahankali, Feng, Hou, Fox, and Gao (2002)

The next study in this review dealt with quite a different simulation of lying—feigned malingering. Subjects (6) were asked to carry out forced-choice memory tasks feigning memory impairment. The fMRI images were generated by subtracting actual recalled responses from false forgetting (intentional forgetting) in two kinds of experimental protocols—a digit memory task and an autobiographic memory task.

The results reported in Lee and his colleagues' study showed that a number of regions were differentially activated in the feigned memory condition. They concluded that the cerebral hemispheres were bilaterally activated in the following regions when a subject was being deceptive:

- Prefrontal (BA 9, 10, 46)
- Frontal (BA 6)
- Parietal (BA 40)
- Temporal (BA 21)
- Subcortical caudate region

D. Ganis, Kosslyn, Stose, Thompson, and Yurgelun-Todd (2003)

Ganis and his colleagues added another type of deception task to the ones already described. In this experiment their subjects (10) were asked to lie in two different ways. In one protocol, the lie was a part of a coherent story and was generated more or less spontaneously from that story. In the other, the lie was a well-rehearsed distortion of a true fact. Their results for the two conditions highlighted the idea that different kinds of lies existed and that the brain responses to each might be different. A condition in which the subjects were required to tell the truth was also added as a control.

Ganis and his colleagues reported that many brain regions were differentially activated by both kinds of lies. When the spontaneous lie was compared to (i.e., subtracted from) the truth, the following areas indicated increased activation:

- Right middle frontal gyrus (superior BA 10)
- Left middle frontal gyrus (superior BA 10)
- Anterior cingulate (BA 32)
- Right middle frontal gyrus (BA 8/9)
- Left precentral gyrus (BA 4)
- Right pre/postcentral gyrus (BA 3/4)
- Right fusiform/parahippocampal gyrus (BA 36/37)
- Left fusiform/parahippocampal gyrus (BA 36/37)
- Right cuneus (BA 17/31)
- Right precuneus (BA 7)
- Left cerebellum

On the other hand, when a well-rehearsed lie was compared with the truth, the following regions exhibited increased activity.

- Right middle frontal gyrus (superior BA 10)
- Right middle frontal gyrus (inferior BA 10)
- Left middle frontal gyrus (superior BA 10)
- Right fusiform/parahippocampal gyrus (BA 36/37)

- Left fusiform/parahippocampal gyrus (BA 36/37)
- Right cuneus (BA 17/31)
- Right precuneus (BA 7)
- Left cerebellum

The conclusion that was drawn from these results by Ganis and his colleagues was that not only could the pattern of fMRI results distinguish between truth and lying, but that their results suggested that their method could distinguish between different kinds of lying.

E. Spence, Hunter, Farrow, Green, Leung, Hughes, and Ganesan (2004)

In 2004, Spence's laboratory returned to specifically consider the suggestion (based on the four papers already discussed) that lying primarily activated the prefrontal and anterior cingulate cortices. Alternatively, telling the truth was not associated with any localized regional activation. To support this hypothesis, this study briefly reported a very preliminary experiment using a new paradigm. Their idea was to add to the paradigm a third condition—"defy-comply"—beyond the two standard ones—lying and truth telling. This third condition unfortunately was not described adequately for us to be clear about its meaning. However, the results of this pilot study suggested that lying was associated with increased activations in the following regions:

- Right ventrolateral (BA 47)
- Orbitofrontal cortices (BA 11)
- Right medial frontal gyrus (BA 6)
- Right inferior parietal lobule (BA 40)
- Left premotor cortex (BA 6)

These were different locations, they acknowledged, from those identified in their earlier study (Spencer et al., 2001) and did not correspond to their original hypothesis of the special role of the prefrontal and anterior cingulate cortices.

F. Kozel, Revell, Loberbaum, Shastri, Elhai, Horner, Smith, Nahas, Bohning, and George (2004)

In 2004, a new complication crept into the scientific studies exploring the possibility that the fMRI might be used as a lie detector. Kozel's laboratory at the Medical University of South Carolina submitted a patent application for the procedure. He and his colleagues became associated with what was intended to be a profit-making corporation offering lie detection services to the legal community.

It is not entirely clear what the basis of their specific instantiation was that distinguished their methods from the work of his predecessors that would justify a patent. Nevertheless, an entrepreneurial spirit was exhibited here that was quite different than the pioneering scientific studies previously discussed.

Kozel and his colleagues quickly published three papers on the topic of an fMRI lie detector. In this section I consider the first one. Consistent with what were now the applied interests of their laboratory, a new protocol for lying research was introduced in the first of Kozel's reports—truthful and deceptive answers to questions involving hidden money—a simulated crime. The results of their experiment, however, showed no consistent activation pattern among their subjects (8). Instead, one subject showed no activation difference when the truthful answers were subtracted from the deceitful ones and the others varied substantially, one from the other, in terms of activated areas.

Kozel and his colleagues had originally hypothesized that deception would be signaled by activity in the orbitofrontal region, the right anterior cingulate gyrus, and the amygdala. In fact, none of their subjects displayed any amygdalar activity. Instead, the areas activated varied substantially over the brain including other regions that were not designated by Brodmann areas:

- Left middle temporal gyrus (BA 21)
- Right precentral gyrus and the right inferior frontal gyrus (BA 44)
- Left inferior temporal gyrus (BA 37)
- Right middle frontal (Orbital frontal) region
- Cerebellum (Bilateral)
- Superior temporal gyrus
- Right anterior cingulate
- Right superior frontal gyrus

In sum, the results presented in this study were quite irregular as well as being dispersed across the brain. They did not support the author's original hypothesis. Increased activations were found over broad areas of the brain. Their own summary of the paper reflect some of the general frustrations stimulated by research in this field:

The other areas of activation that were not hypothesized can only be considered to be exploratory. (p. 301)

G. Kozel, Padgett, and George (2004)

In this follow-up study, Kozel and his colleagues once again found a substantial degree of diverse activations from a new group of subjects (13). The experimental protocol was slightly different; subjects were asked to lie or tell the truth about the whereabouts of $50 bills (hidden under objects encountered in a familiarization session prior to the acquisition of the brain images) when pictures of the objects were presented while the subjects were in the fMRI system. When the data for lies minus truths were accumulated for all subjects, statistically significant activations were found in six areas of the brain:

- Right anterior cingulate
- Right inferior frontal
- Right orbitofrontal
- Left middle temporal
- Right middle frontal
- Left medial temporal[15]

However, when the data for individual subjects were considered there was a much more diverse set of responses. Two of the 13 subjects showed no activated regions at all, two displayed activity in four regions, and all others in only two or three regions. Furthermore the right anterior cingulate region, one of the regions often associated with lying, was activated in the brain of only one subject.[16] Kozel, Padgett, and George concluded:

> The technique was not able to detect, within individuals, consistent activation patterns. (p. 855)

H. Kozel, Johnson, Mu, Grenesko, Laken, and George (2005)

Following their earlier reports which showed wide variability between subjects and diverse activation areas across the entire brain, Kozel's group proceeded to seek a means of identifying lying in individual subjects rather than extrapolating from group data. It was becoming clear at that point that the diversity of individual responses was so great that it was not possible to use group data as a standard criterion of lying since so many regions were only idiosyncratically activated.

In this study Kozel and his colleagues asked their subjects (in each of two conditions) to "steal" either a watch or a ring and then to hide it. The subjects were then placed in the fMRI imaging system and asked questions about the stolen object as well as some neutral questions.

At this point, their analytic approach becomes very much more complex. They built a "model" of activations produced by lying by asking their subjects to participate in a mock crime. This model permitted them to develop an analytic method that they believed could then be applied to another group of subjects as a test for lying. For each subject, the analytic model was applied in a two-step procedure. The individual subject was first tested in the context of the mock crime and the pattern of activations then used as a standard. The subject would then be tested in the real (but artificially staged) situation and their fMRI images compared to the results of the mock condition. Under these conditions Kozel and his colleagues claimed to have success of 90% percent for detecting deception by the individuals of their test group.

The areas they found responsive to lying and showing the largest activations were, once again, widely spaced and dispersed over and within the brain. The following list tabulates regions that they reported to be significantly associated with lying in individual subjects:

- Right supplementary area (BA 6 and 8)
- Right anterior cingulate (BA 32)
- Right orbitofrontal (BA 47)
- Right insula (BA 47)
- Right inferior frontal (BA 44)
- Left orbitofrontal (BA 47 and 38)
- Left and right angular (BA 39 and 40)
- Left and right caudate nuclei

I. Langleben, Loughhead, Bilker, Rupare, Childress, Busch, and Gur (2005)

This report illustrated, as did the previous one, the increasingly complex experimental designs that were deemed to be necessary to accommodate the increasingly complex findings from these brain image studies of lying. It was now becoming evident that not only the deception task required of the subjects, but also the type of analysis could produce widely differing results. Even as simple a factor as the threshold that was used to determine the extent of the activations could drastically affect the interpretation of the findings.

Trying to untangle what were obviously the effects of many different causal factors, therefore, became a challenging part of this kind of research. Langleben, one of the earliest pioneers in this type of research, but now working a different group of colleagues, designed a card recognition experiment in which their subjects (26) were told to admit possession of one card and deny another when presented with a series of cards on a visual display.

When the imaging data for the lie minus truth conditions were examined, local maxima were found in five regions:

- Inferior parietal lobule (BA 40)
- Inferior frontal gyrus (BA 9)
- Superior frontal gyrus (BA 6)

- Right Inferior frontal gyrus (BA 9)
- Cerebellum

In addition, many other areas were also activated to a lesser degree. For example, the inferior parietal activations that were maximum in BA 40 were also observed in BA 1, 2, 3, 4, 5, 6, 7, 24, and 32. Areas activated in association with four other maxima in BA 6 and 9 included BA 13 and 44 as well as many regions of the cerebellum. Once again, a very diverse set of regions seemed to be activated and even within this wide distribution, the level of activation depended on many analyses, tasks, and subject variables. Despite this substantial variability, Langleben and his colleagues claimed 78% accuracy in identifying lying by their subjects.

J. Davatzikos, Ruparel, Fan, Shen, Acharyya, Loughhead, Gur, Langleben (2005)

Davatzikos and his colleagues were most interested in the development of a pattern recognition algorithm that could discriminate between truth and lying. In doing so, they tacitly assumed that the key to lie detection was not the activation of a particular localized area, but a dispersed pattern of activity. They used a group of 22 subjects and a card test in which a subject had to acknowledge or deny which of two cards were in their possession when a sequence of cards was displayed during the fMRI examinations.

The resulting brain images were then processed by a pattern recognition algorithm in the hope of distinguishing general patterns that discriminated between truthful and deceitful responses. Davatzikos and his colleagues developed a mathematical "hypersurface" simultaneously representing many dimensions and regions of the brain response. This hypersurface was used as the key to determining differences between lying and truth telling. Although the mathematical details of their pattern recognition procedure are not germane to the present discussion, both their figures and their tabulation of the most important areas are of special interest.

Their major result was that the patterns of activity observed during lying were different than when telling the truth. The areas that increased in relative activity when a person was telling the truth were widely dispersed over many of the areas of the brain ranging from the cerebellum in the rear to the parietal lobes in the mid regions to the frontal lobes. Those areas that seemed to be relatively more active during lying were, however, primarily in the frontal regions. From this wide distribution, Davatzikos and his colleagues concluded that the most "informative regions" (by which I assume they mean the areas displaying the largest difference for lies minus truths) included the following regions:

- Right inferior prefrontal gyrus (BA 6)
- Right superior prefrontal gyrus (BA 44)
- Bilateral superior temporal gyrus (BA 38)
- Bilateral inferior parietal gyrus (BA 40)
- Bilateral pericentral areas (BA 2, 3, 4)
- Cerebellum

The work of Davatzikos and his colleagues depended upon high dimensional pattern recognition procedures that they believed overcame the disadvantages of group data. On this basis they claimed 100% correct rates in detecting lying within the conditions of their experiment.

K. Phan, Magalhaes, Ziemlewicz, Fitzgerald, Green, and Smith (2005)

Phan and his colleagues used a modification of the playing card GKT originally used by Langleben et al. (2005). Fourteen subjects were instructed to always lie about one particular card and to always tell the truth about another. Control and irrelevant cards were also presented. The results seemed to be identical for comparisons of the lie minus truth conditions and the lie minus control conditions. The following regions were reported by this group to be increasingly activated during lying:

- Ventrolateral prefrontal cortex (BA 45 and 47)
- Superior temporal sulcus (BA 21, 22, 37)
- Dorsomedial prefrontal cortex (BA 8)
- Dorsolateral prefrontal cortex (BA 9)
- Angular gyrus (BA 39)
- Supramarginal gyrus (BA 40)[17]

L. Lee, Liu, Chan, Ng, Fox, and Gao (2005)

Lee and his colleagues returned to the feigned memory impairment paradigm when they followed up on the Lee et al. (2002) study carried out three years previously. In this study of 27 subjects, they were especially concerned about the effect of different stimuli, gender, and language background in determining the activated regions. In general, they found no significant effects of these variables. All three of the experiments for which they reported results produced the same pattern of results—bilateral activation of the frontal, cingulate, and parietal areas (with some minor exceptions). The main activated areas included bilateral activation of:

- Premotor (BA 6)
- Dorsomedial prefrontal (BA 8)
- Dorsolateral prefrontal (BA 9)
- Fronto-polar prefrontal (BA 10)
- Orbito-prefrontal (BA 47)
- Superior parietal (BA 7)
- Supramarginal (BA 40)
- Left cingulate (BA 23) or right anterior cingulate (BA 32)

On the basis of these results, Lee and his colleagues suggested that lying was a function of a bilateral network of prefrontal and parietal areas.

M. Nunez, Casey, Egner, Hare, Hirsch (2005)

In 2005, Nunez and her colleagues specifically acknowledged that there were substantial inconsistencies among all of the research reported so far. They sought to standardize results by manipulating the conditions of the simulated lying. Their method was to use a test in which autobiographical and non-autobiographical questions were asked of the subjects (20) who participated in their experiments. For example, an autobiographical question was "Have you ever told a lie?" and a non-autobiographical question was "Is New York City in Ohio?".

In some conditions their subjects were instructed to lie; in others to tell the truth. Their results added even further complexity to the data reported previously by other researchers. When true responses were subtracted from false responses, it was the cingulate region that responded with the highest activation level. This result compared poorly to other studies in which it seemed to play a secondary role and emphasized the inconsistency of all of these results. However, as usual, broad expanses of the brain were differentially activated when one compared lies and truth.

Specifically, they reported that activations occurred in the following bilateral (unless otherwise indicated) regions when a subject was lying.

- Left anterior cingulate (BA 32)
- Superior and medial frontal (BA 6)
- Left inferior frontal (BA 44, 45, and 47)
- Left precentral (BA 6)
- Medial frontal (BA 6, 8, 9, 10)
- Right frontal (BA 9, 10, 46)
- Caudate
- Thalamus

N. Abe, Suzuki, Tsukiura, Mori, Yamaguchi, Itoh, and Fujii (2006)

Abe and his colleagues moved away from the prevailing card test method to a different procedure in which their subjects (14) were asked to pretend not to know or, conversely, to know about some real-world experience. A further change in instrumentation also differentiated their study from most previous ones; quite unlike most of the other experimenters, they used a PET imaging system rather than the ubiquitous fMRI device. Their procedure required their subjects to carry out some realistic activities such as painting a picture. Experience with the content of the picture was considered to be equivalent to the "truth."

In subsequent tests, the subjects were then asked to respond in four different ways. They were to answer truthfully ("I know") if a test picture was presented that they had previously seen or ("I don't know") if a new picture was presented. In two other conditions they were asked to lie – to answer falsely ("I don't know") if a familiar picture was presented or ("I know") if an unfamiliar picture was presented.

The results of this experiment were complex; they differed depending upon whether the subject was pretending to know or pretending not to know, another factor exemplifying the difficulty of defining what a lie was. When the subjects were pretending not to know, the following areas were activated.

- Left medial frontal gyrus (BA 10 and 46)
- Right inferior frontal gyrus (BA 45)
- Right medial prefrontal gyrus (BA 9)
- Right anterior cingulate cortex (BA 24 and 32)

However, when the subjects were pretending to know (the other condition of lying) the cingulate cortex was not activated although all other of the aforementioned areas were. This, of course, contradicted some of the earlier results I have reviewed here.

O. Grezes, Berthoz, and Passingham (2006)

Another interesting experimental paradigm tested an unusual aspect of lying — whether the subject or another person was perceived as being lied to! Grezes, Berthoz, and Passingham tested this distinction and found very different brain regions to be involved in the two situations. Six subjects were placed in situations in which the experimenter lied to the subject about either the behavior of an actor or that of the subjects themselves as depicted in a video.

The results were, once again, idiosyncratic and complex — they were inconsistent with virtually all of the findings from all of the experiments reviewed in this section. For example, the amygdala and the fusiform gyrus were activated only when the subjects felt they were personally being lied to. On the other hand, whenever the subjects felt that actors in the videos were being deceived, the superior temporal sulcus and the anterior cingulate cortex were activated.

Grezes, Berthoz, and Passingham attributed this diversity of results to the fact that being lied to personally was perceived as a threat, but observing someone else being lied too was not personally threatening. Therefore, they speculated that a different set of regions was activated than in the personally nonthreatening act of seeing someone else being deceived.

When the subjects perceived themselves as lying or the actor was perceived as lying the following regions were activated. (Unfortunately, Brodmann areas were not identified in this article.)

- Bilateral anterior and lateral orbital gyrus
- Right cinculate gyrus
- Left putamen
- Left short insular gyrus

An important consideration is that in this experiment, a different pattern of activated regions, not previously involved, was involved in the perception of the target of the lie, than in the act of lying. Even more salient to the present discussion was the fact that additional factors were shown to be implicated in lying. The picture emerging at this stage of this meta-review is of an increasingly varied set of responses to an increasing number of variables that influence the mental act we refer to as lying. It is also clear in this case how a response to an emotional situation may be misconstrued as something specific to lying.

P. Mohamed, Faro, Gordon, Platek, Ahmed, and Williams (2006)

Finally, the most widely dispersed activations reported so far come from one of the most recent studies. Mohammed and his colleagues used a relatively small number of subjects (12) and found activity across virtually all of the brain from the occipital lobes to the frontal lobes. Furthermore, the subject's task in this situation was also the most realistic of any protocol discussed so far. The subjects were told a story in which they were supposed to have participated in some crime and then told they would be rewarded if they were not "identified" as the criminal when examined in the fMRI system. In this experiment, Mohammed and his colleagues found 14 brain regions to be activated at levels that exceeded background levels (i.e., when the "true" images were subtracted from the "false" images. These included:

- Left medial frontal gyrus (BA 9)
- Left Inferior frontal gyrus (BA 10)
- Bilateral precentral gyri (BA 6)
- Right (temporal) hippocampus (BA
- Right medial temporal (BA 19)
- Bilateral parietal precuneus (BA 40)
- Right inferior parietal lobule (BA 40)
- Left lingual occipital (BA 18)
- Anterior cingulate
- Posterior cingulate
- Right Fusiform gyrus
- Right sublobar insula
- Thalamus

This final study in our meta-review emphasizes the general result that regions supposedly responsive to deception are scattered throughout the brain. It is also important to remember that these were the regions that exhibited the highest levels of activity and probably do not fully describe the spread of subthreshold but correlated activity. Thus, I must reiterate the basic fact that it is likely that all of the studies reported here underestimated the extent of the brain activity induced by this kind of mental activity—lying. These raw findings and initial interpretations set the stage for the following summary of the 16 published studies.

3.4 A Summary of the Sixteen Experiments on Brain Images and Lie Detection

In the previous section, I reviewed the results from the 16 identified experiments that attempted to find a sign or signal of deception using brain imaging measures. In the following sections, I present a discussion of them from three points of view:

1. A tabulation using the location of the single maximum peak of activation as a criterion. Consistency among the maximum peaks reported in the 16 experiments would speak strongly for ideas of cognitive modularity and circumscribed localization as well as the general idea that cognitive modules can be represented by localized regions of activation. As it turns out there is no such consistency observed.
2. A tabulation of all of the areas identified in each study associated with deception. Consistency in this case would support a broader distributed representation of cognitive processes albeit not narrowly localized. Such consistency is, however, not observed at this level either. Instead, we see that each experiment reported an almost unique pattern of responses.
3. A summary of some of the key issues highlighted by these findings.

Table 3.1

Experiment	Location of Maximum (Largest Voxel Volume)	Location Of Maximum (Max Z-score)
A.	#	BA 47
B.	BA 24 and 32	BA 24 and 32
C.	BA 10 and 46	#
D.	BA 32	BA 10
E.	#	BA 40
F.	#	BA 21
G.	#	BA 23
H.	BA 8, 32, and 6	#
I.	BA 47	BA 6, 8, and 9
J.	#	#
K.	#	BA 45 and 47
L.	#	#
M.	BA 32	BA 32
N.	BA 10 and 46	BA 10 and 46
O.	#	#
P.	#	BA 18

(# = No Entry)

A. Which Areas are Identified as the Point of Maximum Activity?

Most of the studies discussed here attempted to make some estimate of the parts of the brain that responded maximally to lying in accord with their individual experimental protocols. Although there were many differences in procedure, especially in what was considered to be lying, the goal was to determine which areas had distinctive maximum activation levels or peaks when a subject is lying. (It should be noted that this approach essentially dotes on the idea that a modular cognitive function, i.e., lying, is encoded or represented by a particular region or a system of regions of activity.) Presumably, should the experiments all have agreed and the brain was encoding "lying" at a particular place or at a particular group of places, then the points of maximum activity should be relatively close to each other. As a first approximation, therefore, it is worthwhile to examine the locations on the brain at which these maximum regions of activation occur.

There are two ways in which the location of these maximum activation peaks can be identified from the reports I reviewed here for analysis: (a) by determining the location of the maximum cluster of responding voxels or (b) by determining the maximum z score (the statistic representing the greatest deviation from the mean value of all voxels measured in standard deviation units) of the places where peaks occurred. Not all of the studies presented both kinds of data so there are some blanks in Table 3.1, the tabulation of these maximum values. I identify each experiment by the subsection heading used in the previous section.

A major limitation of this approach is that there were so many different experimental protocols and deception tasks that we should not have expected great consistency at the outset. Although this is a property of most psychological research and is probably unavoidable to at least some degree in brain imaging, as we now see, the magnitude of the inconsistency among the reports of the various experiments belies any hope of developing a brain image criterion of lying based on the activity of a single, albeit maximum, location. As much as we would have hoped to have seen some semblance of replication among these 16 experiments, this was not to be.

There are other problems in evaluating these data. For example, with the exception of the very first (A.) study, individual articles always reported more than one region of maximum activation for different experimental conditions. Furthermore, not all experiments organized their data in the same way as is done here. To the maximum extent possible, I have selected the lie-minus-truth condition as the prototype for the comparisons now being made.

All of these caveats not withstanding, this table is a first approximation to the rhetorical question—is there a unique localized center which is maximally activated in the brain when a subject is lying?

To make this data more interpretable, I have superimposed these areas of maximum activity on a drawing of the Brodmann areas in Figure 3.2. The main conclusion that can be visually drawn from this chart is that there is no consistent report of any single maximum region that is reliably associated with lying. This figure shows, instead, that reported maxima of activity may occur in any of the major lobes of the brain including the frontal, the parietal, the temporal, and even, in at least one instance, the occipital lobes of the brain when a subject is asked to lie.

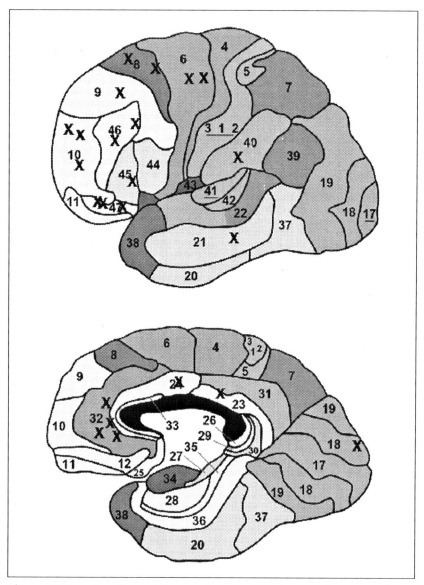

Figure 3.2 The location of the maximum activation peaks reported in each of the studies on lie detection discussed here.

B. What Areas, Other than Maximum Peaks, Are Involved?

The tabulation in the previous section asked—is there any evidence of a single re-liable localized area responding selectively to deception? There answer is clearly no! Quite to the contrary, the maximum peaks, as identified by either statistical significance or voxel volume, represented only a small part of the brain response. It is much more likely, for both empirical and technical reasons, that these few maximum peaks of activity drastically and arbitrarily understate the true extent of the brain responses. These data argue, to the contrary, that the brain's response is better characterized as widely distributed activity than as activity in a singular location. Therefore, a much better understanding of the extent of the brain activity associated with a mental act such as lying may be obtained by carrying out a similar exercise, not just for the peaks, but for all of the activated regions identified in the 16 experiments.

I now consider this alternative and tabulate all of the responding areas, not just the peaks, whose magnitudes were reported to be statistically significant in both a tabular and pictorial form. Table 3.2 lists all of the activated areas reported in all of the experiments. In this case, I also use the Brodmann area notational system as a means for comparing the various findings. An important additional caveat is that even this exhaustive list understates the true extent of the respond-ing regions. Each identified peak or maximum is but a portion of the differen-tially activated brain tissue, the true extent of which is arbitrary and depends on the experimenter's decision concerning the threshold at which "activity" will be considered to be "an activation."

This tabular information can also be presented in a graphic and more in-tuitive form by superimposing all of these locations onto a plan of the Brod-mann areas as shown in Figure 3.3. The conclusion one is impelled to draw from these displays of the data supplements the conclusion drawn from the analysis of the peak data; not only are there no reliable individual peaks as-sociated with lying, but the brain responds with widely dispersed activations across this group of studies. There is no consistency (i.e., reliability) reported here.

Table 3.2

Experiment	Brodmann Activation Areas									
A.	47									
B.	1	2	3	6	8	24	32	40		
C.	6	9	10	21	40	46				
+ Caudate										
D.	3	4	7	8	9	10	17	31	36	37
+Cerebellum										
E.	6	11	40	47						
F.	21	37	44							
+ Cerebellum + BA 11 (?)										
G.	Brodmann Areas Not Specified									
H.	6	8	32	38	39	40	44	47		
I.	6	9	40							
+Cerebellum										
J.	2	3	4	6	38	40	44			
+Cerebellum										
K.	8	9	21	22	37	39	40			
L.	6	7	8	9	10	23	32	40	47	
M.	6	8	9	10	32	44	45	46	47	
+Caudate + Thalamus										
N.	9	10	24	32	45	46				
O.	Brodmann Areas Not Specified									
P.	6	9	10	18	19	40				
+Anterior and posterior cingulate +Fusiform +Insula + Thalamus										

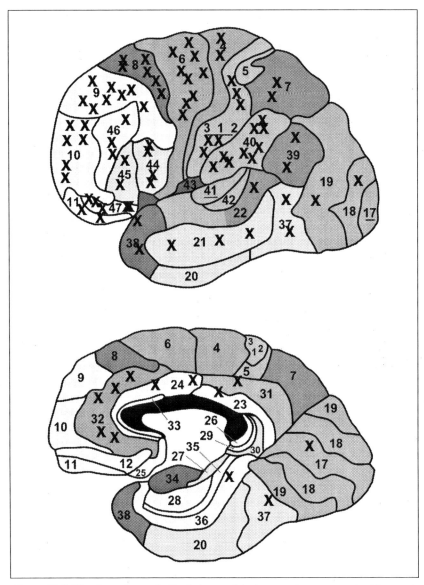

Figure 3.3 *The location of all of the activation regions reported in each of the studies on lie detection discussed here.*

C. Some Inescapable Conclusions

This analysis of the data obtained from what is believed to be a nearly complete review of the cognitive neuroscientific literature on brain images and lying has left us with two inescapable conclusions.

1. There is no evidence of a single localized area associated with deception.[18] Peaks of activation are reported throughout the brain in what seems to be a virtually random manner by this group of experiments.
2. There is, furthermore, no evidence of any reliable broad pattern of activations associated with deception. Statistically significant responses occur scattered about nearly all portions of the brain in a manner that varies from report to report.

Based on these empirically based conclusions, the old phrenological assumption, even as girded in its new modular-localization raiment, clearly cannot be supported. There is no evidence of narrow localization; indeed, there is no suggestion that any identifiable group of brain regions is activated more often than any other when people are asked to lie.

What we see instead is a highly variable and inconsistent set of data produced in a variety of different conditions and using different methods. No region or regions of the brain seemed to be reliably associated with deception. Virtually all parts of the brain were reported by one or another laboratory in one report or another to be activated by lying. This included regions in the frontal, parietal, and temporal areas as well as some auxiliary regions not classified within the Brodmann system. These auxiliary regions included such unlikely locations for the cognitive process we call deception as the thalamus and the cerebellum. In sum, there is no present evidence of any reliable brain image indicator of deception either in terms of a particular location or in terms of a consistent pattern of activations.

There are two possible reasons for the absence of a reliable brain sign of deception. The first is that the field is so beset by different methods and inadequate simulations of real life lying that any brain image correlate is hidden in the noise (i.e., irregular, random, irrelevant, or uncontrolled activity). Thus, the failure to detect deception may be due to a lack of experimental control. Some of the sources of this high level of experimental noise in the system include:

1. The independent variable (i.e., what was intended to constitute a lie) varied from experiment to experiment. The following list tabulates the idiosyncratic nature of the procedures used to induce a simulation of lying.

- Lying In Response To Probe Questions
- Guilty Knowledge Test with Playing Cards (2)
- Directed Lying with Playing Cards (3)
- Directed Lying about Real World Events (2)
- Feigned Memory Impairment (2)
- Well Rehearsed Coherent Lies vs. Prompted Lies
- Novel Lies vs. Routine Truths
- Rewarded Guilty Knowledge (2)
- Denying Mock Crime (2)
- Control Question Procedure
- Target of Deceit: To the Subject or to Someone Else[19]

2. Statistical thresholds for accepting activations, either in terms of their z-scores or voxel count, varied substantially from experiment to experiment allowing background activity to be misinterpreted either as correlated activations or excluded noise.

3. Different samples of subjects were examined on different imaging machines in different laboratories and the data pooled. The problem may, therefore, be a sampling error, i.e. the samples of subjects were not equivalent. Recent work (Aron, Gluck, and Poldrack, 2006) has shown that although individual subjects do reliably replicate their personal pattern of activations, the more data being pooled, the greater the variability of the statistics describing the results.

In fact, none of the 16 studied research studies was specifically designed to repeat any earlier one—each was more or less idiosyncratic in terms of its experimental design. Therefore, specific replication should hardly have been expected. It is possible, of course, that as the field matures, that standards of control will improve and a brain image measure of lying will emerge from the chaos that characterizes the current work. However, for the moment, inconsistency and a lack of reliability seem to characterize this field.

There is, however, a more pessimistic conclusion one can draw from this analysis—that the findings may in actual fact be unreliable because there is no signal; in reality, all activations are essentially random responses. This interpretation suggests that every peak, every distributed response is nothing more than background noise unrelated to the experimental conditions! If this interpretation is correct, the hypothesis that we can determine when a person is lying with a brain imaging device is just patently wrong. Any such effort to find an objective brain image of lying, if this conclusion is correct, is a fool's errand, there being no valid or reliable brain image measure of the cognitive state we refer to as lying. There is, on this perspective, only spurious responses from the brain that have little or nothing to do with deception either directly (as a valid and objective, albeit noisy, measure of the mental state) or indirectly (as a correlate of some associated mental state such as emotion).

Just how broadly this conclusion may be applicable to other cognitive processes is uncertain. However, the initial analysis of the meta-reviews discussed in Chapter 2 points in this direction. In general, meta-reviews show weak reliability and great inconsistency of the experimental findings.

The meta-review of the findings from the 16 experiments that I have carried out here should at the very least leave us with a very skeptical attitude towards the use of brain images as lie detectors. The following summary emphasizes the reasons that may underlay this skepticism.

3.5 Evaluation of the Use of Brain Images as Lie Detectors

The meta-review that I carried out here evaluates what is probably a complete corpus of the currently available scientific evidence concerning the use of brain images as lie detectors. This review sets the stage for further discussions of the many issues, technical and conceptual, that circulate around this field today.

So far we see that the empirical evidence does not support the use of the fMRI or PET brain imagers as lie detectors. In fact, they strongly argue that the whole approach is invalid. Not too surprisingly and in spite of this lack of scientific support, there is still considerable pressure to assume that such a system may be applicable, to at least a limited degree, in some forensic applications. It can be argued that the reasons that this pressure still exists are extra-scientific and have more to do with the felt need for an objective measure of this particular mental activity than with any supporting scientific evidence that it works.

How could we have gotten into a situation in which machine lie detection, so scientifically unsupported, could have such wide use and misuse? Adler (2002) suggests that much of the explanation can be found in social as opposed to scientific justifications:

> …the rise of the lie detector in twentieth century America was a historical response to a specific set of imperatives. These included the popular demand that the state draw a sharp line between lawful and unlawful behavior (among both cops and criminals), the ongoing negotiations that produced a particular regime of intellectual property, and the need for reliability in new hierarchical associations. (p. 24)

These social needs were further interpreted by Adler as (1) the unquenchable desire for a more absolute proof of guilt or innocence in a complex and variable world, (2) the emerging autonomy of workers to the extent that ideas became transportable, and (3) the need for loyalty to large corporations that transcended the small family units of the past.

To this collection of social forces must also be added the predilection of the scientifically naïve to accept as real that which is in reality fanciful and to provide answers where only imponderables exist. Furthermore, there is a certain mystique about "machines" that draw graphs or produce pretty pictures. People want to believe that a "magic" machine can read their thoughts or that an image of brain activity is equivalent to the thought, an idea that is supported by the fact that the signal comes from the brain and the brain is without question the organ of the mind. In fact, reliable and robust empirical evidence for such a speculation is almost completely absent.

In this section, I identify a number of the problems that face brain image based lie detection and expand on why the movement has such persistence despite the lack of scientific support. These problems include:

- Most important of all, the empirical results concerning the relationship of brain images and deception are inconsistent and variable. There is no single place or group of places in the brain that has been shown to be uniquely associated or even modestly correlated across the board with deception or any other high level cognitive process. To put it in the simplest possible terms—IT DOES NOT WORK!
- Brain images do not measure mental activity any more directly than does the polygraph.
- Lying or deception is an ill-defined process probably composed of many different kinds of mental responses and combinations thereof. Therefore, the control of experimental conditions is extremely difficult.
- Beyond the issue of reliability, there is no way to establish the validity of the proposed brain image measures of deception, even in the remote future should they be shown to be reliably correlated. There are other plausible explanations of the correlation beyond "reading the mind."
- Furthermore, there remain a number of practical problems noted by researchers in the field that continue to obstruct application of brain imaging as a lie detector including:
  - ◊ Ultimately countermeasures will be developed.
  - ◊ Decision rules lead to false positives and missed deceptions.
  - ◊ Statistical anomalies distort lie detector success rates.
  - ◊ Averaged data does not help in predicting individual responses.

◊   Examinee cooperativeness is required.
◊   The imaging procedures are cumbersome and time consuming.
◊   The subtraction process does not work.
◊   Double blind experiments are infrequently used.

A. There is No Single Place or Group of Places that Has Been Empirically Associated with Deception or Any Other Mental Process

Because we cannot study brain function at the detailed microscopic network level, the presumed level of neuronal activity that is likely to be the actual source of mental processes, we do what we can do. In traditional cognitive neuroscience this has been embodied in the search for localized areas in the brain that are supposed to encode specific cognitive processes, much in the same vein as the basic assumption of the long-ago rejected phrenology. There has been a powerful tendency to substitute a different kind of research question—"where" does something happen?—for the question of "how" the brain produces the mind. This is the heart of the twin assumptions of psychological modularization and brain localization that continue to pervade much of cognitive neuroscience. All of the 16 studies reviewed here are "localization" studies in which it is only asked "where" the brain is activated when a person tells a lie. Even if it was possible to answer this question (and the answer is not discernible in these publications) there is a vast difference between this kind of knowledge and an understanding of how the brain generates mind. Indeed, one may fairly ask—what contribution to mind-brain theory would be forthcoming from even the most complete answer to the "where" question?

As we have seen in this meta-review, even the "where" question is not answered in the sense originally hoped; the activation peaks associated with lying have been shown in this corpus of scientific reports actually to be widely distributed across and within the brain. Although each report reports some degree of activation in multiple areas, the collective impression produced by the meta-review as shown in Tables 3.1 and 3.2 and Figures 3.2 and 3.3 is one of very great dispersion of the brain responses. There is no evidence of any special place or group of places in the brain whose activation can be associated with lying.

The best current answer to the "where" question, therefore, is "almost everywhere!" There is no question that the phrase "distributed neural responses" more closely describes the actual situation than does the phrase "localized responses." The conclusion of widespread and dispersed distribution is the basic empirical result of the entire body of meta-research—a long delayed, but necessary attack on the logic behind the emphasis currently based on the "where" question.

B. Brain Images Do Not Measure Mental Activity Any More Directly Than Does the Polygraph

A brief consideration of some of the properties of conventional lie detectors will help to set the stage for the following discussion. Each of the older classes of lie detector methods (see those tabulated under Class I earlier) suffered from one or another major disadvantage. The first class, including the classic polygraph, was based on the recording of some autonomic or motor response that was only distantly related to the purported mental process of deception. For example, no one considers the blood pressure as measured by the sphygmomanometer to be the psychoneural equivalent of the mental process itself; at best, it is only a correlated indicator of the body's response to stress or emotion, mental states that themselves were only indirectly associated with lying per se.

Members of the second class listed, Class II, including the EEG and other similar indicators of the electrical measures of brain activity, do seem at first glance to be somewhat more direct indicators of mental states. After all, it is argued they come from the brain and most cognitive neuroscientists agree that the brain is the organ of mind. However, we do not definitively know where these microvoltage-level brain recordings originate or what their relationships are to mental activity. There is, therefore, serious doubt that they reflect mental states any more directly than do the autonomic responses.

Then the fMRI and PET brain images appeared on the scene. Their seemingly more direct measurement of brain activity provided them with a kind of face validity that was not enjoyed by the autonomic or electrical wave measuring instruments. Brain images record what is asserted to be direct manifestations of the brain's information processing activity, not an elusive global electrical signal such as the EEG. Furthermore, there seem to be demonstrable differences in the activated locales reported in individual studies, a fact that fit well with the long-standing assumptions of both brain and mind modularity.

Thus, the idea of using brain images as lie detectors is entirely consistent and timely within the context offered by the prevailing model of mind-brain relationships. Unfortunately, the currently available empirical data suggest that however consistent and timely, the strong conclusion that brain imaging devices directly probe the brain mechanisms of lying is probably not justified.

The point is that because they come from the brain, brain images have a kind of special face validity and conceptual potency that is undeserved. Quite to the contrary, when examined in detail, it becomes clear that fMRI brain images are as indirect measures of mental activity as are the autonomic or electrical measures. Technically, they are metabolic measures of the Blood Oxygenation Level Difference (BOLD) in the brain—an aspect of the brain's metabolism—only indirectly of the neural activity that is presumably the equivalent of mental activity.

Even here there is great uncertainty. There remains considerable controversy in the field concerning the exact relationship of BOLD both to the brain's metabolism and the information processing carried out by neuronal networks. There is, therefore, no question that the brain images are not direct indicators of what we would consider the equivalents of mental activity. The chain of logical connections between our thoughts and the brain images is as long and disjointed as that between our thoughts and autonomic responses used in the polygraph. Here, for example, is a list of the links in the logical chain implicitly adhered to when one attempts to relate brain images with cognition.

Cognitive activity is assumed to be represented by an accumulation of:

Local Field Potentials (Synaptic) Activity >
Increased Glucose (?) Metabolism >
Increased Oxygen Demand >
Increased Oxygenated Blood Flow >
Decreased Deoxygenated Blood Level >
Changed fMRI Signature

(Where > means "which is assumed to lead to.")

All of these steps introduce multi-second delays between the thought and the fMRI response and, thus, uncertainty about when the critical response occurred. The conclusion to be drawn is that the final image is not a direct measure of the salient neural equivalents of thought any more than the measure produced by a sphygmomanometer. Both are secondary manifestations of the neuronal networks that actually account for our thoughts and which control our behavior.

In summary, although there has been an enormous amount of research in the field called cognitive neuroscience, in fact the basic question of what aspect of brain activity is the equivalent of mental activity remains poorly understood. The best guess right now is that the mind is encoded by the state of activity and the informational interactions of the network of billions of neuronal cells as mediated by synaptic junctions. Unfortunately none of the imaging techniques operates at this level. Like the EEG, brain images are cumulative, low resolution summaries of the activity of multitudes of cellular interactions. All such measures lose or obscure all of the critical microscopic detail that actually is thought to be the root of our mental life. As such they, too, are indirect responses of the brain, at best correlated with the fundamental brain activity subserving mental processes, but not the actual equivalents of that mental action. The brain image, which is indisputably one of the most important developments in medical science, is just operating at the wrong level to understand mind-brain relationships.

C. Lying or Deception is an Ill-Defined Process Probably Composed of Many Different Mental Processes

Another problem with this entire body of research is that the persistent difficulty of defining and controlling the mental process of lying has not yet and may never be solved. Indeed, in the published literature I surveyed in this chapter, experimenters have resorted to a diverse set of laboratory simulations of real-world lying. Most have used some version of the GKT, typically modified and manipulated by directing responses to the status of playing cards or false theft situations. Others used feigned memory impairment, instructions to distinguish between real and false memories, or asked their subjects to lie or tell the truth in contrived situations with or without some kind of monetary award.

The important point of this diversity is that lying was idiosyncratically defined in many different ways in the experiments reviewed here. None of these simulations was a priori wrong, but collectively they illustrate a clear example of the general difficulty of defining cognitive processes. The fundamental source of this continuing problem is that we still do not have good psychological theories, concepts, or even adequate definitions about the nature of mental processes to closely approximate the emotional and cognitive overtones of real-life lying. The nineteenth century phrenological list of mental faculties has been superseded by equally ambiguous terms in modern psychology such as a learning, perception, executive decision making, fear, and general emotion among many others. However, these faculties or mental processes still elude precise definition, simulation, and control.

Nowhere is this ambiguity made clearer than in what we mean by deception. Real-life lying comes in many different guises and is driven by many different motivations. The degree of self confidence on the part of liars, their personalities, the context in which the lie is offered, and for these experiments, the nature of simulated deception task, can evoke any number of different kinds of unknown mental activities. The observed absence of any semblance of replication of results in the 16 experiments reviewed here is due, in substantial part, to this lack of a good or even a common definition over what was meant by lying. Given that replication is the prime criterion for good science, this is a frail foundation on which to base such important decisions as should this deeply flawed new version of an objective lie detector test be used in our judicial proceedings. Unfortunately, the expectation that a precise definition can be formulated is also unrealistic.

Cumulatively and individually, none of the results from these 16 studies support the contention that lying produces consistent responses in either narrowly circumscribed or distributed regions of the brain. To the contrary, they provide additional support for the argument that virtually any psychological function, no matter how carefully we attempt to define it, can and does activate widely dispersed portions of the brain. (The corollary to this conclusion is that virtually any part of the brain is activated by many different psychological processes.) The conclusion to which we are once again inexorably drawn is that no local activation or pattern of activations is uniquely associated with deception.

D. Validity of the Measures

This brings us to one of the most subtle and complex conceptual issues involved not only in deception testing but throughout the science of neuropsychology. Even if the findings from the various laboratories were consistent and the same or similar brain areas were being activated in the different laboratories, there remains the question of the validity of the fMRI method in this mind-brain context. That is, are we measuring what we think we are measuring? The answer to this question is that so far there has been no rigorous proof that these recorded brain measures are actually measuring deception itself. Because it is so difficult to define and control stimuli, it is also difficult to guarantee that the brain images are directly associated with lying per se. Of course, the problem of validity is always a challenge when one is attempting to measure something that is not directly accessible. In the case of mental processes such as lying, however, all of the traditional difficulties are exacerbated.

Of course, reliable brain images that were highly correlated with lying would be of interest and could serve as a lie detector even if they came from a third mediating variable (e.g., emotion). That is, the system could be reliable even if its validity could not be established. It would be encouraging if there was a high correlation between some activation area in a brain image and lying; this, at least, would provide some face validity to the idea that the brain image is accurately measuring some aspect, however uncertain, of the mental state of lying. Unfortunately, there is still no evidence of such a correlation; therefore, the whole issue of validity cannot be resolved—the minimal conditions for scientific explanation are not being met.

In summary, the lack of a good definition of lying (or any other mental state) and the absence of any theory of how the mind emerges from the brain leads to the following specific difficulties in empirical and theoretical studies.

- Poor control of independent mental state variables in experiments
- Ambiguity and variability of dependent response variables
- Paradoxical responses
- Questionable validity
- Extreme variability

Most of the issues I have discussed so far are scientific, technical, and theoretical. I now turn to some of the practical problems that mitigate the admissibility of brain images as lie detectors in our courtrooms. These practical considerations speak directly to the third of the *Daubert* criteria, to be discussed later in this chapter.

E. Practical Problems

Let us assume for the moment, for the sake of argument, that all of these conceptual and scientific issues could be overcome and a reliable brain image correlate of lying developed. Even in that unlikely case, there still are many practical obstacles to its admissibility into the judicial process. I now consider a few of those practical problems that would make even the best vetted brain image lie detector difficult if not impossible to apply and certainly disqualify them from participating in legal matters.

1. Ultimately Countermeasures Will Be Developed. One of the major problems with lie detectors of any kind is that it is relatively easy to develop countermeasures that will inevitably cripple widespread application to any other than the most naïve subjects. Thus, like the conscious control of autonomic responses that is achievable by behavioral techniques, it is likely that sophisticated examinees could learn to control their brain responses. Simple diversions of attention, forced recollections, or mental arithmetic are likely to be extremely effective countermeasures. Recent developments suggesting that it is possible to consciously control mechanical devices (such as prosthetic limbs) by conscious control of brain responses also attest to how easy it would be to consciously modify any putative brain responses to lying.

For some personality types, it may not even be necessary to make a conscious effort to counter the test's goals. Intrinsic "countermeasures" may come easily and naturally to the sociopathic personality who simply does not have the emotional or cognitive reactions to deception that are presumed to be the foundations on which any fMRI test of lying would eventually be based. Other more normal personalities can be trained to overcome any weak associations between lying and brain images that may emerge in the future. The effectiveness of training in lie detector countermeasures can be inferred from the fact that there is no record of any spy ever being caught by a polygraph despite its widespread use throughout the government and industry.

2. Decision Rules Lead to False Positive and Missed Deceptions. There is another aspect of variability that also has to be taken into consideration when examining the plausibility of using brain images as lie detectors. Even if something better than a modest level of correlation between lying and brain responses could be obtained, the association is never complete. The outcome of even the most successful lie detector will have to be phrased in terms of overlapping distributions. There will, therefore, always be the problem of false positives and missed lies as best conceptualized in the language of Signal Detection Theory (SDT).

SDT is a powerful means of explaining why variable data with overlapping distributions will always produce some false positives (i.e., the examinee who is telling the truth is reported to be lying) or misses (the examinee who is lying is reported to be telling the truth). The four possible decisions are shown in a tabular form in Table 3.3.

This is an inevitable outcome of a system with overlapping distributions, that is, with less than perfect (1.0) correlations.

The problem highlighted by this kind of analysis is that if the criterion for accepting a response as a lie is set high enough to minimize false alarms (assuming a lie is being told when it is not), there will be a number of missed lies (assuming that the truth is being told when the examinee is actually lying). If, on the other hand, the criterion is set too low, so as to maximize the number of hits (assuming that a subject is lying when they are, indeed, lying), there will be an increased number of false alarms (assuming a subject is lying when he is telling the truth). For systems with any degree of variability and overlap of their respective distributions, there is no way to avoid this pattern of false alarms and misses: If you decrease one, you will increase the other.

The proportion of false alarms and misses can be quite considerable. It is certainly much worse than the much higher level of certainty exhibited by a DNA test or even what is now becoming increasingly evident in the modest levels of successful identifications using fingerprint comparisons and ballistic evidence. (See Saks and Koehler, 2005, for an up-to-date consideration of the failures of this kind of forensic evidence to meet high standards of proof.)

The problem for society then becomes an ethical one, not a technical one. How many false convictions based on false positive alarms is society willing to accept so that the net can be broadly enough cast (by using a low enough level criterion) to convict a satisfactorily large number of real liars? In other words, there is no way to avoid false convictions other than to acquit everyone!

Table 3.3

	Lying	Truth Telling
Lying Detected	Hit	False Positive
No Lying Detected	Miss	Correct Rejection

3. Statistical Anomalies Distort Lie Detection Success Rates. Although occasional studies report high levels of success in discriminating lies from truth, it is becoming obvious that the raw "percentage correct" scores reported may distort the actual success rate. At the most elementary level, it must be remembered that a "hit rate" of 50% in a two alternative test (e.g., a person is judged to be lying or to be telling the truth) in which half are liars and half are telling the truth constitutes essentially random results. Thus, reported scores or 60% and 70% actually represent relatively poor performance on the part of a putative lie detector.

4. Averaged Data Does Not Determine Individual Behavior. If there is any fundamental truth to be observed generally throughout psychological research, as well as in the meta-review of these 16 studies, it is that individual behavior cannot be predicted from group statistics. Because human behavior is so variable, we must necessarily subject it to a statistical examination to approach even the most basic understanding of the *likelihood* that a person will behave in one way or another. Therefore, we do not have the option of predicting individual human behavior based on the resulting group data.[20] The best that we can say is that there is a probability that a person will behave or has behaved in a specified manner based on observations taken from what is a random (an assumption not always justified in psychological research) sample of groups of individuals.

In the same vein, barring impossibly high correlations, group data from a number of fMRI scans is variable enough so that there is no possibility of telling with certainty whether or not an individual is lying. No matter how many subjects and how many responses are pooled, the veracity of an individual response is not absolutely determinable from the pooled and averaged data. Individual brain images can fall any place on the distribution of responses observed in the group data. Therefore, there is no absolute way to determine that a given individual's score is evidence of deception. It depends as much on the investigator's selection of criterion levels as on the variable behavior exhibited by the sample of subjects used in the experiment. At best, psychology is a correlative and statistical science. The ethical issues that this undeniable fact raises for judicial proceedings are profound. To use such ambiguous data in determining the guilt or innocence of an accused is little improvement in effectiveness over medieval judgment by trial or ordeal.

5. Examinee Cooperativeness. Another technical problem is that the measurement of a brain image requires a great deal of cooperation on the part of the examinee when placed in a brain imaging device. Both physical posture and the head's stability must be severely controlled for what are often extended periods of time. Indeed, it is not only necessary to ask the examinee to maintain position but it is equally necessary to ask the examinee to cooperate by "controlling" the wandering of their thoughts because of the extended time required to produce an fMRI image. Such control is difficult even in the most pristine laboratory setting; in the highly stressed and relatively unstructured arenas of a field investigation or a judicial proceeding, many would agree that it is impossible.

A degree of cooperation on the part of the examinee is thus required that transcends even that required for a standard polygraph. Furthermore, the need for cooperative and compliant examinees opens the door to the use of counter-measures and the fraudulent use of the brain imaging system by people who have a vested interest in a preordained outcome.

6. Cumbersome Procedures. Exacerbating the requirements of subject coop-erativeness is the simple fact that the measurement of an fMRI brain image is a cumbersome, time-consuming, and expensive procedure. Routine application of the procedure is currently very expensive, costing upwards of several thousand dollars for a simple medical examination. This raises the question of who would be examined and the possibility of justice tempered, once again, by wealth or its absence.

Of course, future technological developments may overcome these technical problems and permit a brain image to be collected as easily as a camera snapshot is taken. However, other technical and experimental design problems remain that cannot be conceivably overcome even in the distant future. One of these is the subtraction method that is the basic tool for comparing control and experimental conditions.

7. Subtraction or Differencing. A major problem for brain imaging is the stan-dard paradigm of subtraction used to identify a putative localized activation. In brief, the image results for a control condition ("don't think about a cow") are subtracted from the experimental condition ("think about a cow") and the differ-ence in the activated areas is presumed to indicate where the idea of a "cow" is represented in the brain. The basic assumption on which this procedure is based is that activity appearing in the experimental condition but not in the control condition identifies the "cow" region.

Unfortunately this method is deeply flawed. The brain, all neuroscientists now agree, is a heavily integrated system in which high levels of activity in one location may actually represent areas prohibiting or inhibiting activity in other distant areas. Similarly, other high activity regions may actually enhance distant activity by disinhibiting activity in other areas. High (or low) levels of brain image activation, therefore, are not necessarily associated with high levels of mental activity. This kind of uncertainty has plagued cognitive neuroscientists throughout its history. Each of these problems may reflect a basic inability on the part of any experimenter or theorist to parse out the actions and interactions of a complex system. (See the discussion of the work of Hilgetag, O'Neil, and Young, 1996, for an elaboration of this difficulty.)

Furthermore, it is not a priori true that an absence of a difference in the fMRI image between a control and an experimental condition means that the area under study is performing the same function in the two conditions. Some areas that show no difference in the two conditions in the BOLD determined image may actually represent two vastly different neural configurations if examined at the microscopic level. To draw a somewhat superficial analogy, a computer may exhibit no difference in the energy consumption or the electrical field strength around it as it carries out two very different programs. Although the average values may not change and no difference in cumulative activity may be indicated, the actual details of the underlying programs may have changed drastically.

Therefore, we must conclude that the differencing or subtraction approach, so broadly (and, some would argue, necessarily) adopted in the brain imaging field, rests on an assumption that is much too simplistic to permit robust conclusions about the significance of the observed activation levels. Indeed, the subtraction process may actually cover up what are essentially the failings of a totally ineffective means of studying the brain.

8. Double Blind Experiments are Rare. One of the most important means of guaranteeing the robustness of a scientific experiment is to use a double blind experimental design. A double blind experiment is one in which neither the subject nor the experimenter (and sometimes even the scientist who analyzes the data) know what are the various experimental conditions such as which subjects are in a control group and which are in an experimental group. Even more important is that no one involved in the actual running of the experiment be aware of its expected outcomes. Only in double blind protocols can the effect of bias driven by expectations, hopes, and personal theoretical positions be minimized. Robust scientific procedures using double blind experimental designs have been remarkably absent not only from studies of deception but also from a substantial amount of the cognitive neuroscience research carried out in the last two decades.

When we are dealing with an experiment in which the independent variable is controlled by asking the subject to carry out some cognitive process, it becomes extremely difficult to avoid this kind of bias. How, indeed, does one keep the subject from knowing the conditions of the experiment when the subjects are the ones who must conjure up the mental states in response to the directions of the experimenter? The opportunities for bias and placebo effects are especially ripe in brain image studies of cognitive functioning.

3.6 Interim Conclusions

We have now arrived at the point at which some interim conclusions can be drawn from what must be considered to be an extremely modest corpus of research concerning the use of brain imaging as a detector of deception. Our analysis supports what should be obvious—there is no substance to the idea that a machine, even one as complicated as the fMRI, can read the human mind with a precision sufficient to justify its use as a lie detector. This skeptical conclusion is also supported by such authors as Talbot (2007), who has expressed many of the same reservations noted here.

Of course, no one can predict the future; it is always possible that future research will uncover an unanticipated link between lying and BOLD activity (or some comparable measure of brain activity) that may ultimately be associated or correlated with cognition. However, given the lack of any semblance of reliability in the current data and the fact that extraneous social and personal needs have led to a persistence of an otherwise fallacious pseudoscience—polygraphy—it seems that popular, if not judicial and scientific, enthusiasm is running far ahead of the science.

It is important to understand that the articles that I reviewed here are all from respected scientific laboratories. These studies represent a substantial step in scientific quality beyond those discussed in the NAS (2003) report on polygraphs. Nevertheless, almost by their role as researchers in this field, the investigators are advocates and believe they are providing the scientific foundation for what some day may be an effective brain image lie detector. However, all express some concern and doubt about what they collectively consider to be highly preliminary work. For example, a culling of their cautionary comments includes the following:

- "...our protocol requires refinement"
- "Our experimental evidence provides some initial evidence"
- "...our two dimensions for the characterizing of lies are just the beginning"
- This is a "pilot study"
- "Further work is required"
- "Future studies could examine the effects of...countermeasures and physiological states on the accuracy of fMRI based lie detection.
- "...the approach could potentially be used"
- "Funding for these studies was provided by Cephos..."[21]
- "The consistency of these findings suggests that the fMRI...may have potential as a reliable lie detection device."
- "...simulated deception in laboratory experiments cannot be view as being the same as deception in real life"

- "...in other words, [our results] could probably be generalizable to future scientific studies of deception in various clinical and forensic populations."
- "A major limitation of this study...."
- "These results are preliminary...and it is too early to predict whether functional MR imaging will replace other methods of examining deception."

Nowhere in this list of comments is a strong conviction expressed that the brain imaging process is yet ready to be applied to judicial and investigative activities.

Furthermore, it is also important to appreciate that because of the cost of this procedure, the number of subjects run in each experiment is relatively modest for a data set of such variability. Many statisticians would argue that it is below the number at which acceptable levels of significance tests could be achieved. If one examines comparable (in complexity) drug testing procedures (which typically involve hundreds of subjects and which produce only small changes, modest levels of significance, and all-to-often reversals of their respective initial hypotheses) it seems that these 16 studies are, at best, very preliminary explorations that do not recommend anything beyond the need for "further research." They certainly do not justify the introduction of brain imaging techniques as an admissible "lie detector" into the legal system at this point. Indeed, there is every indication given the lack of repeatability and reliability in these studies that the effect is either very small or nonexistent and that, as the NAS has stated for the polygraph, the justification for "further research" is quite weak.

This raises the ethical issues to a different plane. It is just not a matter of the violation of our privacy or protections against "unreasonable search" should the system actually work. Instead, it is a matter of what now appears to be the premature use of a scientifically unsound procedure. If one worries about the ethics of applying a *method that works*, consider how much more serious would be the ethical issues involved in using something that has been shown *not to work*. It is clear that this is not only a possible outcome but also an immediately likely one given the history of the traditional polygraph and the present results. Although not admissible in most courtrooms as evidence, use of this pseudoscientific device still percolates through the judicial system.

It is also interesting to consider the nature of the explanatory theories that have been used to explain these findings. Whatever the results obtained in these 16 experiments, the efforts to explain them in terms of the presumed functions of various regions of the brain are unlikely to bear fruit. Not only do serious questions remain about the role that any particular area may play in deception, but the whole idea of modular cognitive functions assigned to localized regions of the brain is coming under increased attack, as discussed in earlier chapters.

Beyond that general issue is the mathematical fact (highlighted by the work of Hilgetag, O'Neil, and Young, 1996) that complex systems whose units are heavily interconnected with feedback, feed forward, and lateral communication lines are indeterminate in terms of their hierarchical structure. That is, none of the ad hoc theories, which assert that a given region performs a specific function or influences other regions in a particular way, can be confirmed or denied. Thus, any theoretical discussions in which specific functions are assigned to specific brain modules ultimately must be considered to be arbitrary and quite possibly unachievable.

It is important that the nature of the research carried out in this chapter on lie detection be compared to the requirements of the *Daubert* criteria for admissibility. In addition to being relevant and reliable, the *Daubert* criteria include:

- Any theory or method must be falsifiable, refutable, and testable in a scientific sense. This criterion implies that sufficient data must be available to demonstrate that it actually works.
- It must have been previously published in an outlet that requires peer review.
- There must be some quantitative measure of its error rate and maintenance and calibration must be up to appropriate standards. This criterion implies that the error rate must be low enough to justify its admissibility as evidence.
- It must be generally accepted by an appropriate scientific community. This criterion implies that substantial, although not necessary total, agreement among relevant investigators is required for admissibility.

The *Daubert* criteria are not unambiguous and there still remains a great deal of uncertainty about which scientific evidence should or should not be admissible. Accepting that the use of the fMRI as a lie detector is being researched and published, and that its validity could conceivably, someday, be confirmed (or refuted) on the basis of solid scientific evidence, at present it must be concluded that the data do not yet support its acceptance by the scientific community. It is, therefore, the third criterion that the brain imaging lie detectors fail to satisfy most completely. The current state of the brain image-lie detector field is neither reliable nor can any estimates be made of its error rate—beyond the bald fact presented here, that it does not work! As shown earlier, not even the investigators involved in this activity unequivocally support the hypothesis that brain images are potent detectors of lying.

Therefore, at the present time the following conclusions concerning brain images and the detection of deception seem appropriate.

1. There has been enormous progress in both the neurosciences and psychology in recent years.

2. Nevertheless, there remains an enormous gap between the two domains of discourse. We still have no well-substantiated technology that will allow us to read minds, detect lying, or determine guilt.

3. There has been a sea change occurring in the field of mind-brain relationships. Where once modular mental functions were supposed to be localized in circumscribed regions of the brain, it is now becoming apparent that the brain operates on a much more global basis in which many areas contribute to what still remain very ill-defined mental activities.

4. The current corpus of experimental literature (consisting of only about 16 studies) on the proposed use of the fMRI or PET brain imaging techniques as lie detectors is inconsistent and unreliable. No objective measures of its error rate exist because of this inconsistency. Nothing in the meta-review carried out here suggests that it can work as a lie detector.

5. Using such devices in judicial proceedings is, therefore, premature at best.

6. Those few entrepreneurs who jumped the gun by setting up commercial enterprises to offer imaging services to investigators and courts are at serious risk of seeing their companies fail for the best of scientific reasons. To persevere in the context of the low level of reliability of current scientific findings suggests that they are intentionally purveying a pseudoscience, albeit one cloaked in the scientific aura and attractiveness of one of the most important scientific developments of modern times.

7. I appreciate that stamping out the attractive idea that there are machines that can read minds is as difficult as killing vampires.

8. However, perhaps a few "wooden stakes" of scientific scrutiny may help to abort what is all too likely to become the same kind of persistent pseudoscientific fad as polygraphy. My hope is that we will be able to kill this new "vampire" before it becomes an irreversible part of our legal system.

9. My expectation, unfortunately, is that our courts are going to be confronted with this kind of pseudoscience for many years.

Endnotes

1. Hammurabi's first law dealt with ensnarement. ("If any one ensnare another, putting a ban upon him, but he can not prove it, then he that ensnared him shall be put to death.) The meaning of the word "ensnare" in this context is not clear but it may be akin to kidnapping or illegal restraint.

2. The exact date of the formulation of the Ten Commandments is unknown. The traditional date is about the thirteenth or fourteenth century BCE during the exodus. Another view, expressed by the minimalist school of biblical scholars and archeologists, asserts that they were written down around the eighth century BCE when the Old Testament was first composed and compiled from oral histories. (Finkelstein and Silberman, 2001)

3. An interesting current attempt to use behavioral indicators as indicators of deception can be found in the training given to Taekwondo professionals. Although acknowledged to be fallible, the mentioned clues to lying include 40 different behavioral signals such as slouching posture, touching the nose, and rubbing the ears.

4. The word trial is used here in the older sense of a physical challenge, even combat, rather than in the modern jurisprudence sense.

5. The autonomic nervous system of the body consists of a series of nerves and nodes lying outside the spinal cord and brain that serve to regulate bodily processes such as pulse rate, blood pressure, pupillary dilation, and skin resistance. Their activity is mainly automatic in that we do not consciously decide to speed up the heart or change the electrical resistivity of the skin, as relevant examples. Negative emotions, threats, and physical challenges of all kinds as well as positive emotional experiences are all known to produce changes in autonomic activity.

6. Trovillo (1939a) points out that the use of these devices as lie detectors was not mentioned in the first edition of Lombroso's book. It is, however, mentioned by his daughter in her translation (Ferrero, 1911/1972) of this classic work.

7. Grubin and Madsen (2005) tell the interesting story of Marston's popularization of the idea. He was the author of the comic strip series "Wonder Woman," a character possessing a magic cord that would force a person to tell the truth. Obviously this was a spin off from his scientific work.

8. The *Frye* criterion for admissibility was short and sweet. It required only "general acceptance by the relevant scientific field." The *Daubert* criteria are much more stringent.

9. It is interesting to note that despite this contribution, Keeler was one of the first to challenge the idea that the polygraph was an accurate lie detector only four years later. (Keeler, 1934)

10. The definitive National Academy of Sciences report states that—"we conclude that in populations of examinees such as those represented in the polygraph research literature, untrained in countermeasures, specific-incident polygraph tests can discriminate lying from truth telling at rates well above chance, though well below perfection." (p. 4, NAS, 2003).

11. Although PET scans have infrequently been used in this research, most of the work I discuss in this chapter involves the fMRI procedure. The results and conclusions presumably hold for both methods.

12. As shown later in this chapter, even this glimmer of "promises" has not been achieved during the past few years. Indeed, the situation is just the opposite; the idea of a brain image lie detector seems to be a fantasy that is not just "not supported" by the relevant scientific research but is rejected by the empirical findings.

13. An even newer system has been proposed by Talairach and Tournoux (1988) in which measurements (in mm) are made in a three-dimensional space from landmarks on a standard brain. It is not yet clear what advantage this may have given the variability in brain sizes and shapes; however it promises to be more effective than the Brodmann system based as it was on neuronal types. Other methods involving standardizing the shape of the brain by distorting it may also be useful.

14. Brodmann area[s] is hereafter designated by the abbreviation BA[s].

15. Unfortunately, this study did not use the Brodmann localization system to identify activated regions. They were, therefore, not used in our summary analysis.

16. All of the positive findings discussed here were for a lie minus truth type of analysis. When the lie was subtracted from the truth, no significant activations were observed.

17. BA 39 and 40 were not activated in the lie-control comparison.

18. It is not unreasonable to assume that this conclusion can be generalized to all other theories relating brain images and cognitive functions. This extrapolation is supported by the meta-studies reported in Chapter 2.

19. This tabulation does not add exactly to 16 since some of the experiments commingled two experimental protocols.

20. I appreciate that some of the 16 studies did attempt to detect individual behavior. However, it was done on the basis of comparisons of an individual with themselves and not with group data. The admonition that group data cannot adequately predict individual behavior still holds.

21. "Cephos" and "No Lie MRI" are two companies that have been set up to provide commercial brain imaged-based lie detector services to the legal and investigatory communities. Given the very preliminary and unreliable nature of the scientific database, it seems that these activities are premature and deceptive in the same manner as are conventional efforts to commercialize polygraphy.

Chapter 4

The Brain and the Control of Aggression

Synopsis
4.1 Introduction
4.2 Who are the Neuropsychologists?
    A. Neuropsychologists
    B. Forensic Neuropsychologists
    C. Cognitive Neuroscientists (Physiological Psychologists)
    D. Psychiatrists (Biological and Functional)
    E. Neurologists
4.3 What is Neuropsychology?
    A. Case Studies
4.4 The Problems of Neuropsychological Test Reliability and Validation
    A. Neuropsychological Tests
    B. Reliability
    C. Validity
4.5 Classic Physiological Psychology and Definitions of Aggression
4.6 A Traditional History of Brain Mechanisms of Aggression and Violence
4.7 The Modern Empirical Literature on Aggression
    A. The Limbic System
    B. The Papez Circuit
4.8 Human Aggression and Brain Mechanisms
4.9 Interim Conclusions
Endnotes

**MYTH: We know which regions of the brain control aggressive behavior.
TRUTH: Knowledge about the role of particular brain regions in determining aggressive behavior is inconsistent and incomplete.**

4.1 Introduction

There is abroad in both the lay and professional worlds a widely accepted idea that we have made enormous progress in understanding how the brain and the mind are related. As we have seen in previous chapters this near consensus is far from reality. Although we have made much progress in understanding both human behavior and the physiology and anatomy of the brain, respectively and

121

separately, theoretical bridges between the two sciences do not yet exist and the empirical facts are still inconsistent and uncertain. Some of the most profound questions of human nature, furthermore, may be poorly formulated, conceptually confused, and, in the long run, represent insolvable problems. For example, one question repeatedly asked concerns which areas of the brain encode, represent, or regulate aggressive behavior. By now it should be clear that not only is there great uncertainty about the nature of the underlying mental processes (our inferences from behavior are far from rigorous and our definitions far from precise) but that the whole idea that a mental process such as aggression is localized in or on the brain may be seriously misleading.

Nevertheless, contemporary use of cognitive neuroscience in the courtroom as well as in the laboratory dotes on this approach. Courts are frequently confronted with the question—should we admit neuroanatomic evidence as a defense for criminal behavior? Indeed, a major new issue arising in the application of neuroscience in the courtroom is the use of questionable associations between specific brain lesions or disease and behavior that is abnormal or illegal. More and more frequently, evidence suggesting the presence of abnormal brain anatomy or physiology is being offered as an exculpatory defense against charges involving violence or aggressive misbehavior. The ethics of this application of cognitive neuroscience is complex and many issues remain unresolved. The purpose of this chapter is to consider the scientific evidence for the association of specific brain dysfunction with aggressive misbehavior—a necessary but often overlooked task prior to the application of this evidence in judicial proceedings.

There is little question, nevertheless, that some legal defenses are increasingly being made on the basis of brain damage or dysfunction. This is especially evident when the issue is aggressive or violent behavior. Although some of the early cases involved the use of the EEG or the ERP (or some enhanced version of these standard clinical tools such as the BEAM[1]), most of the newer case actions have been stimulated by the extraordinary developments in the PET and fMRI brain scanning technologies. For example, a typical case reported in Arizona in 1990 involved the use of a BEAM map as evidence that a Mr. John Zimmerman was insane as a result of brain abnormalities and, therefore, should be acquitted. This claim was rejected.

Another of the early efforts to use brain function as a defense was the famous murder trial of Herbert Weinstein in 1992 in the city of New York. This defense was based on the fact that a PET scan showed only that a cyst was pushing on Mr. Weinstein's brain rather than a specific malfunction or malformation of a particular portion of the brain. Nevertheless, the issue was raised whether or not some kind of brain dysfunction was a causal factor in Mr. Weinstein's misbehavior. This claim was admitted but with the caveat that nothing could be said about the relation between the cyst and criminal behavior.

Perhaps the most famous case was that of John Hinckley who attempted to assassinate President Reagan and was acquitted in 1982 on the basis of insanity at least partially on the basis of an admitted CAT scan that showed an anatomical brain irregularity.

Since that time, there has been a great increase in the number of cases in which errant brain anatomy or physiology has been used as an argument that the accused was not responsible for his actions. Marchant (2007) has exhaustively reviewed this legal application of neuroscience knowledge. He listed a number of the more significant criminal cases in which a defense was based on the fact that the accused's brain was abnormal. It was Marchant's general conclusion, drawn from his review of the legal literature, that the courts have been erratic in sometimes admitting and sometime rejecting neuroscientific evidence. Some of the legal reasons drawn by judges and cited by Marchant (2007) for not admitting brain information into criminal trials are of interest. They include:

1. "It was an interesting research tool but it had not been authenticated so far."
2. "…there was substantial evidence from which the court could conclude that BEAM is not generally accepted in the neurological community."
3. "[Such] tests would add nothing new to the existing psychological evaluation of defendant."
4. "…no evidence exists that Brain Fingerprinting[2] has been extensively tested, has been presented and analyzed in numerous peer-reviewed articles in recognized scientific publications, has a very low rate of error, has objective standards to control its operation, and is generally accepted within the relevant scientific community."
5. "QEEG[3] is apparently used quite extensively as a research instrument but is not widely used by clinicians as a diagnostic tool….QEEG is not considered reliable in the professional organizations."

Similarly, some of the reasons for admitting "brain" information are also of interests and include.

1. "While the competence and persuasiveness of the offered testimony can be questioned, the relevance of the subject matter cannot be."
2. PET scan results were admitted "despite evidence that such pathology has no known link to criminal behavior."

What all scholars in the field now seem to accept is that the admissibility of evidence from brain imaging devices will be clouded for the foreseeable future by a great deal of uncertainty and ambiguity concerning the scientific status of this kind of neuroscientific evidence. As we see throughout this present chapter and the ones following, there is a long history of studies that seek to explicate these relationships. Unfortunately this long scientific history is as beset with ambiguous empirical results, flawed interpretations, and conceptual misunderstandings as is their application in the courtroom.

The basic problem remains: most of the arguments presented in a courtroom concerning how neuroscientific evidence correlates to mental functions not only do not meet the *Frye* or *Daubert* standards but are still active areas of dispute and contention among cognitive neuroscientists. It is, therefore, too much to expect people trained only in the legal arts to make definitive decisions concerning their use. It is only by a thoughtful analysis of the scientific literature that the ethical and technical problems facing legal decision makers will ultimately be solved.

A major goal of this chapter is to evaluate what cognitive neuroscience indisputably knows about the relationship between brain function and violent and aggressive behavior and what it does not know to see if this fog of uncertainty can be clarified. In general, as this discussion develops we will see that the scientific reasons for not admitting this kind of information are gradually outweighing those that suggest that they should be.

Indeed, there is an entire field of specialty, which is called forensic neuropsychology, in which making the case for admission of these findings has been the traditional goal. Forensic neuropsychology is a subfield of a broader field called neuropsychology which is supposed to provide the scientific foundation for the forensic application. Neuropsychology, itself, is a human-oriented subfield of what used to be called physiological psychology and what is now referred to as cognitive neuroscience. Neuropsychology is a profession mainly inhabited by non-medically trained clinical psychologists who work in conjunction with neurologists and other medical professionals. I will deal with the differences in the professional skills offered by each later in this chapter. Whatever the professional training, the original forensic goal was to find some sort of an explanation of misbehavior in the malfunctioning of the organic brain.

A traditional definition of neuropsychology can be found in a recent paper by Harley (2004):

> To explain the patterns of impaired and intact performance seen in people with brain damage in terms of damage to one or more components of normal cognitive functioning. (p. 5)

The goal in this case is to develop a theoretical model of the mind by observing the differences between "normal" and intact people. In this case brain injuries are used as a means of parsing the mind into modules. Such a theory is based on the assumption that the mind is modular, a questionable axiom at best as we have seen in previous chapters.

A second definition has quite a different goal. It is based on the idea that the behavioral observation can be used to tell us something about the nature of a brain deficit. As Harley pointed out, this, however, depends upon the assumption that the behavioral deficit is simply and directly associated with the brain deficit. With the development of the field, however, it has become increasingly clear that this second goal is probably not achievable and neuropsychology has moved away from its "neuro" roots to being more concerned simply with psychological assessment.

The reasons for what is an emerging negative evaluation of the application of neuropsychological findings in the courtroom are clear. The field faces one enormous problem in developing its empirical facts as well as its theoretical foundations. That special problem is the limits on controlled experimentation on human subjects on which to base its conclusions and findings. Instead, neuro-psychologists, neurologists, and others who testify in court must largely depend on fortuitous insults to the brain due to trauma, disease, age-based dementia, or ischemic accidents (i.e., strokes) to provide the scientific foundation for their theories. This essentially means using idiosyncratic "case" or individual studies as its main source of scientific evidence.

For this reason, the scientific literature of neuropsychology is not as orga-nized as that emerging from well-controlled experiments on animals. The vari-ability of the associations between human brain states and behavior produces a highly idiosyncratic collection of observations and findings from which it is very difficult, if not impossible, to draw stable general conclusions about what brain area does what. Indeed, the very axiomatic assumption—that specific behaviors are encoded by specific regions of the brain—underlying such a quest may be deeply flawed.

Sometimes, this assumption is based on extrapolations from work done on animals in which intentional lesions were surgically or chemically made on the brain and the behavioral results observed.

Sometimes, and this is a much more fragile approach to the problem, infer-ences are drawn from behavior to inferred human brain anomalies. Such "reverse engineering" is often based on suggestions from the empirical literature, but some-times they are based on unsupportable and leaps of logic or remote analogies. In many cases the brain disorder underlying some misbehavior cannot be identified and for many years the phrase "Minimal Brain Dysfunction" (MBD) was used as a hypothetical "cause" for any misbehavior. In this context, all that MBD had to offer was a reaffirmation of the scientific and ontological idea that all mental and behavior processes are aspects of brain function. This, of course, is a philosophical statement that offers little in the way of scientific understanding or content. MBD was used as a crutch to indicate that something was probably different in the brain when a person consistently misbehaved. However, the nature of the brain dysfunction was "minimal" (i.e., below the threshold of observation) by implication, therefore, beyond the ken of empirical science. Therefore, the idea of MBD represents nothing more than the ontological assumption that the brain is the unique organ of mind, something which few cognitive neuroscientists would disagree. In principle, to assign misbehavior to a MBD, however, violates the most basic rules of empirical science. In practice, it has no diagnosis or therapeutic value.

To authenticate a particular association between some brain dysfunction or locus and some behavior, neuropsychologists have based much of their research on animal research or the very variable and idiosyncratic clinical results from persons whose brains had been damaged by trauma, disease, or age. Another goal of this chapter, therefore, will be to evaluate this corpus of scientific knowledge and draw conclusions about its admissibility into the judicial process. As we see, the empirical data supporting some of the associations drawn between behavior and brain are very tenuous indeed. In preview, I note here that I will eventually conclude that one of the most ill-founded arguments in cognitive neuroscience is the idea that it is possible to assign aggression to a particular part of the brain.

4.2 Who are the Neuropsychologists?

Given that the general theory behind the utility of neuropsychological testimony is that there are specifiable and direct relationships between localized brain regions and behavior that should allow it to be admitted into a judicial proceeding, a number of different professional skills may become involved in courtroom testimony. Among these are:

- Neuropsychologists and other clinical psychologists
- Forensic neuropsychologists
- Cognitive neuroscientists (physiological psychologists)
- Psychiatrists (biological and functional)
- Neurologists

Each of these professions has been trained in a different style, methodology, and content. Each approaches the problems of neuropsychology in what can be a distinctively different manner. Each has a varying degree of competence in dealing with controlled laboratory situations, statistical analysis, trauma, brain injuries, and behavioral testing. Each, inevitably, brings a different point of view to the courtroom. As a result, there is often considerable controversy and inconsistency in testimony from professionals in this field, especially when it comes to predicting future behavior. Thus, consensus is rare among their respective testimonies. It is also important to remember that, like psychology itself, the professional titles used are often ambiguous. What constitutes a neuropsychologist, for example, may be very different from one individual to another just as the word psychologist is, at best, an imprecisely defined title. Different neuropsychologists may have different views of what are their professional skills. Therefore, the following comments are, to a certain degree, cartoons, exaggerating the skills and training of each profession.

Within this context of ambiguity, let's begin with the professionals who call themselves neuropsychologists.

A. Neuropsychologists

It is important to understand that neuropsychologists are primarily clinical psychologists. That is, their training is mainly concerned with the treatment and measurement of human behavior as it may be evidenced in social and personal relations. The main tools of clinical psychologists have always been the person to person psychotherapy (talk counseling) originally modeled by Sigmund Freud, although highly modified over the years from his original formulation. Neuropsychologists add to this traditional tool kit, expert competence in the administration of tests of psychological abilities and what is claimed to be skill in predicting propensities for future behavior. The distinguishing characteristic of the neuropsychologist (as opposed to ordinary clinical psychologists) is that neuropsychologists are more likely to be using tests of cognitive, sensory, or motor performance, often ascribing any observed deficiencies to brain injuries or dysfunctions. Indeed, prior to the development of the brain imaging procedures, their tests were among the few means of measuring brain dysfunction in intact human beings. The inability to perform some cognitive task was extrapolated to a brain malfunction on the basis of these tests, an extrapolation that is not justified in the present scientific context.

At the present time, some neuropsychologists have changed their rationale from defining brain-behavior relationships to one that is mainly aimed at measuring cognitive capacities and predicting behavior. These days a neuropsychologist may be essentially ignoring most of the traditional mind-brain correlations and simply developing and applying tests to measure cognitive capabilities and, to some questionable degree, attempting to predict future behavior (Chaytor and Schmitter-Edgecombe, 2003). As such, the phrase "neuro" becomes somewhat grandiose and irrelevant. Nowhere is this made clearer than in the *Handbook of Cognitive Neuropsychology* (Rapp, 2001) in which the brain is hardly mentioned once beyond a historical chapter.

B. Forensic Neuropsychologists

Forensic neuropsychologists represent a group of applied neuropsychologists who offer their services to investigatory agencies and the courts. Typically, they are not active producers of research as are their more experimentally oriented colleagues. Some of the duties of forensically oriented neuropsychologists may involve the determination of legal liability by demonstrating the presence of cognitive deficits with appropriate tests. In other instances they may use the same battery of tests to determine that an elderly person is not able to handle his own affairs. Tests may include those that measure motor skills, sensory and perceptual competence, as well as tests of language understanding, and decision making among other more complex cognitive skills.

Another task of forensic neuropsychologists is to distinguish between a real deficit and malingering. Forensic neuropsychologists should not be called upon to draw specific inferences about the nature of a brain injury or disease that causes the behavioral deficits they measure.

C. Cognitive Neuroscientists (Physiological Psychologists)

Cognitive neuroscientists, who were previously called physiological psychologists, are the basic research arm of neuropsychology. Their contributions add to our fundamental understandings of how the brain and the mind are related. Typically their findings are the results of well-controlled experimental conditions and very often the results of animal experiments. With the advent of the PET and MRI brain imaging devices, however, their attention has increasingly turned to studies of human brain-behavior relationships. Much of the current conceptual database of neuropsychology is based on the basic scientific findings discovered in cognitive neuroscience laboratories. Because of the demand for high levels of control, cognitive neuroscientists typically deal with very simple cognitive processes and well-defined brain lesions.[4] The term "cognitive neuroscience" is far more inclusive than the term "neuropsychology."

D. Psychiatrists (Biological and Functional)

Psychiatry is a specialization of the medical sciences that is mainly aimed at the diagnosis and treatment of mental disease. Its practitioners are physicians who can use drugs and biological interventional procedures (including shock therapy or brain surgery) that are not generally permitted to any of the nonmedical professionals previously mentioned. In other instances, psychiatrists limit themselves, just as do clinical psychologists, to the personal interactions involved in talk therapies. Psychiatrists may be called up to testify about the mental status of an accused but typically will not use the same kind of testing procedures used by forensic neuropsychologists. As such, their judgment of what constitutes normal behavior is less objective than the standards used by neuropsychologists in those cases in which the two approaches may overlap. They depend (as do many clinical psychologists) on the Diagnostic and Statistical Manual of Mental Disorders (DSM-IV-TR, 2000). It is now appreciated that this manual is not based on a sound scientific foundation; rather it was constructed from the clinical opinions of a committee of practicing psychiatrists and psychologists (Spiegel, 2005). It is rare to have a psychiatrist discuss the details of brain anatomy; that is usually left to the next in our line of "neuropsychologists"—the neurologists.

E. Neurologists

Neurologists are also medically trained individuals but their domain is the brain itself treated as a physiological mechanism more than in terms of its psychological functions. A neurologist may apply simple tests of sensory and motor function but is not likely to apply the broad battery of tests used by a forensic neuropsychologist. The neurologist's goal is to diagnose specific nervous system disorders and then to determine by examination of brain images and other biological tests whether the problem with the nervous system is amenable to surgical or chemical intervention. Nervous system surgery of the most extensive kind is within the domain of the neurologist.

Like any classification system, this minitaxonomy obscures the facts that all of these professions overlap to a degree. Neurologists may depend on neuropsychologists for hints about the parts of the brain to which a behavioral disorder may be attributed. Clinical psychologists in such a situation may discover some behavioral clue that may help to pinpoint some neurological disorder. Furthermore, any or all of these professionals may appear in the courtroom testifying about symptoms and conditions for which they individually have only modest credentials.

Of course, there are the generalists whose knowledge transcends a particular field of science and it is often interesting, if not definitive, to listen to their views. More often, however, any one of these practitioners who testifies in the courtroom about the subtle mind-brain relationships that are being discussed here with anything other than a cautious and skeptical demeanor should be held highly suspect.

Each of these professionals brings different skills to the table but none of them is or can be the ultimate authority. "Forensic neuropsychologists" have little or no training that authorizes them to cope with the nitty-gritty of the anatomy or physiology of brain structure or function. Although this may be an offensive and threatening statement to many practitioners in the field, only rarely should a neuropsychologist be permitted to testify about brain function. Professionals in this field have not been trained in the techniques and methods that are demanded to understand brain anatomy and physiology. Their training is mainly in the administration of tests that are assumed, sometimes without sufficient supportive evidence, to reflect some specific brain dysfunction.

Furthermore, only rarely should clinical neurologists and other biologically trained personnel be permitted to testify about the tests and protocols that have been used to evaluate behavioral performance. Their training is mainly in the anatomy and physiology of the brain. Their specific ability, however, to present and interpret the complex tests used to evaluate behavior, with few exceptions, is very limited without extensive cross training.

One final comment, this discussion about the various professionals has been presented as a typology with rigid boundaries. It is obvious that this is not a completely accurate picture of the field of neuropsychology because some of the professionals I have discussed may be more broadly cross trained than suggested here. However, the basic point I wish to present here is that because all of these practitioners deal with the problem of relating the brain to the mind, this does not mean that they all share a common competence in dealing with the various components of this extremely complex subject matter.

4.3 What is Neuropsychology?

The most important point about neuropsychology (and I now use the term to collectively include all of the professions described in the previous section) that must always be kept in the forefront of any analysis is that it is a science based on two fundamental but controversial assumptions. They are the familiar ones that I have already introduced as being central to modern cognitive neuroscience of all kinds—the twin and mutually supporting concepts of cognitive modularity and brain localization. Everything that is done in this field is based on the almost axiomatic assumptions that mental processes can be analyzed into independent functional modules, the function of which can be assigned to particular brain regions. Given the limitations of this approach already discussed throughout this book, these are frail foundations on which to build a forensic science that may have such important ramifications for individual lives.

Probably the best way to make clear what neuropsychology is to examine the methods that are used in the field. There are two that stand out as the archetypes of neuropsychological practice. The first is the case history, a technique thrust upon neuropsychology because of the extreme variability of the brain injuries, the behavioral responses, and the interaction between the two. The second is the use of standardized tests of human cognitive and motor behavior.

In the following section, I present a discussion of the first of these two methods and place them in a context of the standards of scientific research in general. Later, I consider the role of psychological tests in neuropsychology.

A. Case Studies

In general, it is not the task of those who identify themselves as neuropsychologists to do the carefully controlled experiments involving large samples of patients. More often, neuropsychologists work with individual brain injured subjects and attempt to observe how the behavior of a person with neurological damage differs from what is considered to be normal. The problem with a line of research depending on idiosyncratic case histories is that it is largely anecdotal. An individual case may be strikingly suggestive and deeply interesting to both the lay public and the neuropsychological community; however, it is rarely up to the scientific standards of rigorously controlled and statistically analyzed multi-subject experiments.

The main problem is that in place of well-designed, multi-subject, and well-controlled experiments, neuropsychologists have a body of knowledge that is to a considerable degree based on individuals who suffer from fortuitous traumatic lesions or brain diseases.

Many serious neuropsychological studies are, of necessity, also presented in the form of case histories. Some of the most important milestone cases in determining the historical course and current theory of neuropsychology have dealt with individual subjects. Even the widely accepted classic work of Broca (1861), which defined one of the speech centers, was mainly based on a single patient who was assigned the name "Tan" because this was the only speech sound he made. Even today, for reasonable reasons of medical privacy, most brain damaged subjects of interest are often individually identified by abbreviations such as "Jimmie G." (Sachs, 1985/1998) or "Zazetsky" (Luria, 1972/2004). Only occasionally, and in very special cases, are they identified by their full names; for example, in the story of John Hale told by his daughter (Hale, 2007) or in the case of historic figures such as Robert E. Lee who suffered brain damage as a result of the stroke that took his life. Because of the dramatic behavioral effects of brain injuries, these biographies became objects of extensive popular interest and are often the source of best-selling books.

What such cases offer in terms of hard science is much more problematic. At present, even some of the most comprehensive efforts (e.g., Ogden, 1996; Darby, 2004) to codify neuropsychology in book length contributions are forced to deal mainly with case studies. Given the constraints on human brain research, some of the most distinguished students of neuropsychology (I specifically refer to Shallice, 1988) understand both the limits and the necessity of the case history approach arising as a result of the paucity of opportunities to work with group data.[5]

The over dependence on case studies can be seen even in the most modern neuropsychological research. It is not possible to list the many neuropsychological studies that deal with individual cases. However, a sampling of some of the most recent can be obtained by looking over any of the recent issues of a journal such as *Neuropsychology*. The impression one gets is of a small number (very often one) of subjects and modest and inconsistent correlations between various kinds of brain trauma or degenerative diseases and behavioral deficits. The implications of this situation have not gone unnoticed by neuropsychologists. In the place of studies of specific brain locus-behavioral deficits, we now see a very interesting shift to studies of more diffuse brain degeneration that occur in such maladies as Alzheimer's disease. Another main difference between traditional neuropsychological studies and current ones is the new emphasis on purely behavioral studies of patients with various problems such as Attention Deficit Hyperactivity Disorders (ADHD) with a lessened attention to the possible neurological dysfunctions that may or may not attend it. All of these changes reflect the emerging realization that neuropsychology has failed to achieve one of its original goals—reliably linking specific brain disorders with specific behavioral deficits.

Coltheart (2000), in the introduction to *The Handbook of Neuropsychology*, attempts to assuage some of the concerns that arise because of the case history approach that is so prevalent in neuropsychological circles. He poses four standard challenges (underlined) to a case study approach to the science and offers responses to each of them as follows:

Criticism 1: The cases are rare! This challenge implies that the variability of the human mind brain is so great that a few isolated examples are insufficient to provide an adequate theory of mind-brain relationships. Coltheart's response is that we can accept case studies if we assume that "the architecture of cognition is constant across people" (p. 18). Unfortunately, this assumption is highly suspect. There are many examples of how a single idiosyncratic study, even those as widely accepted as Broca's pioneering work, led to misunderstandings about the neurology of speech.

Criticism 2: Cases are never pure! This criticism implies that any model based on isolatable cognitive processes and circumscribed brain areas cannot be established. Typically multiple deficits appear and rarely is a narrow locus the brain injured. Coltheart's response is that it should nevertheless "be possible to find such patients, given enough patients, and patience" (p. 19) to justify a theory of the specific mind-brain relationship. Unfortunately, this hopeful expression does not take into account the extreme complexity of brain interconnections and the serious possibility that additional data will not unscramble the relationship, but actually add to the intractability of the mind-brain problem. (See, especially, my discussion of the work of Hilgetag, O'Neil, and Young, 1996)

Criticism 3: Virtually every case is unique! This challenge raises the possibility that the prime requirement of a science—replicability—is not achievable.

Coltheart answers this by suggesting that we "appeal to the assumption of uniformity of functional architecture across people" (p. 20). The frail logic of this argument should be obvious. The very nature of the idiosyncratic case study argues strongly against this assumption. This assumption of a kind of pseudo-simplicity of the brain-mind system is simply not supported by the evidence. Every experiment we do introduces further complexity into the discussion, rather than conceptual simplification. "Uniformity of functional architecture" trivializes the true complexity of the mind-brain problem.

Criticism 4: Neuropsychological theories are too powerful! This fourth challenge, aimed at neuropsychological theorizing, is that any posed theory will be so general that it cannot be refuted. Coltheart's counterargument is that current theories that explain "all-so-far observed data" (p. 20) are not "too powerful." He argues further that new data always impacts on old theories and, thus, they are always subject to refutation or modification. The counterargument is that there is no universal theory available yet and any microtheory that can be proposed cannot be distinguished from a host of other potential theories. The problem, as I repeatedly allude to in this book, is that the "data" is so underdetermined that it does not point to a unique or even "most likely" theory as opposed to an ex post facto "just so" story. Unfortunately, if viewed from within the context of standards of scientific proof with their emphasis on significance testing and statistical inference, this counterargument just does not ring true.

Nothing could make the difficulties created by the case study approach any better than the following anecdote. Some years ago I was privileged to visit the laboratory of Reginald Bickford (1913-1998) at the Mayo Clinic in Rochester, Minnesota. Bickford was a neurophysiologist and clinical neurologist whose specialty was inserting "depth electrodes" into the brains of patients suffering from some debilitating brain disorder (e.g., epilepsy and tumors) in an attempt to find the locus and, hopefully, the cure for medical problems. A tumor potentially could be localized or a focus of epileptic activation identified by this method.

Bickford had a huge room (an old centrifuge facility that had been used during World War II to select pilots) filled with a multitude of paper recordings of the brain signals recorded from his "depth electrodes." I asked him—"What have you learned from all of these recordings in general about the function of the human brain?" I remember his answer quite well and paraphrase it here—"Very little in general, each patient was different than all of the others. Although we were able to help individuals, there were such enormous differences from patient to patient that few general rules emerged."

Despite enormous amounts of additional research, the situation is not that different nowadays. We have a much expanded corpus of experimental data and clinical observations but they still vary substantially from case to case. The number of different brain areas that have been implicated so far in the control of aggressive or violent behavior, for example, is substantial; one experimental report after another has implicated virtually every area of the brain in either an excitatory or inhibitory role.

The conclusion one must draw from these arguments is that the case history approach is deeply flawed and is not likely to produce a comprehensive theory of mind-brain relationships—only further confusion as individual findings proliferate.

4.4 The Problems of Neuropsychological Test Reliability and Validation

A. Neuropsychological Tests

Modern forensic neuropsychology is largely a profession of test administration to determine the behavioral competence of an individual. A relatively large number of neuropsychological tests are available. One list (Swiercinsky, 2001) tabulates over 60 different tests and this number is probably a low estimate. These tests range from the expansive *Halstead-Reitan Neuropsychological Battery* (Reitan and Wolfson, 1985) which uses a number of different tests to produce an "overall assessment of brain function" to the older *Bender Visual Motor Gestalt Test* (Bender, 1938) which promises to "yield signs of brain dysfunction" to quick tests aimed at evaluating single cognitive abilities such as memory.

From the start of any discussion of this complex matter, it must be reiterated that we have no direct means of measuring mental properties. All that a neuropsychologist can really measure is the overt behavior and, for those with the training and facilities to do so, certain limited aspects of brain structure and function. Therefore, the purported utility of many neuropsychological tests has to be evaluated in terms of the specific intent of the administrator. Several proposed applications of these tests can be identified. Not all of these applications are justified, as we shortly see, from a scientific perspective.

- Neuropsychological tests can be used to identify the cognitive, sensory, or motor impairments exhibited by a subject.
- Neuropsychological tests can be used to predict future human behavior.
- Neuropsychological tests can be used to infer specific neurological deficits.

The first application of neuropsychological tests to measure cognitive, sensory, and motor deficits, although mitigated by such potential problems as malingering or intentional deception, is a plausible and potentially valuable diagnostic tool. Any test, no matter how rigorously designed, that shows discrepancies between normal subjects and clinical patients can be, within limits, of value in a legal inquiry, especially those concerned with competence or the results of injury.

The second use of neuropsychological tests, to predict future human behavior, is, however, far less likely to produce satisfactory results. This application is beset with huge problems of variability of the tests with regard to individual behavior under even the best controlled of life situations. The problem is further complicated by the modest relation between the somewhat arbitrary inferences made by the neuropsychologist from the test measurements and actual future behavior. In the final analysis, any prediction of future behavior is based upon a judgment by the psychologist rather than the objective evaluations of the raw measurements provided by the test. We now know that human behavior is not only dependent on individual conditions but also the social environment within which a person may be embedded. As a result, predicting aggressive, violent, or general criminal behavior is a risky business.

The third potential use of tests to diagnose brain injury or dysfunction is actually a far more complex problem, although at first it may seem conceptually simpler. The problem in this type of application is that what seem to be objective behavioral and neural tests cannot be definitively linked to each other. The bridge between behavior and brain function has not yet been adequately established to justify this application.

The fault in this case is mainly attributable to the current state of neuroscience. As I have discussed elsewhere in this book, these seemingly direct observations are so varied, so idiosyncratic, and so biased by prevailing preconceptions, that the relationship between a specific brain injury and a specific behavioral deficit is always still clouded with great uncertainty. In other words, the findings relating a brain injury to a behavioral deficit are not yet sufficiently well-established to permit us to assert with confidence that a particular test result accurately indicates a particular brain injury. Furthermore, because of the distributed and redundant nature of brain functions, it may well be that the underdetermination problem raises its head again in this context. It is not only possible, but likely, that a well-defined behavioral deficit could be produced by two or more distinguishably different brain injuries.

There are a number of other unresolved problems concerning all of these neuropsychological tests. Many are extremely controversial even within the confines of the neuropsychological field itself. The tests used by neuropsychologists, it must be clearly kept in the forefront of our thinking, are intended to be measures of cognitive functioning and behavior. Any link or inferences drawn from them and actual specific brain dysfunction is tentative at best and based on what is acknowledged to be weak neuroscientific support.

A further problem is that most neuropsychological tests have not enjoyed any degree of validation. One reason for this deficiency is that many different areas of the brain will produce the same behavioral dysfunction. Another is that the cognitive processes that are measured by these tests are only vaguely defined for reasons that I have already dealt with in previous chapters and will return to later in this chapter.

Furthermore, there is a considerable problem with the reliability of these tests. Extreme variability is always the general outcome when efforts are made to standardize or normalize a test. However, the situation is particularly acute with neuropsychological tests. As in any other psychological experimental design, replication is difficult; different samples of experimental subjects produce different results, stimuli are inadequately defined, and methods are never perfectly replicated. Furthermore, individual subjects vary from one to another and thus there will always be a distribution of responses varying from very poor performance (which may be due to malingering as well as performance deficits) to very high scoring individuals. The broad nature of this distribution means that it will be necessary to make an arbitrary decision as to where the dividing line between normal and abnormal performance levels will be set. The problem is terribly exacerbated when this distribution of "normal" responses is used to predict the future behavior of an individual who has displayed socially unacceptable behavior. Now let's consider the problems of reliability and validity in more detail.

B. Reliability

In principle, test reliability is relatively easy to define. It is a measure of how well a test repeats the measurement when it is used repeatedly under the same conditions. The usual metric is the correlation coefficient between two sequential tests. In practice, reliability is not so easy to determine. The problem lies in the fact that there are many ways in which test reliability can be evaluated. In each case the goal is to determine the repeatability and consistency of the test when compared to itself or some portion of itself. The simplest and preferred way is simply to compare the test with itself. However, this method is not fool proof. The conditions for the second test are never the same as the first; at the very least, subjects have had the experience of previously taking the test.

To overcome this difficulty, reliability is sometimes measured by comparing one half of the test with the other half. This procedure assumes that the two parts of the test are sufficiently alike to draw a conclusion about reliability—a premise that may not be justified. One strategy to overcome any residual difference between the two halves of test is to ask the same question in different ways and compare the results.

The difficulty in establishing the reliability of a neuropsychological test is further exacerbated by the design of the tests themselves. Some well-known tests use several subtests, each of which may correlate differently with other comparable tests or portions of other tests. For example, McKay, Casey, Wertheimer, and Fichtenberg (2007) showed that different components of the Repeatable Battery for Assessment of Neuropsychological Status (RBANS) test correlated with other tests that were considered to be similar over a range that varied from -.497 to +.827.

The literature of journals such as the *Archives of Clinical Neuropsychology* is filled with efforts to establish the reliability of the myriad of tests that are being used by psychologists. Over the years, a substantial body of research has shown that the test-retest reliabilities of neuropsychological tests are often quite high, in the .80s and .90s. Other tests do not enjoy even this level of quantification because their outcomes are merely verbal statements, judgments, or even opinions on the part of the test administrator. For example, some of the most widely used tests are totally nonquantitative (they are generally designated as "projective tests") and held to be of questionable utility even by large portions of the clinical psychology. (Hunsley, Lee, and Wood, 2003, for example, examined a number of controversial and questionable tests that are widely used but they believed are based on inadequate scientific foundations. Included in their analysis are such familiar projective tests as the Rorschach Ink Blot Test, The Thematic Apperception Test, projective drawings, anatomically detailed dolls, and the Myer-Briggs Type Indicator, the latter not being a projective test but one with numerical values corresponding to a questionable theory of personality types.)

After a detailed examination of these methods and the relevant scientific literature, Hunsley, Lee, and Wood (2003) conclude that their "questionable" status is justified. They pointed out that much of the scientific literature on projective tests does not meet acceptable standards of scientific research. They also noted that the individual psychologist is often confronted with the task of evaluating a test's reliability. Above all else, however, most of the tests simply did not receive the kind of research support that should be required considering the importance of the decisions sometimes associated with their use.

An especially cogent issue is the matter of the "norm." Given the variability of human behavior, as well as the variability of the effects of brain lesions, it has not always been possible to precisely determine what is the normal criterion against which either abnormal behavior or brain status should be compared. Establishment of a norm imposes many problems on the developer of a new test; it can be expensive and time consuming and can require very large numbers of subjects to be the control for the inherent unreliability of psychological tests. It is, however, essential if the test is to have any value in neuropsychology.

C. Validity

However uncertain may be the reliability of neuropsychological tests, reliability is not really the main issue in considering their application to the prediction of behavior or the diagnosis of brain dysfunction. Even the most reliable tests may produce meaningless nonsense if they are not measuring what they are supposed to be measuring. Many of the problems of reliability can be finessed by using appropriate statistics and by making, however arbitrary, decisions about what constitutes normal and abnormal behavior. However, the more fundamental problem deals with the problem of validity. Few of the tests used by neuropsychologists have been satisfactorily validated.

Validity is raised in two different ways—how well the tests justify the use of "neuro" in neuropsychology and how well the tests measure and predict subsequent behavior. Let's deal with brain function validity first. By brain function validity, I am referring to how well these behavioral tests actually relate to the brain anomalies they invoke as causal factors in the maladaptive behavior. In later parts of this chapter, I will argue that the relationships between behavior and specific brain mechanisms as observed in the laboratory in which neurological observations can directly be compared to behavioral measures are themselves highly problematic. They are based on some assumptions that are at least questionable, and may, on the basis of new evidence, be wildly incorrect. The suggestion that specific brain anomalies can be attributed to neuropsychological test results is even more uncertain. Most of these tests deal with complex cognitive processes that are extremely difficult to define and even more difficult to localize in specific brain regions.

For example, establishing the validity of a neuropsychological test that purports to indicate injury in a particular part of the brain requires that some independent method (for example, a postmortem or an fMRI examination of that particular brain) be carried out. Unfortunately, as repeatedly noted throughout this book, this kind of association is rarely complete and fraught with conceptual and technical difficulties. The fact that all behavior, as well as mental activity, is mediated, represented, or instantiated in the brain does not obscure the fact that the specific relationships between neural and psychological phenomena are still incomplete and obscure.

Establishing the validity of a neuropsychological test is a much more challenging task than the simple numerical manipulation required to demonstrate reliability. Indeed, philosophers have argued over the years concerning the meaning of validity. However, all of the difficulties that arise when one attempts to establish the validity of a test are exacerbated when it comes to the problem of how the brain and the mind are related.

Why should this be so? The answer to this question is rooted in the inaccessibility of mind and the complexity of the human brain. The end result of the absence of a theory of mind-brain is that the validity of any cognitive model, be it a test, a computer program, or simply a verbal interpretation of some preliminary and incomplete measure of brain activity such as an fMRI or the behavior change produced by a surgical or traumatic intervention is untestable.

How to validate a neuropsychological test, therefore, has been a perpetual one for practitioners in this field. Part of the response to this very serious problem (it is the founding assumption of traditional neuropsychology) has been to redefine the word "validity" in a number of different ways, not all of which are in agreement with the original intent. In the following list, I tabulate the most frequently encountered terminologies and note why not all represent the true idea of validity. As we see, some of these new definitions are merely convenient ways of avoiding the fact that the demonstration of validity is particularly challenging when dealing with any aspect of the mind-brain problem.

Among the most important forms of validity are:[6]

- Content or logical validity:
Do the items in the test measure what they are designed to measure? This, of course, is the classic definition of validity. However easy it is to put this definition into words, it is extremely difficult to determine whether content validity is achievable in general as well as within the neuropsychological context. Therefore the following expedients are often used in its place.
- Ecological Validity:
Are the results of the test predictive of what the patient will do in real life? Ecological validity is, in principle, an ideal criterion of validity IF the sole goal of neuropsychology is simply to predict behavior. It has the advantage of being almost quantitative both in terms of the prediction and the outcome. However, it is free of any "neural" implications and has nothing to say about brain mechanisms. Furthermore, it is sometimes still quite difficult to determine whether a test is ecologically valid or not as discussed by Chaytor and Schmitter-Edgecombe (2003). Nevertheless, it still requires an arbitrary decision on whether or not a particular level of correlation should be acceptable in establishing the test as being ecologically valid. Indeed, these authors suggested that the currently irrelevant question of "absolute reliability" should be replaced by a relative alternative as to "which tests have the most ecological validity?" (p. 193)
- Concurrent, convergent, or criterion reference validity: Does the test correlate with other tests of the same psychological process and not with tests of other different processes. This kind of "validity" has noth-

ing to do with the classic definition of validity. It is a criterion based on agreement among theoretical constructs whose construct validity itself is questionable.

- Construct validity: Do the test scores measure the particular mental construct, for example—the psychological property we call impulsive-ness—in question? This is also an example of a false kind of validity. It is based on the existence of hypothetical constructs that themselves may be no more than current whims or theoretical phantoms. A con-struct is not an entity whose independent reality can be tested to deter-mine if it is that which we desire to measure.

- Discriminant validity: Are the results uncontaminated by other prop-erties than the one it is hoped is being measured. Do they distinguish between the relevant and irrelevant properties? Establishing this kind of validity is usually impossible because of the complexity and vari-ability of human cognitive processes. It is more a hope, than a measur-able property that the test is uncontaminated.

- Incremental validity: Do the results add substance to the diagnosis above and beyond that which is obtained from other tests or inter-views? This is another hopeful aspect of a test for validity but also very difficult to establish in a definitive sense.

- Face validity: Does the test "seem" or "appear" to be measuring what it is supposed to be measuring. Face validity is among the most insidious entries in this list. It dotes on the superficial and prescientific aspects of evaluating a test. It merely asks if "it feels right." It ignores the pos-sibility that the test and the content may simply be analogous or even metaphoric in some superficial sense. Indeed, most logicians would argue that face validity does not represent any kind of logical validity. It is however, probably the most prevalent form of validity testing.

- Internal versus external validity: Can the validity of a test that can be demonstrated within the confines of a well-controlled experiment be extrapolated to real-world applications? The issue of generalizability raised here is extremely important especially in evaluating the util-ity of a test beyond the original research. Well-controlled experiments sometimes do not generalize to the chaos of practical applications; even the best vetted test may fail in the real world.

- Localization validity: Does the test work in the purest neuropsycho-logical sense. That is, does it accurately localize a function in the brain? Keep in mind that this may be based on totally false assump-tions of cognitive modularity and circumscribed brain localization. Furthermore, as discussed previously, neuropsychology is changing away from the task of using behavioral measures to identify brain lesions. Therefore, localization as a criterion of validity is of diminishing importance.

In summary, both the reliability and validity of neuropsychological tests remain open to serious question. The reasons behind this uncertainty are largely due to the complexity of the mind-brain system and the undeniable fact that the science relating brain, mind, and behavior is still undeveloped. To understand why this is the case, we now turn to a discussion of the state of the relevant cognitive neuroscience.

4.5 Classic Physiological Psychology and Definitions of Aggression

Without rejecting or dismissing out of hand the observations of the classic Greek, Roman, Arabic, and Renaissance neuroanatomists, the first scientists to systematically explore the relation between brain and behavior began their work in the seventeenth century. The early history of what was to become cognitive neuroscience has been detailed in Chapter 2. In general, most of these pioneers worked on motor and sensory processes which had the advantage of being directly anchored to the physical environment. In the twentieth century, however, an explosive expansion of this work occurred; at that time the first scientists who we might call physiological psychologists or cognitive neuroscientists began to explore the brain mechanisms of more complex, central, cognitive processes that were not so directly anchored to the physical measures of the stimulus and the response. Topics such as the specific brain mechanisms of attention, emotion, violence, fear, pain, pleasure, hunger, thirst, sex, learning, memory, intelligence, and even personality and their disorders came under the researcher's purview. In virtually all of these experiments, the term "specific brain mechanisms" was embodied in a search for the locations on the brain that were presumably associated with this gamut of cognitive processes. From the non-localization perspective that is gaining credibility these days, such an activity may represent one of the greatest wastes of psychobiological talent and energy in history.

In this section, I continue the history of what was then traditionally called physiological psychology and what is now called cognitive neuroscience. These are the scientific foundations of what we now refer to generically as forensic neuropsychology in the legal arena. My goal here is to identify some of the critical initial experiments that extended mind-brain studies into the domain of aggression in particular. I also detail some of the many persisting reasons that the field is filled with such inconsistency and uncertainty about specific mind-brain relations, even something as behaviorally overt as aggression.

The classic Aristotelian trichotomy divided mental activity into sensory, central, and response categories. All three areas come into play in the courtroom. It is relatively easy to determine the extent of a sensory or motor deficit that might be due to some traumatic injury. An inability to fully move a limb or to be blind is relatively easy to document. However, a far more difficult task is to determine the effect on high level cognitive processes such as perceiving, reasoning, learning, or most germane, violent aggression.

As usual, caveats are necessary before beginning this discussion. Although it is possible to define the properties of the physical entity we refer to as the brain, it is far more difficult to define the mental attributes for which we now seek neural equivalents. This difficulty arises repeatedly in the following discussion and is one of the most influential reasons that this field remains so refractory to robust answers to questions as simple as where in the brain is language located. The classic literature to be described in this section continues to be the source of considerable controversy and poorly grounded conclusions mainly for this reason. In large part we are searching for the material locus of immeasurable and inaccessible phantoms; cognitive processes that we can only indirectly assay and inadequately define. For reasons that I have alluded to many times already in this book, the problem of defining the mind and mental processes makes the task undertaken by any kind of neuropsychologist very challenging and contentious. The ambivalence of the court system to admit neuroscientific evidence into judicial proceedings is very likely a reflection of this scientific uncertainty.

Another subtle problem faced in this field is that it is often difficult to distinguish between an area of the brain that is *necessary* and one that is *sufficient* for some process; that is, between a brain region that is an integral and inseparable part of some complex system and one that is capable by itself of mediating the cognitive process. Damage to the former may disrupt a system whose overall and collective function is to instantiate a cognitive process. Surgical or traumatic intervention may thus disrupt a process, not because that region was unique, but because the overall function of a complicated system of interacting parts was degraded. On the other hand, an area that is sufficient is one that by itself may be responsible for the observed cognitive process. Herein lays an additional source of variability in the results often invoked by forensic neuropsychologists to substantiate an opinion. Separate investigations may accurately determine that a number of different areas are able to produce the same cognitive deficit when damaged. This occurs because damage to any one of them may disrupt the system's function. Clearly, it is incorrect to assign the process to any one or any few of the individual brain components when it is likely that the whole system is responsible.

In addition, there are many methodological problems that interfere with clear cut conclusions from even the best designed empirical investigations. In an earlier work (Uttal, 2001) I noted the following difficulties that inhibited understanding of cognitive neuroscientific findings even when an experiment might have been deemed to have been successful.

- Inadequate definition of the boundaries of brain regions.
- Difficulty in isolating a lesion to the region under investigation.
- System complexity due to the high level of interconnectivity including feedback, feed forward, redundant coding in more than a single region, massive parallelicity, the interplay of excitatory and inhibitory modules, and finally the multiple roles of single brain regions.
- Variable and idiosyncratic data from human brain injuries
- The fact that, in the main, only behavioral deficits could be localized by lesion methods. In the final analysis all that can be done is to show that behavior is changed from the norm after a brain lesion.
- The effects of inadvertently cutting fiber tracts passing near or under the lesioned nuclei were often misinterpreted as functions of the lesioned region.
- Recovery of function. (Abstracted and appended from p. 153)

Beyond these difficulties, there are a host of other problems with the empirical literature. One, to which I have referred often in this book (and will greatly expand on in the next chapter), is that the actual nature, if not the very existence of specific cognitive deficits, is still a matter of contention among psychologists and philosophers. Given that underlying mental activity must be inferred from behavioral responses, it is not possible to confirm that the behavior is other than a symptom of some vague underlying disorder as opposed to a result of some specific neurological lesion.

The specific difficulty of defining aggression is highlighted by the fact that some investigators (for example, Moyer, 1968) have suggested that we must break this kind of aberrant behavior into multiple types:

- Predatory aggression.
- Inter-male aggression.
- Fear-induced aggression.
- Irritable aggression.
- Territorial aggression.
- Maternal and paternal aggression.
- Instrumental aggression.

Other investigators divide aggression in other ways. For example, Vitello and Stoff (1997) and subsequently Blair (2004) dichotomized aggressive behavior into reactive aggression in response to a threat, on the one hand, and goal directed or predatory aggression. McEllistrem (2004) alludes to "affective" and "predatory" aggression. Other investigators have added social aggression to these dichotomies by which they refer to aggression to establish dominance.

Other tripartite mini-taxonomies of aggression have been proposed by other scholars in the field. Elliott (1983), for example, proposed a division of human beings with aggressive tendencies that is partly based on learned behavior and partly based on organic dysfunctions. His three classes include:

- People with normal brains but who have been brought up in situations in which aggression and violence are condoned.
- People with antisocial personality disorders—the sociopaths and psychopaths—who may or may not have some brain dysfunction.
- People who are raised in normal situations of learned social control and who may behave themselves between outbursts of aggression are likely to have some kind of brain dysfunction.

A further complication in animal research is that cognitive neuroscientists tend to distinguish between different types of aggression depending on how an animal responds. Rageful behavior in which the animal violently attacks a prey is distinguished from behavior of a more quiet kind in which stalking or low levels of aggravation such as "quiet biting" characterizes the aggressive behavior. The former seems to be totally out of control; the latter, on the other hand, seems to be a normal hunting behavior. Which of the two, as well as some other behaviors we deem to be aggressive, is thus arbitrary.

The problems of definition of aggressive behavior are especially egregious when it comes to denoting human aggression. Aggression is thought by Ramirez and Andreu (2006) to actually represent a number of different phenomena that are unique to humans as well as those we share with the rats and cats. These researchers deal with the problem of definition in detail by tabulating a set of behaviors that they believe are "aggressive" in one way or another. They cite several different three-dimensional schemas that they report have been offered to understand the wide variety of aggressive behavior. These include one suggesting that the three dimensions should be:

- Physical-verbal
- Active-passive
- Direct-indirect.

Another three-dimensional scheme suggested by Ramirez and Andreu (2006) suggests that the appropriate dimensions should be:

- Biological
- Social
- Situational

Other investigators, rather cavalierly suggest other dimensions that are descriptive of aggression including:

- Positive-constructive
- Negative-destructive
- Overt-covert
- Proactive-reactive
- Instrumental- hostile
- Impulsive and-premeditated

and many others, all of which are observed in human behavior.

To complicate the matter even further, Ramirez and Andreu (2006) propose that implicit and covert psychological states such as anger, hostility, and impulsivity must be inserted into the analysis to designate the affective feeling that accompanies these dimensions of behavior.

Thus, there is still no consensus about what we mean by aggression or violence. The roots of this kind of misbehavior are now believed by many students of the field to be due to a combination of environmental, experiential, and neural factors. Some investigators use such cryptic terms as "anti-social personality disorders," a terminology that would suit a murderer as well as a person who cheats at cards. The question arising from this plethora of definitions is—are there well enough defined behavioral forms of aggression for which specific brain mechanisms can be identified?

One does not have to delve too deeply in the human cognitive neuroscientific literature to discover that the vast corpus of experimental and clinical case history findings has not yet been summarized or categorized within the context of a scientifically acceptable theory. This is hardly surprising, not only because of the difficulty of defining abnormal behavior (even the most sharply defined lesions produce widely variable behavioral symptoms), but also because many of the regions of the brain, particularly those associated with emotional activities, are heavily interconnected. As noted previously, it is, in general, not possible to determine the effects of a particular node in a complex system. Therefore, any effort to link a particular brain lesion or dysfunction with a particular kind of misbehavior is fraught with difficulties.

The point is that aggression is a highly complex mix of behavioral and mental states in both animals and humans that is not subject to a relatively simple and unique association with a particular anatomical structure. It is not always possible to understand what is the significance of an aggressive act nor to tell if one kind of aggression is actually the same or different from behavioral observations. It becomes understandable in this context how difficult it is to establish a coherent story in the courtroom. To simply ascribe misbehavior to the activity of a particular part of the brain is obviously an oversimplification and represents a class of evidence that should not be admissible in any judicial proceedings.

4.6 A Traditional History of Brain Mechanisms of Aggression and Violence

There is no clear line of historical priority on discoveries about brain mechanism of behavior. Some of the earliest work was done on fortuitous brain trauma occurring in industrial or military operations. Nearly simultaneously, laboratory studies were being carried out by some pioneering brain researchers on animals, most typically cats, dogs, and rats. Nevertheless, all of them, pioneers and currently active workers alike, share a common, but probably incorrect, basic assumption—there is some degree of localization of function in the brain such that it is possible to assign specific behavioral outcomes to specific brain structures. Nowhere is this assumption more misused than when this body of knowledge is applied in the courtroom in order to find some neurobiological exculpation for criminally aggressive behavior. In its place should be an emerging consensus that any mental function is encoded by massively distributed neural networks in which the conceptual system of independent nodes, nuclei, centers, and lobes must be supplanted by the concept of distributed neural systems characterized by massive interactions.

Let's begin by reemphasizing that forensic neuropsychology is, by virtue of its basic assumptions and logic, a practical field application of what we now call cognitive neuroscience incorporating neurophysiological and neuroanatomic ideas, on the one hand, with behavioral and psychological concepts and findings, on the other. The basic ontological principle permeating this entire field is that one is explicable in terms of the other.[7]

The history of the search for the brain mechanisms of aggressive behavior is one in which both physicians and psychologists have contributed. Much of the earliest work was carried out by physicians acting in the role of physician-neurologists confronted with traumatic brain injuries that resulted in behavior changes. Much of this work was anecdotal in that an individual presented with a brain wound and the physician observed what were assumed to be changes from the patient's pre-injury behavior. Among the most famous, and the most seminal in the history of the field was the case of Phineas Gage. Gage was injured when a tamping rod was explosively driven up through his left cheek, passing behind his left eye, and exiting from the top of his head. This injury essentially performed a bilateral frontal lobotomy on Gage.[8] Although, Gage recovered rather quickly (he attempted to go back to work a few months after the accident) it was reported by the attending physician, J. M. Harlow, that he exhibited massive changes in his behavior and personality. Harlow (1868) detailed the changes in personality in what has certainly been one of the most quoted statements in cognitive neuroscience:

> Gage was fitful, irreverent, indulging at times in the grossest profanity (which was not previously his custom), manifesting but little deference for his fellows, impatient of restraint or advice when it conflicts with his desires, at times pertinaciously obstinate, yet capricious and vacillating, devising many plans of future operations, which are no sooner arranged than they are abandoned in turn for others appearing more feasible. A child in his intellectual capacity and manifestations, he has the animal passions of a strong man. Previous to his injury, although untrained in the schools, he possessed a well-balanced mind, and was looked upon by those who knew him as a shrewd, smart businessman, very energetic and persistent in executing all his plans of operation. In this regard his mind was radically changed, so decidedly that his friends and acquaintances said he was 'no longer Gage.'

This extraordinary case set the stage for a long series of observations and experiments in which the frontal lobes of the brain came to be associated with personality, decision making, and social control. Eventually, it culminated in one of the most egregious aberrations of neurological history, the frontal lobotomizing of psychiatric patients as has been so eloquently described by Valenstein (1986) in his highly acclaimed book.[9] In spite of the fact that psychosurgery, particularly as performed on an outpatient basis in a psychiatrist's office, is no longer acceptable as a treatment for mental illness, the Phineas Gage story still has an extraordinary saliency among modern day cognitive neuroscientists. It stimulated the persistent theoretical opinion that particular regions of the brain are the site of such high-level cognitive processes as decision making, choice, and social control.

It is only possible to highlight a few of the many reports that have been published over the century since Gage's accident associating brain dysfunction and aggressive or violent behavior; the literature is enormous, far beyond the point of review and still elusive of synoptic summary. The initial experimental work searching for a brain locus of aggression was carried out by Goltz (1892). Goltz completely removed the cerebral cortex of a dog and observed not only that the animal was able to survive this massive insult to the brain but that it also became highly susceptible to violent aggressive behavior. The conclusion he drew was that the cerebrum was an *inhibitor* of primitive rage, a behavior that was actually *excited* by the lower levels of the brain.

Bard (1928) provided the next major milestone in this biological theory of aggressive behavior by identifying what he believed was the specific structure that was released from this cerebral inhibition thus permitting rage and aggression. Bard identified this ultimate source of aggressive behavior as the hypothalamus, a portion of the midbrain that is now known also to be related to the endocrine system (particularly to the control of pituitary hormones) and to the regulation of bodily or autonomic functions. It is because of this connection to the powerful chemical hormones in our body that a substantial amount of recent work, which has shown that there are chemicals (e.g., serotonin) that can also regulate aggressive behavior, makes sense.

The hypothalamus also occupies an interesting intermediate position between the higher portions of the brain—the cerebral cortex and those lower levels. MacLean's (1990) historically interesting theory of the "triune brain" held that our brains are actually made up of three different "brains." The first consists mainly of the cerebral cortex, the great convoluted hemispheres that overlay the underlying structures, responsible for intellectual activity and rational decision making, and a few minor subcortical nuclei.

The second is an intermediate brain lying at the base of the cerebrum. It consists of the limbic system, a group of centers and nuclei that is largely involved in emotional and other basic forms of behavioral and regulatory control. The limbic system is made up of a number of other structures including the hippocampus, the amygdala, the entorhinal cortex as well as the hypothalamus.

The third part of the triune brain is evolutionarily a very old portion that was assumed to be the original source of our aggressive impulses. According to McLean, we share this region with reptiles and other less evolved animals. This third division consists of the large number of brain stem nuclei such as the medulla, the pons, and the cerebellum (the latter until recently believed to be mainly a motor control unit) that are required for survival by even the most primitive of animals. It is when they are released from the control of the cerebral cortex that aggressive behavior is exhibited.

MacLean's basic idea is that there is a constant tension between this highly emotional lower level—the reptilian brain—and the rational thinking level—the cerebral cortex. (This is an idea that we shall see reemerge in several different forms as this discussion progresses.) The suggestion was that this balance between control and uncontrolled rage is analogous to homeostasis, the maintenance of a balance between other autonomic functions throughout the body. This concept is used to explain why cerebral damage can lead to violent or aggressive behavior; the reptilian brain is "unleashed" when the cerebral controls are diminished.

The major complicating factor in this analysis is the enormous degree of interconnectivity of the various parts of the brain. Pick virtually any of the structures that have already been mentioned and neuroanatomists can assure you that there are either direct or indirect connections to all others. Some of these may be excitatory—stimulating the activity of distant regions of the brain, where others are inhibitory—preventing activity in those distant regions. Furthermore, the situation may be even more complicated by the fact that excitation may be simulated by inhibition. That is, a distant area A may be excited because an intermediate area B, which inhibited A is itself inhibited by the action of a third area A. This manner of inhibition (of B by C) may be misinterpreted as B having an excitatory effect on A—a process referred to as disinhibition.

Obviously, neither the role of the hypothalamus nor that of any other center is going to be simple when viewed from the point of view of a highly interactive system. Decades of research using both lesion and electrical stimulation techniques have shown that the response is complex and different parts of the hypothalamus produce different patterns of response. Morgan and Stellar (1950) presciently understood the complexity of the hypothalamic control of aggression and rage when they said:

> If the higher structures of the cerebral cortex and thalamus are removed, we must have the hypothalamus in order to have a full-fledged emotional response....however, we can make restricted lesions in and around the hypothalamus, sufficient in size to damage all centers and tracts in the hypothalamus concerned with emotional behavior, and we still get complete rage responses. (p. 349)

"This," as they went on to note: "is a kind of situation we often meet in dealing with the nervous system." (p. 349). Their admonition is still valid after all of these years.[10] It illustrates how complex the interactions are among the various parts of the brain. In this case, if this pioneering work of Bard and others can still be our guide, it is clear that the conditions of necessity and sufficiency are barely met. For example, the hypothalamus seems to be at once necessary and not necessary for the expression of rage in decorticated (animals with no cerebrum). Stimulating this region can produce aggression; however, even if removed, the aggression response can be elicited. This kind of situation occurs in a very heavily interconnected system of which the brain is a prime example and in which the region under study may regulate, as opposed to encode or instantiate, the behavior under study. As we see now, modern research on the relation between the hypothalamus and aggression continues to be problematic.

4.7 The Modern Empirical Literature on Aggression

The vast modern database of clinical and forensic psychobiology cries out without fulfillment for some classification and order. Some of the reasons for this intellectual disarray have already been noted. However, the main reason is that cognitive neuroscientists are trying to apply the simplistic Cartesian experimental method (vary one independent variable, hold all others constant to the degree possible, and observe behavior) to a highly integrated system with poorly controlled (i.e., ill-defined) stimuli, an inscrutably high level of interconnectivity, and less than fully quantifiable responses. The reality is that almost every victim of traumatic brain injury that produces some kind of a behavioral effect responds in a unique and complex manner signaled by a diversity of behavioral disorders. The most modern, up-to-date synoptic efforts (among which I include Clark, Boutros, and Mendez and Siegel, 2005), therefore, find it difficult to organize the material because of the anatomical complexity of the brain and the multidimensional aspects of both stimulus and response.

No one could possibly review the huge literature in forensic neuropsychology, much less the full gamut of cognitive neuroscience. The number of research articles is so large both in terms of its methodology and findings that any attempt to systematize it or draw general conclusions about the brain mechanisms of all forms of aberrant behavior is doomed from the outset. The best we can do, therefore, is to sample some of the empirical studies, hopefully with the aide of metareview studies, to give us at least an inkling of what are the some of the views held by scientists interested in this field. My main goal in this section of this chapter is to examine the scientific findings that have emerged in the past few decades and come to a judgment concerning the presence or absence of any general principles. In this way, we can see what progress has been made, if any, in the years since Phineas Gage in making any putative associations between damaged brain loci and aberrant behavior.

One thing we must avoid is drawing overall conclusions from any subset of experiments available to us. The association between brain and behavioral dysfunction is more akin to speculative theory than established and reliable observational findings. Foremost among these caveats is the warning that individual behavior cannot be predicted from the kind of modest correlations that most laboratory experiments produce. In this context, the opportunity for misunderstanding is great and the results obtained are often contradictory. Furthermore, results are often interpreted in terms of outdated assumptions and the equally rigid prevailing zeitgeist. Studies using one technique (e.g., the EEG) often conflict with those using another (e.g., the fMRI). In other instances both produce only modest levels of correlation between brain structure and behavior. For some, the true answers, if they exist at all, are hidden in an entangled network of a vast number of contradictory results.

The profound truth is that for some of the questions we want to ask, there are no answers; not now and possibly, because of the complexity of the brain mind system, not ever. [11] This science does not yet speak with sufficient authority or precision to justify its admission into the courts. It should also be appreciated that none of the criticisms that I express here is new; the most prestigious investigators almost always end their papers with an admission that the data are incomplete and make a plea for "more needed research."

This chapter focuses on the most prevalent and serious social aspects of what are believed to be brain controlled misbehavior—violence and aggression. Of course, even this domain is too inclusive because acted-out violence is obviously a function of many different variables, both neuroanatomic and cognitive, as well as hereditary, and societal. Most of the mentalistic cognitive theories, however, that seek to make sense of the observed associations invoke properties that themselves are vague and imprecise. For example, violence has been associated with subjective emotional states that are not themselves intrinsically violent but which may inhibit or disinhibit overtly violent behavior. Since the theories that describe these findings are hypothetical and suggestive rather than explanatory in any way that approaches definitiveness, only brief mention will be made of these generally descriptive models.

Two types of literature are discussed in this chapter. The first is modern animal research in which lesions or electrical or chemical stimulation are used to inhibit or activate aggressive behavior. Since the pioneering days of Bard (1828) and Goltz (1892), a large number of experiments have been carried out that speak to the role of one or another brain center in controlling misbehavior. The second line of research is that carried out on humans, taking advantage of both fortuitous traumatic injuries and medically necessary therapies. Much of the early human work was done postmortem and it was always difficult to correlate even well localized brain injuries with behavior after a person was dead. In recent years, there has been an increase in the use of brain imaging tools such as the PET or MRI scans in order to assign aggressive behavior to particular brain regions.

The following section is organized in accord with standard brain anatomy. I examine a sample of the literature concerning the relationship between aggression and regions of the brain thought to be related to this kind of behavior.

No one questions the fact that some kinds of brain injury can lead to aggressive behavior. The points to be made here are that the involved areas are very widespread, highly variable, and that there are many influences of an experiential or social kind that also contribute to violent behavior. An important point for our legal system is that very few of the findings reported in the scientific literature are robust enough to permit prediction of aggressive behavior and thus are of limited probative value. Many of the findings reported here, especially those done on humans, are only statistically correlative and do not permit us to say either that a particular brain wound will inevitably lead to aggression or to attribute past aggression to a particular brain injury. All that we can ultimately conclude is that some kinds of brain injuries sometimes lead to violent or aggressive behavior.

One of the most important general points to keep in mind as we try to associate brain regions with specific behaviors is that virtually every area of the brain is connected by direct or indirect connections to almost every other area. It is both literally and empirically impossible to activate one region in total isolation of all of the others. Indeed, as we now see, virtually all regions of the brain have been targeted over the years by one investigator or another as contributing to aggression in either an excitatory or inhibitory way—or often both.

To begin, consider two complex systems of nuclei and cerebral regions traditionally associated with emotional behavior—the limbic system and the Papez circuit. The Papez circuit and the limbic system attracted the major share of research attention to aggression, rage, and violence because of the early findings obtained by Goltz and others. However, new research makes it clear that other regions of the brain, including other subcortical nuclei and some very distant regions of the cerebral cortex are also involved in controlling aggressive behavior. Indeed, there is accumulating evidence that damage to virtually any region of the brain may disturb our normal social behavior in a manner we would call aggression.

Another caveat to keep in mind; although I discuss the various components of the limbic system that have some identified relationship with aggressive behavior, it is very difficult to specifically identify the role of any of these individual components. All are heavily interconnected, not only within the broad reach of the limbic system, but also with other parts of the brain.

Furthermore, many of these regions have other functions in addition to the role in aggression highlighted here. This complexity of both structure and function is part of the reason for the umbrella of uncertainty that lies over the whole field. It is also the basis for claiming that this kind of data should not be admissible into the courtroom. For those who wish to go more deeply into the vast empirical literature in which attempts have been made to demonstrate specific functional-structural relationships specific to the problem of aggression, Siegel's (2005) book is probably the most up to date and complete source now available.

A sampling of the research in each of the constituent brain areas is now presented. To the maximum possible extent, I will draw on studies that meta-review or summarize a substantial body of studies findings associated with the role of a particular brain region in aggression. For those interested in a more detailed discussion of the brain's anatomy relevant to behavior than I present here, I recommend Clark, Boutros, and Mendez (2005). This book is especially useful in pointing out the very complex interconnections among the many regions of the brain.

A. The Limbic System

The limbic system lies at the lower edge of the cerebrum. It is made up of some cerebral and some subcortical structures. It has been shown to have complex, but as yet, poorly understood functions in emotion and memory as well as many other somatic and cognitive functions. Many of its components have been associated with aggression and violence in both animal and human studies. However, there is still great uncertainty about the specific functions of each of the nuclei and regions that are included within the limbic system. The classic result was that electrical stimulation of some of its lower level components, such as the amygdala, led to aggressive, emotional behavior, whereas surgically removing higher level areas (for example, as part of a bilateral temporal lobe removal) led to a reduction of anger and fear (Kluver and Bucy, 1939).

The limbic system, depending on the anatomist, may or may not include the hypothalamus. Regardless of the nomenclature, the limbic system is very heavily interconnected with the hypothalamus and any attempt to disentangle these interconnections by the usual anatomical or physiological techniques may be futile. What is clear is that all of these regions, and many others, are deeply involved in aggressive behavior.

The Amygdala

The amygdala is a complex group of nuclei hidden within the temporal lobe of the cerebrum. It thought to have important emotional functions in the control of fear and arousal and especially in eliciting aggressive behavior. Attention was originally directed at it as the specific locus of the docile behavior observed by Kluver and Bucy (1939) when it was surgically removed. Precisely located electrical stimulation that activated this region, on the other hand, produced hostile and aggressive defensive rage behavior in cats (MacLean and Delgado, 1953; Gregg and Siegel, 2001). Equally precise surgical removal of the amygdala (Emery, Capitanio, Mason, Machado, Mendoza, and Amaral, 2001) produced a reduction in similar kinds of aggressive activity as was observed in Kluver and Bucy's initial work.[12]

The amygdala, however, is not only involved in emotion and aggression. It seems to play an important role in other types of social and emotional behavior. It has been linked by current-day workers to such problems as autism and mental illness on less than compelling evidence. Much the same can be said for any of the other centers discussed here; namely that the function of these areas is not limited to a particular kind of behavior. Despite the extensive attention to the role of the amygdala in regulating aggressive behavior, there still remain many uncertainties about its role.

The Hippocampus

The hippocampus is another complex of several nuclei hidden within the temporal lobe that are considered to be parts of the limbic system. It is located behind and above the amygdala. In addition to being involved in emotional activity, many experiments have suggested that it is also deeply involved in the consolidation of long-term memories.[13] Much of the literature on temporal lobe injuries, epilepsy, and their relation to violence actually may be due to the effects of hippocampal traumas because of its anatomical location, intimately close to temporal lobe. To the degree that we can generalize, it appears from work such as that of Siegel and Flynn (1968) that electrical stimulation of the ventral hippocampus produces predatory attack behavior in cats whereas stimulation of the dorsal portion of this same center inhibits this kind of aggression. The hippocampus works in conjunction with the medial hypothalamus, the amygdala, and the periaqueductal gray matter of the midbrain according to a model proposed by Gregg and Siegel, 2001).

The Septal Nuclei

Located below the corpus callosum is a collection of nuclei that like many of the other limbic structures may be involved in emotional responses but like the hippocampus are probably also involved in memory. The small size and complex network of interactions among these nuclei make their exact function difficult to determine. However, it is now believed that stimulation of the ventrolateral portion of the septal nuclei produces predatory attack behavior whereas other parts of the septal nuclei inhibit this kind of behavior but elicit defensive rage reactions. However, some researchers (Brutus, Shaikh, Siegel, and Siegel (1984) believe that these effects are mediated through the hypothalamus.

In recent years much attention has been directed at the effect of septal lesions in birds. Goodson, Eibach, Sakata, and Adkins-Regan (1999), for example, reported that septal lesions in the field sparrow produced highly aggressive birds that had a reduced repertoire of songs. How this work on birds is related to human brain organization is yet to be determined; many of the other components of the human limbic system do not exist in birds.

The Hypothalamus

The hypothalamus, already introduced to us as the regulator of bodily functions "par excellence" by virtue of its control over hormonal and autonomic functions, is also considered an important part of the limbic system and is known to be deeply involved in aggressive behavior. Since it is responsible for those functions that keep the individual and the species intact and alive, it obviously must play an important role in the regulation of emotion which, in the final analysis, is a necessary behavior for an animal's survival. Both predatory aggression and defensive rage and, although we may be loathe admitting it, violence and aggression are obviously highly adaptive responses in some contexts. By virtue of its sensitivity to hormones in the body, any functions of the hypothalamus are especially sensitive to the administration of chemical agents as well as to electrical stimuli.

Although there is little question that there is a role of the hypothalamus in controlling our emotions and especially in regulating aggression, determining its exact function is further complicated by the fact that different parts seem to be involved in diametrically opposed behavioral functions. The classic view is that stimulation of the medial hypothalamus produces the defensive rage syndrome but inhibits predation. The lateral regions of the hypothalamus, it has seemed to many, produce exactly the opposite effect—inhibition of rage—when stimulated. However, even this cautious assignment of specific behavioral functions to particular brain locations is now questionable. Much of this research has been carried out on rats and cats with very small hypothalamic regions. Kruk, Van der Poel, Meelis, Hermans, Mostert, Mos and Lohman (1983), for example, found vast deviations from the standard model when they electrically stimulated "400 sites in the hypothalami of 270 male rats." They discovered that there were regions of the hypothalamus that were graded in their ability to produce aggressive behavior, but that these regions did not overlap with the classical anatomical subdivisions of the hypothalamus. In sum, they showed that quite different aggressive responses could be produced by stimulating regions of the hypothalamus that are only a short distance from each other.

The significance of the study by Kruk and his colleagues is that the function of the anatomic structures discussed in this chapter may not be as discrete as the simplistic anatomic-functional associations may suggest. Instead, even relatively small subregions of the brain may have functional subdivisions built into them. In such a context it becomes extremely difficult to assign specific functions to structures whose extent has been based on structural criteria that may have little or nothing to do with their functional roles. The anatomical proximity of the various portions of the hypothalamus (as well as that of other regions involved in aggressive behavior) makes it difficult to tease out their independent effects.

There are other problems with "locating" aggression in the hypothalamus. Early work by Ellison and Flynn (1968), for example, showed that the hypothalamus could be surgically isolated from the surrounding structures and aggressive, rageful behavior could still be elicited. Thus, the criteria for necessity and sufficiency become extremely difficult to establish in a system with so many inconsistencies and ambiguities. This problem is exacerbated by the ever-present problem that the cat or the rat brains on which the preponderance of the research in this field has been done may be organized in very different ways than that of the human.

The result is the residual confusion and ambiguity of results concerning the hypothalamus. Nowhere is this better summed up than in the words of Adams (2006) whose review of the field is only one among many recent statements that our knowledge of the relationship between aggression and brain mechanisms is still far from complete:

> Many studies elicit attack behavior by electrical and chemical stimulation of the hypothalamus, but there are problems in interpreting the results. Behavioral results of stimulation are contradictory to the results of neural activity during similar naturally-occurring behavior. Neural activity in the hypothalamus has been found to be either unchanged in activity or inhibited during defense in cats evoked by the attack of another cat, even though electrical stimulation through the barrel of the electrode could often produce affective defense behavior....Furthermore, the nature of the attack behavior elicited in the hypothalamus by electrical and chemical stimulation is ambiguous....A more recent review (Kruk et al., 1998)[14] provides a detailed analysis of the "equivocal outcome of such attempts to classify hypothalamic aggression into the motivational categories of offense and defense..." ...One reason for the ambiguity of stimulation results may be the close proximity in the hypothalamus of cell bodies and axons involved in offense and defense motivational systems at several levels....Another source of paradoxical results may be local inhibitory circuits such as those found in the central gray where single neurons are inhibited by nearby electrical stimulation). (p. 310)

Midbrain Periaqueductal Gray Matter

This region has not always received the attention that it has deserved given its demonstrated role in controlling aggression. It is defined as a region of gray (unmyelinated) nuclei surrounding the fluid-filled duct at the level of the midbrain that passes from the ventricles down through the spinal cord. Some early studies (e.g., Kelly, Beaton and Magoun, 1946) had suggested that the midbrain periaqueductal gray matter was deeply involved in aggression. However, interest flagged in later years with much greater attention being directed to the role of the hypothalamus. Renewed interest has been directed at it as a result of studies such as that carried out by Bandler (2006) that showed that electrical stimulation of the midbrain periaqueductal gray matter produces aggressive responses at current levels that are much lower than that required to produce similar behavior in the hypothalamus. Bandler believes, therefore, that the midbrain periaqueductal gray matter may actually be the main source of aggressive behavior rather than the hypothalamus. This is in line with a somewhat older idea that the periaqueductal gray matter is a central organizing point for several different kinds of rage (Pinel, 1993).

Thalamus
The earliest studies of the role of the thalamus in aggression have shown its activity to be modulated by environmental and individual conditions. Delgado (1966), working with monkeys, showed that electrical stimulation of the thalamus might or might not produce aggressive behavior depending on the social rank of the individual. High-ranking animals responded with aggression when their thalamic regions were electrically stimulated whereas low-ranking individuals cowered submissively when the same stimulus was applied to the same location. In another study, Delgado (1966) demonstrated that the effect depended on past experiences as well as the behavior of other animals. He drew the important conclusion that it was a general level of arousal that was being activated by thalamic stimuli rather than a particular "stereotyped motor response." This conclusion was quite unlike his much more famous work with fighting bulls carried out in 1963. In that classic experiment, the electrodes had been placed in the motor regions of the cerebrum and highly stereotyped responses (including, fortunately, the avoidance by the attacking bull of the good Dr. Delgado himself who was waving a red flag in front of the animal) were induced by appropriately timed electrical stimuli.

Because of the complexities of thalamic stimulation, relative little work has been done in this field in the past few decades. A few recent fMRI studies on humans have been reported with few generalizable results. For example, Raine, Buchsbaum and LaCasse (1997) compared brain images from murderers and normal controls and found that there was a reduction in activity on the left side of the thalamus (along with many other regions of the brain) in the murderers. Its specific role in controlling aggression, therefore, remains obscure when faced with this kind of result.

Many of these inconsistent and variable results may be due to the fact that the thalamus is also composed of a number of anatomically and functionally distinguishable regions. It is also heavily interconnected with other regions of the brain whose influences may be exerted in a complex manner. However, some of the difficulties of tying down the specific role of the thalamus may be due to the vague language of psychology.

In addition to the subcortical nuclei already discussed (and other less familiar structures that I have not considered) several regions of the cerebral cortex are also thought to be involved in emotional and aggressive behavior and are considered to be a part of the limbic system or closely interconnected to it.

The Frontal Cortex
Since the time of Phineas Gage there has been a strong inclination among neurobiologists to assume that the frontal lobes were deeply involved in emotional, if not specifically aggressive, behavior. The usual explanation for this association was that the frontal lobes acted much like Freud's concept of the "ego," a theoretical model of constraining and rational forces that acted to control the irrational and aggressive impulses of the primitive "id." Although the Freudian model of a balance between the ego and the id is no longer generally accepted in the psychological or psychiatric community, vestiges of this theory can still be detected in even the most objective brain experiments. The "ego" has been replaced in many circles by the idea of executive control and rational decision making executed by the frontal lobes. Damage to them was said to release base urges in the manner that the Gage case personified. The concept of the id re-emerges in the form of limbic system propensities towards violence.

There are some relatively recent metareviews (e.g., Kandel and Freed, 1989; Brower and Price, 2001; Bufkin and Luttrell, 2005) of the relationship between the frontal lobes and aggression. All are uniform in suggesting that the relationship is poorly understood and often misinterpreted by those who carry out individual investigations. These reviewers collectively pointed out the methodological and conceptual problems that plague the field.

Kandel and Freed (1989), for example, were among the first researchers to question the specific role that frontal lobe dysfunction played in aggressive or violent behavior. With a broad brush, they criticized individual studies of this kind on the basis of four specific bases. These include:

a. Lack of appropriate controls for possible confounds, such as drug abuse or institutionalization;

b. Inconsistent operational definitions in regard to subject assignment;

c. Procedures that ostensibly measure "frontal lobe dysfunction" but have little or no empirical validity;

  d.   Lack of corroborating evidence [such as neuroanatomical studies]. (p. 411)

Kandel and Freed concluded:

> In summary, the evidence for the association between specifically violent criminal behavior and frontal lobe dysfunction is weak at best. (p. 410)

Brower and Price (2001) reviewed approximately 69 research reports in an attempt to find a statistical association between past frontal brain injuries and behavior. They concluded that although there was a statistical correlation between frontal (especially the orbitofrontal) cortex and aggression, this association was exaggerated by many investigators. Notwithstanding the statistical fact that there was an increased proportion of frontal lobe injuries associated with aggressive or violent behavior, the experimental designs in many of these reports were always clouded by the fact that patient sampling was usually biased. In Bower and Price's words:

> Methodological problems in this literature include a lack of prospective data, small subject numbers, and lack of adequate controls for known [preexisting] violence risk factors. (p. 734)

Bower and Price then came to an important conclusion for legal proceedings:

> No study, however, shows that disorders of prefrontal cortex predict violent crime. (p. 734)

Brower and Price concluded their extensive review by asserting that although there was an increased propensity for violent and aggressive behavior:

> Clinically significant focal frontal lobe dysfunction is associated with aggressive dyscontrol, but the increased risk of violence seems less than is widely presumed. (p. 720)

Although all of these articles make it clear that there is a correlation between frontal lobe brain injuries and aggressive behavior, none of these make any assertion about the frontal lobe being the locus of an aggression center. Instead, they point out many of the conceptual, statistical, and interpretive flaws in this entire research enterprise. Wood and Liossi (2006), for example, stated that:

Aggression is a complex social behavior and its cause is multifactorial. We cannot assume a simple association between brain dysfunction, or specific cognitive impairment, and aggression. More importantly, such an association [correlation] does not imply causation. Specific lesions or diffuse injury may alter the threshold for aggression, but cannot be considered a sole direct cause. (p. 340)

Perhaps the most comprehensive empirical study of frontal lobe dysfunction and aggressive behavior was Grafman, Schwab, Warden, Pridgen, Brown, and Salazar's (1996) examination of Viet Nam War veterans with head injuries. They also questioned the validity of the frontal lobe-aggression relationship when they concluded that:

The presence of aggressive and violent behaviors was not associated with the total size of the [frontal lobe] lesion nor whether the patient had seizures, but was associated with a disruption of family activities. (p. 1231)

The best they could do was to draw from their findings the very soft conclusion that:

These findings support the hypothesis that ventromedial frontal lobe lesions increase the risk of aggressiveness and violent behavior. (p. 1231)

Indeed, their data indicated that only a small proportion of those with frontal lobe injury actually were involved in physical violence (14%).

Consider, also, that the effects of a frontal lesion can sometimes be absolutely the reverse of what is usually intended. Damage to the frontal lobe sometimes leads to aggression and sometimes it doesn't! In some cases it leads to apathy and passivity; I direct my readers to the sorry story of prefrontal lobotomies and their use as a tool for controlling aberrant behavior in psychotic patients as told by Valenstein (1986).

Clearly, the frontal lobes of the cerebrum are involved in a variety of different functions, and injuries to or dysfunction in them can result in a wide variety of behavioral disorders. Hawkins and Trobst (2000), for example, list the following cognitive processes in which the frontal lobes are thought to play some role:

- Directing and maintaining high level attention
- Correlating internal and external information
- Generating intentions, plans and programming activity

- Initiating, monitoring, and adapting behavior
- Apathy
- Emotional lability
- Anticipating, planning, and sequencing deficits (p. 150-151)

All of which, they point out, might well be involved in deficiencies in initiating, monitoring, shifting, adapting, and stopping motor behavior as well as abstract behavior.

Bufkin and Luttrell (2005), speaking of the frontal lobes, adhered to the traditional view that the frontal lobes act to suppress or regulate the aggressive tendencies produced by the components of the limbic system. They concluded, however, that if one examines the recent imaging literature, aggression seems to be controlled by a much more complex interaction between the frontal lobes and the cortical and subcortical regions around the limbic system than that suggested by a simple balance between the two areas. According to this traditional view, should the frontal cortex become dysfunctional, then the limbic areas are unleashed to produce violent behavior. However, as Bufkin and Luttrell also pointed out, few brain imaging studies have been directed at determining the nature of this balance or quantifying it. Furthermore, they also noted, based on the work of Raine, Meloy, Bihrle, Stoddard, LaCasse, and Buchsbaum (1998), that the ratio of limbic and frontal activations depended on what kind of aggressive behavior was being examined. Whereas impulsive violence seemed to be determined by the balance between the frontal areas and the limbic regions, persistent predatory behavior was not. Once again the inadequate or ambiguous definition of the behavioral activity (presumably reflecting our difficulty in inferring the nature of some inaccessible mental process) complicates the analysis.

It is also important to realize that although we concentrate on the putative role the particular regions play in aggression, the very same regions of the brain may have multiple other duties. The corollary of this is that virtually any cognitive process activates almost any area of the brain. The idea of a brain as a phrenological aggregation of independent nodes, if nothing else, is refuted by these studies and the respective, near universal, conclusions of their authors in favor of strong interactions among many brain regions. Whatever the role of the frontal cortex is in this complex interaction, it is not a "center" for aggression or even associated with aggressive behavior in a strongly significant way. As noted, damage there may tend to release aggression; however, it may also lead to extremely passive behavior.

Given the complexity of the interconnections of the human brain, it is certain that such a conclusion could be arrived at for any other part of the brain. Indeed, when one considers that the frontal lobe has been associated with a very large number of cognitive functions, there is ample reason to suggest that any specific role as a particular center for violence is premature, if not downright incorrect.

As noted, methodological issues plague this field. Rare, indeed, is the human study that produces a strong correlation between a particular lesion and a particular aggressive behavior. More typical are those studies that report modest correlations or small numbers of positive cases (aggressive behavior) produced by injuries or electrical stimulation. Pillmann, Rohde, Ulrich, Draba, Sannemuller, and Marneros (1999), for example, used EEGs to examine 220 institutionalized criminal defendants. Of this number, a third had abnormal EEGs and only 20 showed localized or focal cerebral abnormalities. When the group of 20 was compared to those without any abnormal EEGs, there was no significant difference in recorded violent behavior. Only when mental retardation, epilepsy, or brain trauma (i.e., confounding factors) were taken into account, the small relationship between those with left focal abnormalities and those without EEGs became statistically significant.

A similarly motivated experimental report (Tateno, Jorge, and Robinson, 2003) using more modern techniques (CT and MRI imaging) found similar results—weak positive correlations. Only 30 of 89 patients who had measurable amounts of traumatic cerebral injuries exhibited aggressive behavior. For those specifically with frontal lobe damage, only about 40% exhibited any aggression. Clearly the low level of association is common across different measurement techniques and should preclude these findings from admissibility in courtroom proceedings.

In conclusion, we generalize from these results and the metareviews previously discussed, it becomes clear that only a fraction of frontal lobe injuries leads to aggressive or violent behavior. Since these studies are always confounded by social histories, including family relationships and alcohol consumption, any specific attribution of aggression to frontal lobe function, seems far fetched. Even worse would be the use of these barely significant data as exculpatory evidence should someone accused of crime seek relief from punishment because of their brain damage. Although all misbehavior is unquestionably brain-related, no brain abnormality has been shown to be both necessary and sufficient to account for aggression.

Cingulate Cortex

The cingulate cortex lies just above the corpus callosum and thus is geographically as well as functionally close to the subcortical regions of the limbic system. Because it, too, is now known to be very heavily interconnected with other regions of the limbic brain (see, for example, the work of Vogt, Finch, and Olson, 1992) as well as having a role in many different autonomic, sensory, and motor functions, it has been particularly difficult to assign a specific role in aggression to it. At present much of the work on the cingulate cortex is done with chemical stimuli whose effect is difficult to localize. The situation is further complicated by the fact that the cingulate seems to have quite different roles in its anterior and posterior regions, the former being associated by Vogt, Finch, and Olson (1992) with "emotional control" and the latter with "monitoring sensory events." The unsubstantiated, but wide-spread, view among cognitive neuroscientists is that the anterior cingulate cortex exerts its influence by inhibiting aggressive behavior.

The Parahippocampal Cortex

The parahippocampal cortex lies under the corpus callosum and, as its name indicates, surrounds some of the subcortical nuclei of the limbic system, especially the hippocampus. Its proximity to the subcortical nuclei may involve it in aggressive behavior; if so, its exact role remains obscure.

B. The Papez Circuit

The Papez circuit (Papez, 1937), long associated with emotional control, overlaps the system of cortical and subcortical regions associated with the limbic system. Over the years the Papez circuit has grown to include more and more brain structures.[15] The circuit, as originally described by Papez, included a loop of cortical and subcortical structures that fed back onto each other to control normal emotional behavior. Such complex and widely dispersed interconnectivity also reiterates the salient point that the whole idea of seeking specific nuclei or structures in the brain for particular cognitive processes may be misguided. If all (or most or even many) regions of the brain are involved in emotional behavior, the association of a particular brain locale with aggression tells us very little about the actual function of the brain as a whole or the specific role of that region in the determination of behavior. Unfortunately, most modern research is aimed at determining the function of the individual components of the Papez circuit which include:

- The thalamus
- The mammillary bodies
- The hypothalamus
- The hippocampus
- The septal nuclei
- The entorhinal cortex
- The cingulate cortex
- The frontal cortex

Although the Papez circuit has long been considered to be the emotion controlling system of the brain, it is not the only such system that has been proposed. Other emotion controlling systems incorporate new views of the environment and/or social aspects of emotion and aggression and may include or exclude components usually included in the classic Papez circuit. For example, Newman (1999) proposed an alternative emotion controlling system consisting of:

- Medial preoptic area
- Lateral septum
- Anterior hypothalamus
- Periaqueductal gray matter
- Medial amygdala
- Bed nucleus of the stria terminalis.

Such a system, Newman argued, represents a novel network that he believed was especially influential in regulating social behavior. Newman also suggested that these networks were not part of a rigid structure. That is, the same components might be involved in other networks and serve different functions in other situations. For example, a quite different, albeit overlapping, network of various neural structures might account for aggressive social behavior among animals of one's own species than would be invoked for aggression on a prey animal.

Other investigators have proposed that the neuroanatomical network of emotional behavior is sufficiently underdetermined that we must consider violence to be a complex interaction between the network and other influences that transcend the neuroanatomical domains. Violence, for example, according to Raine (2002), is a result of a complex interaction including both "biological and social risks," both of which have their own intrinsic "protective factors." He went on to invoke other genetic and environmental factors as contributing components of emotional responses. The difficulty of measuring, much less isolating, these factors makes it clear that it would be extremely difficult to point to a unique brain or environmental factor that determines criminal behavior.

Two new technologies will ultimately lead to changes in our thinking about the organization of these "emotion controlling" networks. The first, of course, is the ubiquitous brain imaging procedures; the problem is that this technology often produces different results than those obtained with more traditional stimulation and lesioning techniques.

The other source of conceptual change is the increased use of biochemicals on regions and nuclei that are believed to have specific sensitivities to them. For example, neurotransmitter substances such as dopamine produce specific effects on the limbic system and have been shown to modulate aggressive behavior.

Similarly, serotonin, it is now believed by some investigators, acts to inhibit aggressive behavior by virtue of a selective action on the prefrontal cortex which has an unusually high number of receptors for this substance. Its action, therefore, is an excitatory one on a structure (the prefrontal cortex) that supposedly inhibits amygdalar activity. Such a theory is obviously based on the conventional "balance theory of a competition between frontal lobe and brain stem neurological forces." [16]

A further difficulty is that the differences between animal research and human clinical and neuropsychological observations remain substantial. Not only do the brains of humans and cats (or rats) differ but the degree of experimental control that is available in animal studies is vastly different from that available to researchers interested in human aggression. I now consider what we know specifically about human aggression and its brain correlates.

4.8 Human Aggression and Brain Mechanisms

Because of the idiosyncratic results, the ethics of experimenting on human beings, the lack of control over the relevant stimuli, social influences, and a number of other reasons, it has been extremely difficult to ask specific research questions about the relationship between brain function and aggression in humans. As we have seen in the immediately preceding discussion, traditional work on lower animals is fraught with its own set of difficulties. In this context the ability to extrapolate from animals to humans becomes very challenging. Not only does even the limited complexity of the simpler animal brains preclude specific conclusions about the way the various portions of their brains influence emotionality and aggression, but there is an enormous amount of variability in the findings reported over the years.

Superimposed on these conceptual difficulties is the persistent problem of interspecies differences. There is strong suggestive evidence that different lower species encode emotionality in different ways; there is no reason to suspect that those differences would not show up in even more profound ways should comparable experiments have been carried out in humans.

There is, however, a breakthrough that overcomes some of these difficulties. The brain imaging devices, whatever their limitations, do permit us to surmount the ethical problems (because of their noninvasiveness) and study brain activity in the one species that is most important to us—us. No longer do we have to use "model preparations" such as rats, cats, monkeys, or apes; now it is possible to at least ask some of the important questions surrounding aggression and the brain.

Bufkin and Luttrell's (2005) comprehensive meta-review of brain imaging research studies and aggression helps us to understand that although the interspecies, ethical, and social influence problems can be partially overcome, there is still no relief from the problems of complexity and variability that plague cognitive neuroscience. Bufkin and Luttrell meta-reviewed 17 studies that used various kinds of brain imaging techniques to study the brains of patients and convicts who had been deemed to have been violent or aggressive. All of the 17 reviewed studies used samples of aggressive or mentally ill subjects; most, but not all, performed the same measurements on matched controls. In the following analysis, I simply list the brain regions of the aggressive subjects that appeared to deviate from normal. This tabulation is based on Bufkin and Luttrell's (2005) Table 1[17].

Regions involved in Aggression
(N = Number of Times Mentioned)
- Amygdala (2)
- Anterior frontal
- Anterior medial frontal (2)
- Anterior Temporal
- Anteromedial frontal
- Bilateral prefrontal
- Dorsolateral frontal
- Frontal
- Hippocampus
- Inferior temporal
- Lateral prefrontal (2)
- Left anterior temporal
- Left basal ganglia
- Left Frontal
- Left frontal grey matter (2)
- Left temporal (4)
- Medial prefrontal (2)
- Medial frontal
- Medial temporal
- Orbitofrontal (2)
- Parietal
- Posterior parietal
- Prefrontal (2)
- Prefrontal grey matter
- Right orbitofrontal
- Right parietal
- Right prefrontal
- Right subcortical
- Right superior parietal

- Right temporal
- Superior frontal
- Temporal (2)
- Thalamus

In addition, the following general (i.e., distributed) abnormalities were reported in at least one of the original papers.

- Generalized hypometabolism
- Generalized lowered autonomic activities
- Generalized MRI abnormalities
- Generalized white matter abnormalities

This long list makes an important point. Like many other studies of brain-behavior relationships carried out on human subjects, aggression was associated with virtually every brain region with the possible exception of the occipital lobe which is mainly devoted to vision.

The simple tabulation of the anatomic regions that were associated by one or another of these studies with violence or aggression does not do justice to the variability and inconsistency exhibited by the findings analyzed in this meta-review. There are many reasons for this seeming uncertainty. First, of course, is the problem of specifying what is essentially the independent variable shared by the 17 papers. The behavioral and mental problems surveyed make up a diverse mélange of different kinds of aggressive and violent subjects. The population ranged from murderers to schizophrenics to alcoholics to others who were classified as suffering from an ill-defined kind of "personality disorder." Exactly what mental aberrations were being examined in this meta-review, therefore, remains somewhat uncertain; "aggression and violence" is just too broad a category to serve as a precise independent variable.

Second, even at their best, most of the reports did not report high levels of correlation between specific brain regions and whatever each investigator meant by the term "aggression." For example, one study which identified the orbito-frontal region measured this kind of response in only one of 14 subjects. Clearly, the identified associations between brain regions and aggression are more idiosyncratic than real, assuming that they are real and not artifactual.

Third, the abnormal behavior was associated with an increase in activity in some responsive areas whereas, in other cases, the same area's response was characterized by a decrease in activity.

Fourth, there were notable differences resulting from the type of imaging device that was used to measure the brain response.

Although Bufkin and Luttrell point out that 14 of the 17 studies showed some involvement of the frontal lobe, there were three that did not. On the other hand, both increases and decreases in a temporal lobe activity were reported from 7 of the 10 studies that used PET or SPECT[18] imaging techniques. Furthermore, subcortical regions such as the amygdala and the thalamus were involved in some of the reports. All in all, as Bufkin and Luttrell conclude in their extremely useful paper:

> There is no present claim that insights from neuroscience permit a program to control precrime, and it appears neuroscientists understand that the image of aggression and/or violence is far from complete. (p. 188)

What their meta-review did accomplish was to emphasize the distributed nature of neural representations of cognitive processes.

4.9 Interim Conclusions

This chapter examines the relationship between brain activity and aggressive behavior. This is an extremely important topic for jurisprudence simply because so many of our court cases deal with violent and aggressive behavior. The possibility that a region or several regions of the brain could be reliably linked with such misbehavior offers many opportunities for rational and humane decision making in the courtroom. It also raises many problems, ethical and technical, should such a relationship be shown to exist. Unfortunately or fortunately (depending on one's point of view) this review of the technical cognitive neuroscience literature shows that the hope that we can identify a reliable and valid brain measure of aggression has not been realized. At present, the field is characterized by substantial variability and inconsistency; it is but a myth that a particular brain lesion can be associated with this particular kind of behavior.

A number of reasons for this conclusion can be gleaned from the discussion presented in this chapter. They include:

1. The roots of human behavior are exceedingly complex. Not only do brain mechanisms and processes determine our behavior but there are many social and environmental influences that act on the brain to determine how different individuals will respond to the same stimulus conditions. It is extremely unlikely that any particular neurophysiological sign will ever be able to uniquely determine, explain, or predict aggressive behavior.

2. The general state of empirical research in cognitive neuroscience is best characterized as indeterminate with regard to the brain correlates

of aggression. The review of the empirical literature presented here indicates that many parts of the brain (including highly integrated and interacting subsystems such as the Papez circuit or the limbic system) are involved in aggressive behavior. Indeed, much of this research supports the distributed neural system's conceptualization of the human brain. That is, many regions of the brain are involved in any cognitive process and many cognitive processes are able to activate a single area of the brain. Aggression and violence fit this conceptual model quite well; many dysfunctional regions have been shown to be able to induce this kind of aberrant behavior.

3. Much of the data specifically related to aggression comes from individual case studies. Despite efforts to generalize such findings, their idiosyncratic and highly variable nature continues to bedevil neuropsychologists. The intrinsic complexity of the human mind-brain-behavior system is so great that it is difficult to pool or combine case studies.

4. An examination of the classic and modern literature of brain-behavior research is characterized by a lack of convergence onto general principles and conclusions. Despite the enormous amount of research in this field, most important questions remain unanswered. The literature is so huge that almost any hypothesis may find some degree of support, no matter how contradictory it may be to other theories. There are no global theories, merely isolated observations.

5. As a result, the field of forensic neuropsychology is currently moving away from seeking to link brain lesions and behavior and has turned to the less challenging and much more achievable task of identifying and describing behavioral deficits. Although this shift was briefly detoured by the availability of brain imaging devices, the quest to link brain and behavior was just not working. Neuropsychology, thus, metamorphosized into a much more narrowly defined field in which the prefix "neuro" is increasingly inappropriate.

6. It is important to understand that the rather vague definition of the word neuropsychology encompasses a number of different professions. Not all are qualified to give testimony in all areas. Specifically, psychologically trained neuropsychologists are rarely qualified to give expert opinion on the brain, and medically trained psychiatrists are rarely qualified to give expert opinion on psychological tests.

7. For both ethical and practical reasons it is difficult to carry out intrusive brain research on humans in a well-controlled manner. Therefore, much traditional research has used animal models. However, interspe-

cies differences make it difficult to extrapolate results from animal studies to the human domain. Lower animals are also unlikely to be sensitive to all of the social, environmental, and cognitive factors that are now known to influence aggression in humans.

8. Aggression, like any other cognitive process, is extremely difficult to define. There are many different types and categories and often the types are intermingled in studies without adequate consideration for their respective adaptive values.

9. Because of the enormous variability, the great complexity, and the inaccessibility of both mind and brain, it is extremely difficult to validate neuropsychological tests and measures of all kinds. As a result, many tests are of questionable value since there is no scientific proof that they are measuring what they are supposed to be measuring. Validity has often been defined in ways that are not part of the original meaning. For example, they may be "validated" on the basis of their predictability or correlation with other tests. None of these alternative means of establishing validity is acceptable in a deep scientific or philosophical sense.

10. Cognitive neuroscience is still based on some highly questionable assumptions. The most important of these are the neo-phrenological ideas that the brain is decomposable into circumscribed locations that encode or represent modular cognitive processes. Whether these assumptions are correct has not yet been resolved. If these premises are not correct, it explains why the problem of mind-brain relationships have been so vexing and why the field has made such modest progress; it is, to put it simply, going in the wrong direction.

11. Despite these difficulties, there is an increasing number of cases appearing in our courts in which localized brain injuries are being offered as exculpatory evidence. The use of existing research findings in the courtroom is based upon a gross misunderstanding of the lack of progress that has been made in cognitive neuroscience. We still do not know what brain lesions are associated with aggression. Attempts to use any brain abnormality as an excuse meet neither the standards of good science nor the judicial rules of admissibility of evidence. Fortunately, most jurisdictions currently do not admit this type of deeply flawed neuroscientific evidence.

12. Just as there is no way to attribute past violence to brain dysfunction, there is no way to predict whether or not a person will exhibit violent or aggressive behavior in the future.

13. Although there are correlations between brain activity and aggression, at best these associations are statistical and not determinant. This

fact makes the utility of the associations extremely contentious in the courtroom. How could we exonerate or convict someone on the basis of a probability and a low one at that?

Endnotes

1. The BEAM (Brain Electrical Activity Mapping) is a surface map of the EEG obtained over broad reaches of the skull from an array of electrodes. It is championed as having more information about the pattern of brain activity than the standard EEG which is an indication of the activity at a set of disconnected points on the skull.

2. "Brain Fingerprinting" (BF) is essentially a guilty knowledge test based on the P300, a positive wave in an averaged Event Related Potential (ERP) occurring approximately 300 ms after a stimulus. The idea was originally proposed by Farwell and Donchin (1991) and popularized by Farwell and Smith (2001). It has not received warm support from the neuropsychological or legal communities as evidenced by the very critical review by Rosenfeld (2005). His conclusion is that "the claims on the BF Web site are exaggerated and misleading" and that "prospective users and buyers of this technology are issued the usual *caveat emptor*."(p. 20)

3. QEEG (quantitative electroencephalography) refers to a manner of processing standard EEG data that have been correlated with various behavioral states. By digital processing of the signals, a pattern of responses is supposedly identified that is characteristic of that behavioral state. This pattern is used to diagnose the same behavioral state in other subjects that share the same pattern of EEG activity. It too suffers from an absence of authentication.

4. There are exceptions to this generalization. However, the more complex the cognitive or emotional process (e.g., religiosity or maternal love), the less credibility adheres to the study.

5. One of the most curious cases of neglecting data and logic can be found in the work of one of the masters of neuropsychology, Tim Shallice (1988). Nowhere in the literature can I find more cogent augments about the inconsistency of neuropsychological data, against the impossibility of distinguishing alternative forms of systems organization, or the general theory that mental and brain entities are arranged as semi independent modules. In spite of the brilliance and eloquence of his argument, Shallice suddenly shifts gears and states that "From this stage on, these methodological cautions will be abandoned. In general, it will be assumed that a (double) dissociation signifies the existence of an isolable system" (p. 266). Nowhere in the literature of neuro-

psychology are the power of the Zeitgeist and the willingness to do what can be done instead of what should be done more clearly demonstrated.

6. This list has been compiled based on an informal search of the literature on validity. Many of the items are overlapping; some are irrelevant to the true meaning of validity; most suggest a substantial misunderstanding of the true nature of what is meant by scientific or logical validity. I am grateful to my colleague Caleb Burns for the original suggestion that this mini-taxonomy of validities might be useful in alleviating some of this misunderstanding.

7. I have written extensively elsewhere about the fundamental philosophical and scientific difficulties in bridging the gap between these two fields. Here I emphasize the dominant assumption among neuroscientists of all kinds that the mind is a product of the brain and that in principle, mental processes are fully explicable in neural terms. Although there are many practical reasons why this extreme neuroreductionism may never be achieved, it is incomprehensible how a cognitive neuroscientist could search in the laboratory for a brain mechanism of something like aggression without accepting this fundamental ontological assumption.

8. A modern study of the exhumed skull (Damasio, Grabowski, Frank, Galaburda, and Damasio, 1994) revealed that Gage had major damage to the frontal lobes on both the right and left sides of the brain.

9. A similar draconian surgical procedure was also used to control aggressive behavior in humans. In this case, the target region was the amygdala. The procedure is described in a report by Heimburger, Whitlock, and Kalsbeck (1966).

10. There is also the problem that whatever degree of brain localization there may be may not remain constant. Leyton and Sherrington (1917) long ago reported that the motor areas from which they recorded were not stable from trial to trial or from animal to animal (chimpanzees and gorillas). They attributed this "temporal instability" to a number of factors including previous experience and metabolic states.

11. I appreciate that this approach will not sit well with my colleagues in the field of neuropsychology who yearn for answers to what are undeniably important questions. However, mentalist or cognitive theories of aggressive behavior are speculative to the point of permitting almost everything or anything to produce violent behavior. This is not solely a criticism of neuropsychology but a prevailing problem for psychology in general. No strong constraints impinge on the variety of these "just so" stories that can be concocted and, thus, no way to either reject or accept any of them.

12. It is important to note, however, that this result is dependent on the type of social situation in which the lesioned animal is placed. Different environments can produce totally contradictory results, again illustrating the difficulty of assigning specific functions to particular brain regions without considering other influences.

13. This does not necessarily mean that it is the repository of our memories, only that the hippocampus is involved in their transcription from experience to storage.

14. Kruk, Westphal, Van Erp, van Asperen, Cave, Slater, de Koning, Haller, 1998.

15. The way in which the Papez circuit has grown to include more and more regions over the years is suggestive of an important emerging concept, namely that all parts of the brain are now thought to be increasingly interconnected. Although not usually framed in the context of the view that the brain is more holistic than modular, this is exactly what is implied by this new development.

16. A considerable amount of research in recent years has been carried out using drugs and transmitter substances to treat aggressive behavior. The reasons for this are obvious; even if we cannot understand their biological effects exactly, we still may be able to develop effective drugs that modify aberrant behavior. This atheoretical approach captures the flavor of much research in this field.

17. The specific citations for the 17 studies meta-reviewed in the Bufkin and Luttrell article can be found there.

18. SPECT (Single Photon Emission Computed Tomography) is a tomographic technique in which radioactive substances are injected into the body and a measurement made whenever a single photon (i.e., gamma ray) is emitted. It is especially useful for measuring blood distribution in the brain.

Chapter 5

The Neuroscience of Cognitive Dysfunction

Synopsis
5.1 Introduction
5.2 Some Caveats
    A. Prematurity and a Lack of Robust Replication
    B. Legal Culpability in the Face of Neuroscientific Findings
    C. Variability
    D. The Multifactorial Nature of Behavior
    E. Differing Standards and Criteria
    F. Linguistic Confusions
5.3 Some Plausible Relations of Mental Dysfunction and Neuroscience
    A. Cognitive Deficits Attributable to Brain Deficits: The Agnosias, Aphasias, Amnesias, and Apraxias
    B. Consciousness and Coma States
    C. Brain Death
5.4 When "Neuroscience" is not Neuroscience
    A. Mental Illness
    B. Other Behavioral Mysteries Lacking a Neuroscientific Foundation
5.5 Interim Conclusions
Endnotes

MYTH: The neuroscience of cognitive dysfunction is sufficiently well developed to pass the *Daubert* criteria for admissibility.
TRUTH: The neuroscience of cognitive dysfunction still does not meet the *Daubert* criteria for admissibility.

5.1 Introduction

This chapter will deal with a number of topics concerned with deviations from normal cognitive functioning that are increasingly considered to be of common interest to cognitive neuroscience and the law. In researching this chapter it became clear to me that few of the many authors who have written about neuroscience and the law actually spend very much time concerned with the neuroscientific database itself. Rather, legal scholars, much in the traditional manner of philosophers and

175

social scientists in the past, have centered their attention on the philosophical, behavioral, and ethical aspects of behavior. Issues such as free will, moral judgment, and responsibility still dominate legal thinking rather than the neuroscientific studies of the relationship between behavior and the brain. As a result, in my judgment, there has been much too little critical evaluation of the scientific status of topics that cross the boundaries between the two domains. Indeed, it is not widely enough appreciated in legal circles just how much of our cognitive neuroscientific knowledge is still controversial and undeveloped. Despite the fact that there has been a new surge of criticism of the neurophysiological concomitants of behavior in the last few years, legal scholars all-too-easily accept very preliminary and exploratory research in cognitive neuroscience as established fact. In reality, there is a very wide corpus of empirical observations and theoretical interpretations that have not stood the test of time and replication. Naïve acceptance of a great deal of what is actually fanciful still vastly exceeds the solid and robust scientific facts.

It is, of course, true that many new findings do show relationships between mind, behavior, and brain. Some of these correlations eventually may be shown to be directly related to the determination and control of behavior; some, on the other hand, are such distant and fantastic analogs or even metaphors for behavioral and mental processes that they offer little in the way of the prediction and control of behavior, much less in the adjudication of the causes of misbehavior in the courtroom.

The major goal of this chapter is to help legal scholars who are not cognitive neuroscientists understand the complexities and limits of contemporary neuroscientific theories that purport to explain deviations from normal cognitive processes such as consciousness, mental illness, and the agnosias. The point made in this chapter is that there is a wide range of cognitive neuroscientific findings that deserve differing degrees of credulity and relevance in the legal environment. Some neuroscientific data, theories, and methods are of unquestionable legal relevance when it comes to such vitally important issues as, for example, determining when a person is truly dead or in a vegetative state. The legal implications of such decisions are obvious and there is a formidable scientific database that can contribute to good judgment in cases of this kind.

However, it must be appreciated that other cases may invoke controversial ideas that are far beyond current technology to resolve. For example, the searches for the neural foundations of altruism, choice behavior, or even ethical conduct itself remain elusive and so far are unfulfilled.[1] Similarly, some medicalized emotional disturbances (e.g., Post Traumatic Stress Disorder—PTSD) have no known physiological or biological markers.

Despite the lingering doubts of serious cognitive neuroscientists, often the most preliminary reports are given credence far beyond their scientific standing. I have already discussed the false credulity given to the idea of an fMRI lie detector—one clear example of the ability of even the most speculative and preliminary observations to find a degree of acceptance despite what seems to be strong evidence that the promise of a brain image-based lie detector is not likely to be fulfilled.

Why should this misunderstanding be so persistent? There are many possible answers to this question. Part of it is due to the inadequate training of lawyers and judges (along with most other laypersons) to discriminate well-established science from science fiction. Part of it is due to the popular desire to find quick answers to profound questions that have not in point of scientific fact yet been answered. Part of it is due to an unjustified extrapolation from the widely accepted assumption of cognitive neuroscience that all mental and behavioral processes are accounted for, in principle, by brain activity. This ontological assumption—every human mental and behavioral activity is ultimately driven by brain activity—does not mean that every such activity is amenable, in practice, to scientific analysis or explanation. For reasons that I have already made clear in earlier chapters, there are matters of underdetermination and complexity that prohibit our bridging the gap between brain findings and the causes of behavior, much less between brain and some extremely subtle legal issues. Unfortunately, too little has been done to dispel the notion that deep and uncontroversial progress has been made in understanding the relationship between mind, behavior, and the brain. For example, the concept of localization of function, a matter that I have discussed so many times in this book, is still a major part of current legal, popular, and neuroscientific thinking: thinking that lags seriously behind well-established empirical results that argue, instead, for distributed neural systems. As we have already seen, whenever we ask the question—what part of the brain accounts for what part of behavior?—we may be asking not only a "bad question" but an unanswerable one.

The point of this book is that some of the leaps and extrapolations from neuroscientific findings to legal opinions are far fetched and are based on unrealizable expectations. Exceedingly primitive initial observations are thought by some legal scholars to raise deep ethical challenges when the tantalizing observations are premature, incorrect, or unlikely to come to any impactful realization. This does not mean that some of the neuroscientific hypotheses *may ultimately have* no effect, but rather that they *should have* no effect at their present stage of development; it is much too early to accept some of the speculative hypotheses and extrapolations that emerge from what even their originators often consider to be exploratory and preliminary laboratory or clinical research. It is extremely important, I argue in this context, to keep from expending an inordinate amount of energy on what are only current-day phantoms that are unlikely to ever become well-established realities. There are serious ethical and scientific issues that have to be resolved before admitting some controversial idea (e.g., children be held to a more lenient standard because "their brains are not yet fully developed"). The plain fact is that we do not know what the exact relation may be between adolescent behavior and immature brain development.

Although aggression and lie detection are exciting topics of special interest in the context of criminal prosecution and have a long history of neuroscience research associated with them, the role of the cognitive neurosciences in the context of the courtroom is far broader than these topics. Not only are criminal violence and destructive behavior of concern to our society but so, too, are other matters that might come into play in both civil litigation and criminal cases. Judgments about damages that may have occurred as a result of negligence, for example, often require that evaluations of the cognitive, sensory, and motor capacities of an injured person be made and often these handicaps are attributed to specific brain anomalies on the flimsiest of bases. Even more esoteric matters as the possible connection of the human brain to computers and the possibility of artificial brain enhancement by drugs or electromagnetic stimulation loom on the horizon, some of which will eventually relate to judicial matters whether or not they are considered valid concepts by cognitive neuroscientists.

In this chapter I offer my estimate of the validity of a number of topics that exist at the interface between law and neuroscience. These topics can be classified into two types: (A) Cognitive disorders that current neuroscience is in a position to provide some admissible support in legal proceedings as well as legitimate topics for future research; and (B) Cognitive disorders for which there is some suggestive evidence but which have not yet been linked in a substantial way to neurological conditions. The following list tabulates the topic in each of these two categories that I will deal with in this chapter.

(A)   Well-founded Contemporary Neuroscientific Problems
   •   The Agnosias—Impairment of sensory, motor and cognitive processes.
   •   Coma and Consciousness
   •   Brain Death
(B)   Questionable Elaborations of Neuroscientific Knowledge
   •   Mental Illness
   •   Autism
   •   Attention Deficit Hyperactivity Disorder
   •   Post Traumatic Stress Disorder

5.2 Some Caveats
A. Prematurity and a Lack of Robust Replication

Before I turn to the specific topics of interest in this chapter, it is important to set the stage by expressing a few general points about the various topics to be considered. In the last few years, there has been a rush of breathless announcements of a number of extraordinary developments in the cognitive neurosciences. Many exciting phenomena or new techniques promise that the gap between the brain and the mind has been crossed and that we are now in a position to "read the mind" of a person or to explain some mental dysfunction with modern technology. However, as I show when I consider some of the individual cases, much of this bridge-crossing is not only premature but seriously misunderstood with regard to its potential significance and relation to a plausible future neuroscience-based courtroom.

Adding further uncertainty to the use of neuroscientific evidence is the fact that many of these initial reports are isolated events that are never replicated. After a brief splurge of enthusiastic interest, most often in the popular press, they fall into obscurity and are never explicitly denied. Instead, they remain isolated, although admittedly exciting, almost unique phenomena that somehow never lead to the development of either further practical applications or deeper scientific understanding. The worst case is that at least a few of them become part of popular myths and are perpetuated, sometimes persisting for millennia, in much the same way as folktales from our historical past. Brain fingerprinting and unique associations between particular brain lesions and aggression are examples of myths still percolating around the periphery of the legal system.

There are some special empirical problems that face any merging of cognitive neuroscience theory and legal practice. Two issues in particular must be considered here—empirical support and legal culpability. The first concerns the robustness of the empirical findings—do the scientific data support an association between the observed behavior and the neural findings sufficiently strongly to justify their admissibility into the courtroom. As I have shown throughout this book, there is a serious controversy concerning the most elemental questions. It is not yet established that what we know about the mind-brain connection is sufficient to permit us to extrapolate from the neural data to any satisfactory kind of explanation of mind or prediction of behavior. Indeed, there is a strong argument there is too little well enough known about the nature of the mind-brain relationship to justify any leap from neuroscience laboratory to judicial proceedings.

Furthermore, there are at least some critics who believe that the mind-brain problem may never be solved and that the best we can ever hope for is statistical correlations between pooled groups. The main reason for this uncertainty is the strong possibility that the measures used in the EEG, ERP, PET, and fMRI techniques may be providing irrelevant answers to questions posed at the wrong level of analysis. All are based on macroscopic (i.e., pooled, cumulated responses) that do not describe the truly salient activity—the complex of microscopic interactions at the neuronal (i.e., the cell) level that are widely considered by cognitive neuroscientists to be the true equivalents of our thoughts and behaviors.

Should the problem be so challenging that we shall never be able to unravel the mind-brain complexity,[2] then a second set of issues would no longer be scientific, but rather ethical, social, and philosophical matters. On the other hand, should some of these matters turn out to be empirically testable, we are then obligated to move on to determine their possible role in the courtroom. Obviously, to expend a lot of time and energy on neurophysiological examinations of concepts that can or are likely to be shown to be fallacious or empirically unsupportable is wasteful and has the potential capability to lead us astray from whatever understanding of human nature we may ultimately be able to achieve.

Throughout this chapter in particular, the quality and robustness of the empirical "proof" of an experiment or observation continually arise. Many of the topics considered here simply do not meet the simplest criteria of scientific credibility. In the main, there is little incontestable scientific evidence that whatever measurable associations between behavior and the brain have arrived at a level of proof that should permit them to influence legal decision making. All of this must be colored by the one basic assumption held by most cognitive neuroscientists: all mental and behavioral functions are controlled by the brain. Given that axiom, it is easy to see how even the most outlandish, prescientific ideas gain such traction in our legal system.

B. Legal Culpability in the Face of Neuroscientific Findings

The second issue concerns something far more subtle, philosophical, and not subject to the raw impact of the empirical data. Suppose, for the sake of argument, that the empirical data were sufficient to show that some form of criminal behavior was associated with a specific aspect of brain dysfunction. The legal problem arising in this case is the degree of responsibility that an accused perpetrator would bear in the presence of a definable neurological "cause." Should, it might be asked, such a relationship between a brain dysfunction and criminal behavior provide a degree of exculpation for the accused?

There are profound arguments on both side of this question. Certainly, some might argue, we already have built into our legal system excuses from penalties based on mental illness, an inability to think rationally, or self defense. Why, then should not an abnormality of the brain (given that it is sufficiently well connected to an abnormality of behavior to pass tests of scientific credibility) absolve an accused from responsibility for a crime? This conundrum leads immediately to a number of other complex questions that highlight the controversy and confusion that inevitably lay at the interface between the law and neuroscience. Is it not the individual's brain that accounts for all normal and abnormal behavior? Does criminal behavior itself not reflect a brain abnormality since all behavior is brain related? Is there any difference between misbehavior due to a tumor and misbehavior due to a subtle information miscalculation in a brain that is reflected in antisocial behavior?[3]

These are not questions that are going to be answered by further neuroscience research. No matter how sound the association between the brain state and the behavioral response, the issue of responsibility for one's behavior as well as for one's brain's activities will remain a formidable ethical issue for the law. Indeed, it is not at all certain that neuroscience has much to say about the issue of responsibility. All that it can do is to provide knowledge about possible relationships. Society and the legal system must make the final decisions.

There is considerable debate concerning the way in which the responsibility issue will be resolved even if the scientific merits of some mind-brain association are substantiated. Knowing that a person's brain state produced a specific behavior does not automatically resolve the legal and ethical problems; in the final analysis it will always be a matter of human judgment, mores, and folkways rather than a scientific issue. After all is said and done, we are our brains and our brains are us. A major legal debate then must resolve whether or not we should make our decisions based on the brain state or on the basis of the behavior. Objectively unanswerable questions on such matters as free-will and neurological determinism then must be answered by decisions that transcend empirical observations. Given our strong proclivities to seek out explanations and the almost preternatural force of face validity, even the most ridiculous and unsupported brain metaphor is capable of exerting a strong influence on judicial decision making. It is, therefore, necessary to cull the absurdities, first at the level of their scientific plausibility, and then in terms of their ethical and legal implications. Unfortunately, even those that do not pass the test of empirical credibility may still continue to play a role in our legal system in much the same way as does the polygraph.

C. Variability

A further problem for cognitive neuroscience, and ultimately its application in the courtroom, is that all cognitive neuroscience data is highly variable. As I demonstrate in previous chapters, correlations may range from little or nothing to equally strong and opposite positive and negative values in various research reports. This kind of variability is accepted and, to a substantial degree understood, in scientific research. Statistics is a highly developed branch of mathematics, and both descriptive and inferential approaches are available to analyze data. For example, tests of significance can used to provide estimates of the likelihood that a particular experiment's results can be taken as strongly suggestive if not "proof" of some hypothesis. The great variability of biological and behavioral activity (compared to the behavior of machines and other physical entities) demands that statistical rather than deterministic mathematics be used to accommodate the range of possible responses obtained in a cognitive neuroscience experiment.

This type of probabilistic or stochastic thinking would be anathema to a judge or a jury. Based on the "reasonable doubt" principle, unanimity is typically required in most types (especially criminal proceedings) of jury trials. The equivalent of a .05 significance criterion is a single holdout juror. In a scientific experiment, the results, equivocal and variable as they may be, are accepted as just another property of experimental findings to be made orderly by the application of statistical methods.

In the jury room, however, such equivocation is unacceptable and deliberations must continue until some resolution of this discrepancy is achieved. Judges and juries are not equipped, nor are they permitted, the kind of leeway permitted in a statement such as "we consider the accused guilty with a 95 percent degree of assurance." The introduction of what is usually variable scientific evidence into courtroom deliberations places them in a special category. Jurors are more easily able to deal with a witness who is lying or telling the truth than to understand the role of statistical correlation coefficients, central tendencies, ranges, and variance.

The question of how the two cultures of decision making can be reconciled is a profoundly complex one, given that the relevant decision rules are almost axiomatic in each environment. Garland and Glimcher (2006), for example, asked—would our juries be able to evaluate information with this level of variability into their deliberations in a manner that would please scientists who depend upon levels of significance rather than absolute certainty? Should any correlation less than 1.00 be used in evaluating guilt or innocence or, even worse, in selecting an appropriate punishment? Of course, jurors accept ambiguous information in their deliberations all the time; indeed, the reason for most trials is that there is some degree of ambiguity in proffered evidence. Nevertheless, juries are called upon all the time to evaluate evidence and come forth with an absolute, binary, yes-no decision.

D. The Multifactorial Nature of Behavior

A further complication, noted by Saunders (2005) among many other legal scholars, is that there rarely is any single causal factor to which criminal misbehavior can be attributed. As we see in the previous chapter, whatever neurological and genetic predispositions there may be to crime, aggression, or violence, they are always heavily modulated by life experiences and environmental factors. The simple, straightforward, single causal answers that a court would like from cognitive neuroscience may just not be possible because of the complexity of the mind-brain system and variety of causal factors that drive our behavior.

This misunderstanding is exacerbated by the multifactorial nature of human development. Not only do neurological systems develop and change as a function of the individuals' genetic heritage, but also because the individuals' experiences during her or his lifetime are now suspected to exert a powerful influence on brain development. These two factors are almost always conflated in experimental studies. It may be that they cannot be separated with any plausible experimental protocol. In point of historical and scientific fact, the classic nature-versus-nurture problem has not been resolved, despite the efforts by some cognitive neuroscientists (e.g., Steinberg and Scott, 2003)[4] to "explain" the changing behavior of children as they mature by allusion to coincident changes in synaptic connectivity.

E. Differing Standards and Criteria

Beyond the differences in acceptable criteria for decision making in the courtroom and the laboratory, respectively, there is another level at which neuroscience and the law conflict. Saunders (2005) pointed out that courts tend to look to historical precedent and preexisting standards (e.g., the first amendment). Science, quite to the contrary, seeks a progression of novel discoveries that are intended to overturn or to modify preexisting knowledge. Where the law looks to the past, science looks to the future for guidance.

Thus, the legal system and cognitive neuroscience operate on the basis of fundamentally different value systems. As a result, there will always be a barrier that prevents science from rapidly changing existing social and legal traditions. The most robust scientific finding can be disputed in the courtroom and this dispute will be especially severe when dealing with scientific matters that are still controversial, such as those involving the relationship between behavior and the brain. A number of scholars, such as Morse (2004) and Green and Cohen (2004), have pointed out that it is not likely that neuroscience will replace, supplant, or substitute for long standing concepts of jurisprudence. Ambiguous behavioral and legal concepts such as "rationality" and the "ability to tell right from wrong" will continue to serve as criteria for the adjudication of truth or innocence whether or not there is demonstrable evidence of some correlated brain damage. Certainly, it may change the way we interpret some such processes. However, even the most dramatic and unexpected development in cognitive neuroscience is more likely to be encompassed within the existing legal system than the reverse.

The primary reason for the difference in conceptual foundation between science and the law is that the legal system is primarily a nonreductive, behavior-based edifice operating at the relatively high (i.e., molar or holistic) level of social interactions. Cognitive neuroscience, to the extent that it has achieved or ultimately will achieve its goal, is a reductive enterprise whose goal is to seek causal relationships between the behavioral level and underlying neural processes. Even in the unlikely event that the "explanatory gap" between the mental-behavioral and the neurological is bridged, it is not likely that the law will surrender its prerogatives to behaviorally control human behavior to some arcane neuroscientific criteria. As Greene and Cohen pointed out:

> Neuroscience is unlikely to tell us anything that will challenge the law's stated assumptions. However, we maintain that advances in neuroscience are likely to change the way people think about human action and criminal responsibility by vividly illustrating lessons that some people appreciated long ago. Free will is an illusion generated by our cognitive structure. (p. 1784)

All of this finesses the primarily scientific issues concerning whether or not the scientific theories supported by the data are generally considered to be valid or not. The neurological evidence for a behavioral concept such as "free will" will always be as elusive as has been the search for the solution of the mind-brain problem in general.

F. Linguistic Confusions

Not all of the difficulties that are faced when cognitive neuroscience impinges on judicial theory and practice arise from the matters discussed so far. Another important problem area concerns the interplay between the words "cognitive" and "neuroscience." The prime materialistic, monistic, neuroscientific ontological assumption is that all that is implicitly mental (and all that is overtly behavioral) arises from the neuronal processes of the brain. A misunderstanding occurs when this axiom is taken so literally that it is incorrectly assumed to mean that the demonstration of a behavioral phenomenon is, ipso facto, an explanatory statement about a definable neurological state. For example, one of the many myths percolating around in the pseudo-neurosciences is that the two halves of the brain process different human mental capabilities. This leads to false processes such as "teaching to the brain"—a pedagogical approach that is as meaningless as the prime assumption that mind-brain equivalence is meaningful. Of course, since the brain is the locus of all of our memories and thoughts, all teaching is done "to the brain." Efforts to squelch the right-brain, left-brain distinction have been continuous (e.g., Efron, 1990); however, the suggestion that "...the concept of hemispheric specialization explains right left performance asymmetries" (Efron, 1990, p. 65) still resonates in the halls of our educational institutions.

Similarly, it has become popular to believe that some severe behavioral problems are the result of some subtle brain order, often neologized by the obscure term "Minimal Brain Disorder" or MBD. The basic problem is that our lack of knowledge about how the brain produces the mind makes these linguistic artifices nothing more than loose metaphors.

The fallacious linguistic usage illustrated here may be called "pseudoneurologizing," that is, attributing anatomic or physiological properties to the brain on the basis of behavioral observations. The logical flaw is the "one to many" issue that I have mentioned previously—the idea that there are many possible inferences that can be made about neural mechanisms from behavior. Thus behavior is indeterminate regarding those mechanisms. In short, one cannot reverse engineer the brain by observing behavior.

Of course, all mental and behavioral manifestations are due to neurological mechanisms. However, the error lies in the usage of a neurological language to explain behavior that has not been empirically linked in any way with the inferred neural mechanism. This often leads to a search for neural correlates that are so ubiquitous that it is hard not to find some kind of support for even the most meaningless concept. Nevertheless, it is well known among statisticians that concomitancy is insufficient to serve as a basis for determining causal relations. The potential for error in assigning causation to correlation (Yule, 1926) cannot be underestimated, particularly during this early stage of development of the cognitive neurosciences.

The real crux of the problem is that much of this pseudoneurologizing is not necessary—the strategies for ameliorating, if not correcting, behavioral problems are, both in the short and long runs, most likely to be behavioral. Little is added to remedial techniques by papering them over with the terminology of a more neurological language that seems to suggest much but actually means little. The most significant progress in treating such disorders as autism and ADHD has come from the dedicated work of behavioral scientists, not from any knowledge of the brain mechanisms that underlay these serious behavioral disorders.

5.3 Some Plausible Relations of Mental Dysfunction and Neuroscience

This task of the remainder of this chapter is to evaluate the neuroscientific status of a number of cognitive disorders that have gained considerable respect in recent years. Although many neurological-behavioral correlations turn out to be whims and fantasies, the ones discussed in this section have legitimate neuroscientific contributions to make in our courtrooms.

A. Cognitive Deficits Attributable to Brain Deficits: The Agnosias, Aphasias, Amnesias, and Apraxias

Despite the dual difficulties of defining cognitive processes and associating them with specific brain lesions, early in the eighteenth century pioneering workers such as Marc Dax (1836) began to notice extraordinary and often unique cases of defective speech processing that seemed to be associated with specific brain injuries. These behavioral deficits seemed to be both more subtle and more complex than motor paralyses or sensory communication deficits. Dax attributed these speech disorders to a damaged region on the left side of the brain. A historical note was that Pierre Paul Broca (1824-1880), who was subsequently given credit for the location of what is now known as Broca's area, initially disputed Dax's discovery, arguing that the brain areas for speech were widely scattered about the whole brain. Broca (1861) subsequently identified the specific region on the left side of the brain for which he is well known. However, even in his earliest work, he presciently (and not unreasonably in light of present research) involved other areas such as the frontal lobes in the speech process.

Broca's aphasia, as this disorder came to be known, was characterized by an inability to produce comprehensible speech. A parallel aphasia (more properly referred to as an auditory agnosia) in which the patient could speak but could not understand speech was reported by Wyllie (1866) and then associated with particular anatomical lesions by Wernicke (1874). Wernicke, not surprisingly, had his name attached not only to this particular kind of dysfunction but also to the region on the left side of the brain to which it appeared to be related.

Agnosias (deficits in recognition) became of extreme interest with the publication to the classic paper on the topic by Lissauer (1890/1988). Lissauer supplemented the initial observations by distinguishing between "apperceptive" and "associative" forms of these cognitive deficits. Speaking specifically of visual agnosias, he noted a symptomatic difference between an inability to see an object—an apperceptive deficit—and an inability to ascribe meaning to what otherwise was a competent visual experience—an associative deficit. The diagnostic test distinguishing between the two kinds of agnosia was the observation that an apperceptive agnosiac would be unable to draw a picture of an object that could otherwise be seen and reported in some separate sensory-perceptual sense. On the other hand, patients with associative agnosia would be able to draw a picture of an object but not express what its use was. At the present time, it is generally agreed that most agnosias are actually mixtures of these two subcategories.

From the late nineteenth century, the concept of aphasia was deeply entrenched in neuroanatomic and psychological theorizing. This led to a furry of discovery of new behavioral anomalies and ultimately to a plethora of different conditions which were classified as associative disorders. The field has always been subject to great uncertainty, not the least concerns the search for the neural correlates of the more subtle disorders. Thus, this work has played an important role in the localization-distribution debates that still characterize the field of cognitive neuroscience.

This brief historical discussion introduces us to the huge variety of cognitive dysfunctions with all of the complexities and uncertainties to which the field is subject. From the outset, we have to acknowledge that it is going to be difficult to precisely define these subtle kinds of cognitive dysfunction for many of the same reasons that it is difficult to read the minds of participants in other kinds of psychological experiments. All that we can do is observe the behavioral responses, seek some correlated brain damage, and attempt to infer the relationship between the two domains. As we see shortly, this is a far more difficult task than it may seem at first.

To illustrate the difficulty, consider how many alternative explanations there might be of a symptom that Lissauer would have designated as an associative agnosia. One possibility is that there is damage to a specific brain mechanism that ties together the perception of an object's shape and its meaning or use. This would lead inexorably to a kind of theoretical model that would be consistent with the kind of localizationist theory (e.g., a specific region had evolved for the singular purpose of adding meaning to a percept) permeating so much of cognitive neuroscience.

However, it is equally plausible to assert that the lack of an appreciation of the meaning of the object is a result of the disruption of a distributed system whose location and function are far less specific and far more general than the first alternative suggests. Following this line of thought, an entirely different theoretical scenario for the dissociation of the sensory experience and its meaningful use would naturally evolve. That all of this must occur in a scientific context of enormous variability in anatomic and behavioral data severely complicates the matter.

The uncertainty of the causal forces at work in accounting for the increasing numbers of dysfunctions diagnosed as agnosias, aphasias, apraxias, and amnesias is not entirely unexpected given what has already been discussed concerning the vague definitions of various kinds of mental activity. At present neither cognitive nor neurobiological conditions accounting for these cognitive symptoms can be definitively designated. The best we can do is to describe the various cognitive deficiencies in terms of their behavioral consequences. The worst we can do is to assign these dysfunctions to specific neurological lesions on the basis of the inadequate data now available. Furthermore, as we see shortly, even the behavioral symptoms are sometimes hard to define.

The next question we must ask in this review of these associative disorders is—what are the behavioral symptoms that distinguish this set of cognitive dysfunctions from simpler and more obvious impairments such as blindness due to sensory factors or paralysis due to motor conduction problems? The set of dysfunctions now being discussed are more subtle and complex and are superimposed on what may otherwise appear to be perfectly competent sensory and motor powers. Unlike blindness, to take one example, the agnosic patient may be able to behaviorally report the presence of an object or the presence of a face. However, the agnosia is defined as the inability to process the information so that the perceived image makes sense. For example, they may not be able to use or to verbally describe the use of a tool or distinguish one face from another. Agnosias of this kind are not restricted to the visual sense; they can occur in all other sensory modalities.

Associative perceptual deficits (generically referred to as agnosias), however, are not the only domain in which high level cognitive dysfunction has been observed. A variety of high level speech dysfunctions may be exhibited by people who have no obvious damage to the mechanical parts of their speech mechanism. Such disorders are generically referred to as aphasias. Aphasias are particularly complex and difficult to categorize because speech employs so many different aspects of nervous system function, not to mention other mechanical parts of the body. Therefore, there has been a proliferation of different kinds of aphasias, each of which may be only slightly different from another, if at all.

Nor do these aphasia and aphasia-like conditions exhaust the array of observed cognitive deficits. Loss of memory is designated amnesia and can also be observed in many different varieties. The degree of forgetfulness may range from a total lack of recall of one's life's history to minor defects in short-term memory as we age.

A fourth category of cognitive inadequacy is referred to as apraxia and refers to an inability to control and coordinate motor functions even though the motor pathways are intact. (A paralysis or lack of coordination due to a break in a motor pathway or damage to a motor region of the brain would not be considered to be an apraxia just as sensory pathway interruption leading to blindness would not be considered to be an agnosia.)

All four of these major categories (agnosia, aphasia, amnesia, and apraxia) of cognitive dysfunction are often associated with some kind of brain lesion; however, unlike blindness and paralysis, the emphasis in this category is on the associative regions of the brain rather than on the primary sensory or motor areas. The exact neurological manifestation of each dysfunction is often subtle and complex. Agnosic patients may have perfectly good visual capabilities in some contexts (e.g., reading) although fail miserably in others (e.g., face recognition). Aphasic patients may exhibit equally specialized failures of language; for example, an aphasic may be able to appropriately manipulate objects (e.g., a shovel) but not to name the object. Amnesiacs may have selective loss of short- or long-term memory. Apraxia patients may exhibit equally specialized disorders, usually involved with skilled motions. For example, an apraxic may be unable to ride a bicycle or tie a shoelace even though there is no overall impairment of motor function inhibiting the use of their hands or legs in other tasks.

A major diagnostic characteristic of all agnosias, aphasias, amnesias and apraxias is their selectivity. The particular cognitive defect is typically quite specific and related cognitive capabilities may be unaffected to the limits of clinical observation. For this reason, each of four major categories of mental dysfunction has traditionally been separated into a cluster of narrowly defined, but related, subcategories. This leads to a very large number of these cognitive dysfunctions. Three important lists of these subcategories are of special interest. Nielsen (1936), Dubin (2008), and the anonymous authors of the internet encyclopedia (Wikipedia, 2008) have all provided long lists of specialized cognitive dysfunctions, many of which fall into one of another of these four basic categories and each of will be discussed in later parts of this chapter. Several important points should be made clear, however, at the outset of this discussion.

First, the various cognitive defects are very poorly defined; it is difficult to discriminate among some of the inabilities tabulated here. Few of them are so pure or clear cut that they do not overlap with some of the others. This, as I have noted several times previously, is a general problem faced whenever psychological processes are investigated—the ambiguity of the mental terminology and the overlap of specific items. In this case, the implications of this overlap, however, are especially serious. An initial impression is that this whole system of listing and classifying these dysfunctional processes is exceedingly arbitrary. Their very numerousness makes the whole enterprise of using them as specific diagnostic categories questionable. Nowhere, was this made clearer than in Nielsen's (1936) classic work on the topic. This book listed 87 different diagnostic categories on pages 258-271. In this list, Nielsen mentioned 16 different kinds of visual agnosias. This gives us an idea of the nomenclatural and taxonomic difficulty in this field. Furthermore, he then went on to add to the diagnostic confusion by offering an alternative list on pages 271-274 consisting of approximately 60 categories organized in a totally different way. Obviously the diagnostic precision that these categories purport to offer is much less than the reality. Even more unrealistic would be any effort to attribute any meaning to the neural implications of such a diagnostic muddle.

The problem is exacerbated by the multiple ways in which the nomenclatures of these dysfunctions are used. Nielsen (1936) makes the case that there are three ways in which meaning may be attached to a term such as Broca's aphasia. First, it may be used in a neuroanatomical sense to describe a region of the brain where damage is purported to lead to a particular behavioral dysfunction; a point of view that, as should be clear by now to my readers, is a highly questionable procedure. Second, it may be used as a name for a generalized but unspecified physiological disorder of the brain—a nearly useless truism comparable to the definition of and probably unobservable "minimal brain dysfunction." Third, it may be used as a purely psychological concept describing the dysfunction. It is only the last of these three possibilities to which any clinical utility can be attached.

The next issue challenging the utility of these terms in defining neurological entities concerns the less well appreciated ambiguity of the neural lesions themselves. Damage to the brain, particularly concerning the human ability to speak and to comprehend speech, is rarely associated with damage to well-demarcated regions. Individual differences are substantial and even the most precise experimental lesion induced in a laboratory animal may be inadequate to establish the actual extent of damage.

The imprecision in defining the extent of laboratory lesions, much less the uncontrolled size and extent of a traumatic brain injury, has been well known for years, even in some of the iconic cases of brain injury that led to the early observations of Broca's and Wernicke's aphasias. Although these forms of aphasia are often attributed to two different specialized regions of the brain, respectively, there is ample reason to suspect that the neural representation of speech is not that simple. Many modern scholars including Penfield and Roberts (1978), Lennenberg (1974), and Damasio (1991) have all implicated other areas of the brain. Lennenberg, for example, noted that:

> ...there do not seem to be any sharply delimited or structurally well defined areas that are alone responsible for the appearance of critical specific clinical language deficits....In other words, there are gradients of probability for the occurrence of a symptom complex that may appear in connection with a lesion for a given area. (p. 524)

It should not be forgotten that even in the first reports by Broca, the involvement of other regions beyond that of "his" area was accepted doctrine. Not even the great neuroanatomist himself believed that there was a specific place in the brain that uniquely accounted for aphasia. Nevertheless, the idea of specific localization of cognitive processes remains widely accepted in contemporary neuroscience theories of aphasia.

In the past, the most compelling evidence for the association between a particular brain region and a particular human cognitive capability has come from studies in which the behavior of an individual is directly compared with anatomic evidence of brain damage. Traditionally, this had always been a matter of postmortem examinations; however, with the arrival of brain imaging devices, these comparisons can be made on the living and relatively intact human beings. Reports discussing the relationship between various kinds of behavioral dysfunctions and brain imaging are now increasingly becoming available. In the following paragraphs I have selected a couple of samples from each domain (agnosia, aphasia, amnesia and apraxia) as representatives of the kind of neuroscientific findings that are now beginning to appear in the literature pertaining to this class of cognitive dysfunctions.

In preview, it is important to note that there is very little evidence associating a particular dysfunction with a specific brain region even with the new addition of these remarkable brain imaging devices. There are many reasons for this lack of support for localized representation of these subtle cognitive disorders.

First, there are so many different types of closely related dysfunctions and the symptoms are so often idiosyncratic that experiments infrequently deal with exactly the same phenomenon. Exact replications are, therefore, unusual.

Second, the results obtained in experiments that are purported to be the same are, in fact, very variable in terms of the implicated brain regions. For example, the traditional allocation of the face recognition mechanism to the right hemisphere's FFA (Fusiform Face Area) and IOF (Inferior Occipital Gyrus) regions are frequently contraindicated as other brain regions on both the ipsilateral and contralateral sides of the brain are found to be associated with this apperceptive defect.

Third, a surprising amount of the discussion of cognitive dysfunctions and brain lesions is based on unique case studies. This is epitomized by the repeated occurrence of one particular patient know as DF in the literature. This is not at all surprising given that archetypical cases of agnosia or aphasia cases are relatively rare.

Fourth, it is well known that recovery of function often occurs. Therefore, there may be MRI signs of abnormal brain activity in the absence of any abnormal agnosia and vice versa.

Fifth, the actual impairment may be below the threshold of observation of brain imaging devices. In such a situation, a subtle brain malfunction might well go unnoticed. A substantial portion of the published literature alludes to the absence of any observable brain anomalies, either structural or functional, even when severe behavioral anomalies are presented.

Sixth, the diagnosis of one form of visual agnosia may be conflated with another. For example, form and color aspects of a stimulus may interact in such a way that color processing inhibits form recognition, an interaction noted by Steeves, Humphrey, Culham, Menon, and Goodale (2002). The behavioral dysfunctions are rarely as pure as we would like them to be for the purposes of our experiments. Language difficulties are especially prone to this interaction; an inability to comprehend a word may be the result of any number of different processes combined in complex and unknown ways. Words may be understood when presented visually but not aurally, and vice versa. Furthermore, some dysfunctions are linked to what otherwise may seem to be unrelated phenomena; for example, Broca's aphasia is often associated with right arm weaknesses (Hillis, 2007) possibly because of adjacent motor and speech regions.

Seventh, there is a strong influence of scientific culture at work that tends to modify our interpretations of empirical results. A pioneering experiment in which a particular brain region had been associated with a specific behavioral deficit may set the stage for the preponderance of future studies. Other involved areas may be ignored simply because of the aura provided by the initial study. The attribution of failures to recognize faces to the ventral occipito-temporal regions on the right side of the brain by Damasio, Damasio, and Van Hoesen (1982) may be an example of the conceptual impact of a dramatic and compelling early seminal study.[5] Most of the experiments that followed constrained their research to this general area. It is likely that much has been overlooked concerning the role of other areas in prosopagnosia.

Eighth, many of the results reported show that there is no association between cognitively specific dysfunctions and the brain regions usually associated with them. Behrman and Avidan (2005), for example, found that people suffering from congenital prosopagnosia exhibited "…normal BOLD activation of the fusiform face area and other ventral cortical structures…" (p. 186). This negative finding, and other similar ones, raises serious doubt about the techniques we are now using to explore the relationship between localized macroscopic brain areas and perceptual dysfunctions.

Ninth, it is not always possible to distinguish the overt effects of a measurable brain lesion from the more subtle effect of a psychiatric or covert neurochemical problem. Although the symptoms may be the same, there are always many possible explanations for the same behavioral anomaly. Some of these are macroscopic; some are microscopic. Damage to a particular brain region may produce an agnosia that is indistinguishable from one whose origins are due to an immeasurable information transaction far below our ability to measure.

Tenth, as I have discussed several times previously, the extent of a brain lesion in even the best controlled experiments is rarely precise enough to demarcate a unique region and, therefore, to associate it with a particular cognitive symptom. The simple extension of the size of a lesion may change the nature of the cognitive deficit in substantial ways. As Hillis (2007) pointed out, this is a complication of even the best known of the auditory cognitive deficits—Broca's syndrome—which may change from a "high level" cognitive process to a "simpler" motor apraxia as the extent of a lesion varies. In such a dynamic context (not to mention the perennial problem of recovery of function) any attempt to make a unique association between a given brain region and a specific behavioral dysfunction becomes untenable.

Eleventh, like all other problems in cognitive psychology, the symptoms, diagnoses, and experimental findings are all phrased in a very imprecise language. We have no precise definitions of many of the key terms. This imprecision characterizes not only the extent of the activations displayed in a brain image (a factor we know that depends on the arbitrary threshold of activation as well as the task difficulty according to Fridiksson and Morrow, 2005) but also on the measurements we make of the cognitive dysfunctions themselves.

To sum up these arguments, the empirical results obtained so far in this application of brain imaging devices to the study of cognitive processes are far below the quality needed to support the specific ideas of either specific localization of any of these cognitive processing deficits or the general idea that the brain is organized as a modular patchwork of quasi-independent skills.

The result of these technical, biological, and linguistic difficulties is that virtually all researchers in the field agree that identifying the brain correlates of these cognitive dysfunctions remains an unsolved problem.

1. Agnosia

Agnosia comes in many different kinds. The following list tabulates the currently identified major conditions.

- Visual Agnosias
  - ◊ Form agnosia: Inability to perceive whole objects, only parts or details.
  - ◊ Associative agnosia: Inability to recognize visual scenes and objects even though they can describe or even draw them.
  - ◊ Apperceptive agnosia: Inability to distinguish visual shapes and discriminate between different visual stimuli.
  - ◊ Mirror agnosia: Inability to recognize objects or activity on either their left or right field of view.
  - ◊ Color agnosia: Inability to recognize colors without a known deficiency in color vision.
  - ◊ Prosopagnosia: Inability to recognize familiar faces, including one's own.
  - ◊ Expressive agnosia: Inability to perceive people's moods from their facial expressions.

◊   Alexia: Inability to read written or printed matter. (A more general term is dyslexia which refers to the inability to properly read or write.)

◊   Anomia: Inability to name objects.

- Auditory Agnosias

◊   Verbal auditory agnosia: Inability to process word meanings.

◊   Receptive amusia: Inability to recognize musical notes, rhythms, and intervals.

◊   Phonagnosia: Inability to recognize familiar voices, even though the words may be understood.

- Somatosensory Agnosias

◊   Astereognosia or tactile agnosia: Inability to recognize objects by touch based on its texture, size and weight.

◊   Pain agnosia: Inability to recognize and process pain.

◊   Finger agnosia: Inability to distinguish the fingers on the hand.

Visual Agnosia: With these caveats in mind and at least a mini-taxonomy in hand of the main types, let's consider some of the specific research forthcoming from the application of fMRI techniques to the complex task of finding brain correlate of cognitive dysfunction. It is a widely accepted idea in cognitive neuroscientific circles dealing with visual agnosias that there are several main regions (the Fusiform Face Area—FFA, the Inferior Occipital Gyrus—IOF, and the Anterior Inferotemporal Cortex—AIT) on the right side of the brain involved in face recognition (Kanwisher, McDermott, and Chun, 1977). Although some researchers have pointed to dysfunction in one or more of these areas as the correlate of prosopagnosia (for example, see the work of Kriegeskorte, Formisana, Sorger, and Goebel, 2007; Bentin, DeGutis, D'Esposito, and Robertson, 2007), a number of fMRI studies, including one by Avidan, Hasson, Malach, and Behrman (2005) have found normal activation levels in these areas even though some patients were severely visually agnosic. In other cases, the neurological anomaly was the absence of a response in the targeted area when faces and non-face objects were compared, another confounding property of the FFA that had been observed earlier by Kanwisher, McDermott, and Chun (1997). Thus, the evidence associating gross morphological and functional neuropathology with face recognition deficits remains equivocal.

A more balanced approach, it seems to me, is to contend that none of these areas is uniquely responsible, i.e., sufficient, for face recognition. Instead, it has been proposed by Rossion, Caldara, Seghier, Schuller, Lazeyras, and Mayer (2003) and Hadjikhani and de Gelder (2002) that the FFA, IOF, and AIT regions, probably in conjunction with other brain areas involved in the acquisition of the visual input, must act as a coordinated system to account for normal face recognition.

Auditory Agnosia: The cognitive deficit we call auditory word agnosia is known in an even smaller population of patients but with a greater range of behavioral deficits. It is defined as an inability to understand the meaning of language even though speech sounds are heard normally. The key indication of auditory agnosia is that other language abilities are relatively unaffected. The brain mechanisms accounting for this deficit are also uncertain. Often no gross differences between normal and auditory agnosic patients can be observed in fMRI recordings (Kaufer, Nuwer, and Benson, 1995). In other experiments surprising and unexpected results have been obtained. For example, Bergerbest, Ghahremani, and Gabrieli (2004), reported that auditory repetition priming (a behavioral test of the ability of patients to respond more effectively to repeated acoustic stimuli than to single presentations) changed activity in the auditory as well as visual and multimodal regions of the brain.

Other investigators have associated quite different brain regions with agnosias. Thierry and Price (2006), for example, link both visual and auditory agnosias for words and attribute the defect to both the middle and superior portions of the temporal cortex, outside of both the primary and auditory regions. Engelien, Stern, and Silbersweig (2001) invoke the frontal regions as well as the temporal regions usually identified with auditory agnosia. Wise (2003), furthermore, adds the basal ganglia and the thalamus to the possible regions directly involved in language understanding and production.

All of these data are a far cry from the simple model of attributing auditory agnosias exclusively to Broca's and Wernicke's area, a hypothesis that dominated thinking in previous years. This new view also speaks to two important general points: (1) cognitive processes are not the result of unique localized regions and (2) the brain operates as a distributed network of interacting regions, all of which must be intact for cognitive processes to function normally.

There are many problems associated with the diagnosis and treatment of auditory, as well as other sensory, agnosias. I have already alluded to the problem of distinguishing between an identifiable brain lesion and what would be referred to in another context as a psychiatric problem. Such high-level and vaguely defined cognitive processes as "uncontrolled" or "uncontrollable allocation of attention" may also simulate agnosic disorders. Speech disorders are particularly susceptible to this difficulty. Thus, it is often difficult to distinguish between deficits attributable to the physical attributes of a stimulus and the semantics of the communication. Undoubtedly, several interacting processes and mechanisms are involved in the reception and interpretation of any kind of sound, whether it is music or speech. In general, it is considered to be more difficult to determine the primary cause of an auditory agnosia than a visual one.

2. Aphasia

This brings us to the equally vague concept of aphasia.[6] Aphasia is defined as the inability to communicate with spoken or written language. This overly broad term embraces a wide variety of different functional causes and effects and, like many other of the cognitive deficits discussed in this chapter, remains elusive both of precise description and of association with particular brain regions. The following list is a tabulation of the major forms of aphasia now being diagnosed.

APHASIAS[7]
- Global Aphasia: A generalized inability to understand or create language. May be expressed as a combination of Wernicke's and Broca's aphasic symptoms.
- Broca's Aphasia or Alalia: Inability to produce coherent language even though it can be understood. May be characterized by repetition, and/or meaningless babbling. (Also known as aphonia.)
- Wernicke's Aphasia: Inability to understand language either in sentences or in individual words even though it can be produced. (Otherwise known as "auditory agnosia.")
- Aprosodia: Inability to vary speech rhythm or tone.
- Dyslogia: Difficulty in expressing ideas even though one can speak.
- Anomic Aphasia: Inability to name objects that can be discriminated and otherwise perceived.

Cognitive neuroscientists are beginning to realize that the terms "speech" and "language" are actually composites of a number of motor and ideational processes that are exceedingly difficult to parse into smaller units; as a result, no good taxonomy of aphasias exists, just tabulated lists of the kind shown previously. The varying disorders exhibited by patients who have had strokes of injuries to the "speech" regions makes it even more difficult to carry out research on this complex cognitive and neurological topic.

Broca's aphasia, the generic term for the inability to produce coherent speech, has long been associated with damage to the region known as Broca's area—a more or less vaguely defined region of the left inferior frontal region of the brain. It differs in this regard from damage to Wernicke's area, usually located at the posterior portion of the left temporal lobe, which is more typically involved in the comprehension rather than the production of language. However, the two regions are directly connected by a band of nerve fibers known as the arcuate fasciculus. It is apparently this connection that leads to their interaction and confusion over what is a production aphasia and what is a comprehension agnosia. Damage anywhere along this tract can itself produce dramatic changes in speech production and comprehension suggesting a complex interaction of at least these parts of the brain during normal language behavior. Furthermore, as Wise (2003) has noted, the more cognitive a process, the more broadly distributed it is in the brain. Semantic comprehension, for example, seems to have its neural correlates widespread throughout the temporal, frontal, and parietal lobes.

As Bookheimer (2002) has so cogently pointed out, the traditional association of Broca's area with aphasia has largely been based on a long history of research and therapy that associated macroscopic regional associations with the inadequately defined behavioral symptoms. Thus, extreme theories of localization (e.g., the suggestion that "language production" is represented in Broca's area) have tended to characterize the main stream of thought about aphasia. In its place, Bookheimer proposes that the system is much more complex. She says:

> In particular, it is apparent that large-module [i.e., a module such as Broca's area] theories are clearly incorrect; rather, the language system is organized into a large number of relatively small but tightly clustered and interconnected modules with unique contributions to language processing. There is increasing evidence that language regions in the brain—even classic Broca's area—are not specific to language, but rather involve more reductionist processes that give rise to language as well as nonlinguistic functions. Finally, functional imaging has indicated far greater involvement of the right hemisphere in some aspects of language processing than previously appreciated. (p. 153)

This modern approach is a major conceptual step forward and strongly supports the idea that the functions of the brain are far better conceptualized from the perspective of a distributed neural system than from that of localized and function specific regions associated with modular cognitive processes. Indeed, Bookheimer argues that Broca's area has far more general functions than just speech and may act in a coordinated fashion with other brain regions to deal with semantic processes in general and not just those involved in spoken utterance. No longer is it sufficient to look upon the left hemisphere's Broca's area as a unitary system accounting for spoken language. Instead it must be considered to be a part of a complex system involving many distributed parts of the brain. Where Bookheimer diverges from a pure distributed neural systems approach is her continued dependence on very small, highly specialized modules for which there is little evidence. In point of fact, a system of such small and specialized modules would be very difficult to distinguish from a purely distributed system.

Unfortunately, Bookheimer's analysis seems to have gone mainly unappreciated and much is still being done and taught based on the traditional concept that Broca's area is the unique and specific area for language production. Part of this is due to the perseveration on the classic role of Broca's area; however, part of it due to the usual difficulty introduced by poorly defined neuroreductionist mechanisms and mentalist concepts and the increasing complexity of both the data and the interpretations as cognitive neuroscientists delve deeper into the mysteries of the mind-brain.

A further complication facing any research on aphasia, which should be noted once again, is the well-documented ability of the brain to recover some of its linguistic functions following cerebral trauma or stroke. Behaviorally there is no question that recovery of both speech production and comprehension abilities occurs over months and years for many patients. However, several investigators have pointed out the many unknowns involved in this process. For example, Crinion and Price (2005) stated flatly that the "neural basis of speech recovery following stroke remains unknown" (p. 2858). Beyond the fact that the normal left hemisphere speech regions seem to be able to recover from small lesions by expanding into areas not previously involved in language skills and the fact that the right hemisphere seems to be recruited when the lesions are large (Marsh and Hillis, 2006), recovery of function remains a mysterious process.[8] Much of what constitutes the neural basis of functional recovery must certainly occur at the level of microscopic neuronal network processes that are far below the threshold of measurement of an fMRI machine.

Further generalizations about recovery of function have been drawn by a number of investigators. Cao, Vikingstad, Paige-George, Johnson, and Welch (1999), for example, used fMRI techniques to show that recovery was better in those patients who "repaired" or reorganized a damaged left hemisphere than in those that had to recruit right hemisphere substitutions. A curious difference in the timing, however, was reported by Fernandez, Cardebat, Demonet, Joseph, Mazaux, Barat and Allard (2004), who showed that recovery seemed to occur in the contralateral (right) hemisphere long before the left hemisphere recovery occurred—a month compared to as much as a year.

3. Amnesia

Each and every one of the cognitive deficits I discuss in this section is beset with its own as well as common problems. Amnesia—abnormal forgetting—is especially complex because it, even more than any of the other cognitive deficits discussed here, can occur in the absence of any measurable neurological problem.

That is, loss of memory may be due to the nature of our thoughts as well as damage to our brains.[9] Psychogenic, functional, or dissociative amnesia, as these psychologically generated amnesias are variously called, can result from logical or emotional causes that are so complex that we are probably never going to be able to determine their microscopic neural parallels. This is not to say that they are not neurological in some fundamental sense but rather that they are the results of unidentified informational manipulations that are not only currently unidentified but also beyond our scientific measurement abilities in the foreseeable future.

The psychogenic sources of true amnesia are not the only way that forgetfulness may be exhibited in the courtroom. Amnesia may also be due to feigning or deliberate dissembling to avoid blame or the consequences of a criminal action. Some of these deceptive practices may, therefore, be totally conscious whereas other forms of forgetfulness are oblivious to the individual. In the courtroom, deliberate forgetfulness and the normal logical restructuring of our memories merge into each other and function as serious impediments to the progress of justice.

A particular problem with amnesia is referred to as confabulation. This is the process of filling in the holes in an incomplete memory. For example, a person with a selective memory loss may be able to recall the events surrounding and following some incident; the problem is that they may falsely fill in the forgotten gaps with invalid reconstructions based on logical plausibility or to meet some vested interest on their part. In the courtroom, this may lead to inaccurate testimony even though the amnesiac fully believes that a truthful account is being given about an incident. Such flawed testimony would be much harder to identify than the complete amnesia for all of the events in an accident.

This section will deal with both kind of amnesias, those that have been suggested to have identified neurological sources as well as the psychogenic ones that are more likely to be the result of defensive, emotional, or similar nonorganic causes. The first kind includes those amnesias that are responses to injury, disease, or drugs. The second kind includes those for which there is no known or detectable organic cause. Of course, since the list that I provide here is based in large part on the symptoms, it is not always clear into which category a particular syndrome should be placed. The following lists are certainly not mutually exclusive and can hardly be considered to be inclusive, given the variety of reported overlapping and redundant memory dysfunctions. The tabulation presented here is further complicated because some conditions are defined in terms of their instigating cause whereas others are defined by their observed symptoms.

Amnesias attributable to organic causes come in many types, both generalized and specific. A list of the various types (collected from a number of different sources) is presented in the following list and includes the following syndromes.

- Anterograde amnesia: Inability to recall events that just happened for more than a short time—the period of short-term memory. Anterograde memory is demarcated from retrograde memory by the moment of the instigating episode or injury. Anterograde amnesia is a failure to remember things and events occurring after an injury.
- Retrograde amnesia: Inability to recall events that occurred prior to an instigating incident.
- Transient anterograde amnesia: A brief period of anterograde amnesia that is a common compliant after single episodes of overindulging in alcoholic beverages.
- Transient global amnesia: A combination of retrograde and anterograde amnesias that may last for a relatively short period of time. It is often attributed to short-term reduced blood flow to the brain, especially in elderly patients.
- Traumatic amnesia: Amnesia that may be exhibited in many different forms due to head injuries.
- Korsakoff syndrome: Amnesia associated with cognitive confusion (separately referred to as Wernicke's Syndrome). Korsakoff's syndrome is often a result of long-term alcoholism. The amnesia is usually characterized by an inability to remember logically coherent sequences such as a short story. Short-term memory may be relatively normal.

In addition, identified forms of amnesia have been observed for which there is no obvious organic cause but seem to be mainly psychogenic. They are included in the following list.

- Posthypnotic amnesia: Inability to remember events that may have occurred or that were instructed to be forgotten during a hypnotic session.
- Fugue amnesia: Inability to remember a single event due to its strong emotional or traumatic overtones. Typically recovers in a few days. Also known as lacunar amnesia.
- Source amnesia: Inability to know how or where an experience occurred.
- Distrust amnesia: Distrust of one's own memory. Both source and distrust amnesia may be coupled together into a single syndrome.
- Dissociative amnesias: Failures of memory due to psychological factors
- Auditory amnesia: Inability to remember sounds.
- Verbal amnesia: Inability to remember written or spoken words.

The situation is even further complicated by the fact that there are many diseases or injuries not initiated in the brain that can result in amnesias. Although they presumably all work on the brain—the organ of all of our memories or thoughts—amnesia may be caused by ailments affecting virtually any other organ systems of the body. Amnesias may also be indistinguishable from aphasias or agnosias (or vice versa). There is often little functional difference in a failure to recognize an object's use and a failure in memory.

Another persistent problem confronting any such tabulation of amnesias is that there are many steps in the process of memorizing (recording information) or remembering (retrieval or recall from stored knowledge). Any one of the steps can produce indistinguishable behaviors from the point of view of the neuropsychological investigator. The possibility that failures in memory can be due to organic or functional causes makes the study of amnesia a particularly fuzzy topic for the neuropsychologist.[10] Perhaps, it is, in part, for this reason that it has played such a role in our popular literature and movies, hundreds of which have played out the theme of some kind of forgetting.

Furthermore, the concept of memory is not a simple one. Psychologists have described many types of memory that may be selectively manipulated in their purely cognitive experiments. For example, Tulving (1972) suggests one taxonomy of memory which includes such varied memorial skills as:

- Declarative memory which consists of memories we can talk about (i.e., declare). It consists of two subtypes:
  ◊ Episodic memory: Memories of special events specific to our individual past experiences.
  ◊ Semantic memory: General knowledge of the world that is not a part of our personal experience.
- Sensory memory: Very short-term memory of sounds or pictures briefly exposed to our sense organs.
- Procedural memory: Learned skills and patterns of movements.
- Priming: The effect of a previously presented stimulus to enhance or inhibit the recall of a memory.

The picture is even further complicated by the variety of methods that can be used to test our memories:

- Recall: The participant in a memory experiment is asked to retrieve a memorized item without cues of any kind.
- Recognition: The participant in a memory experiment is asked to say whether or not certain information has been presented previously or not.

- Reconstruction: The participant in an experiment is asked to reconstruct an object or cognitive structure from a set of parts or ideational components.

Obviously, there is a continuing difficulty in structuring memory tests to diagnose the various kinds of amnesias given the multidimensional nature of this class of cognitive task. Furthermore, given the idiosyncratic neurological evidence associated with amnesia, the confusion of organic and psychogenic causes, and a lack of replicability, the tale now to be told is neither complete nor straightforward. As with any other neuropsychological reductionism, the complete details of how the brain acquires, encodes, and retrieves experience are not yet fully known, a fact that is fully acknowledged by virtually all neuropsychologists working in this complex field.

The story being told here is that the parts of the brain that are involved in storing and retrieving information are numerous and complexly interconnected. On the one hand, specific regions of the brain have been associated with the process of storing information about our experiences in the brain.

On the other hand, we have absolutely no information where or how memories are stored in this remarkable organ. This is the often posed as the classic "engram problem," originally posed by Semon (1921) and further elaborated in one of the classic studies of human memory of the 1920s and 1930s reported by Lashley (1950).[11] What we do now know is that the active process of storing and recalling memories, wherever and however they are stored, has been closely associated with the structures of the medial temporal lobe. In particular a collection of nuclei and regions located in this general region seems to be necessary for the acquisition and retrieval of declarative memories. These temporal regions include the hippocampus, the entorhinal, perirhinal, and parahippocampal cortices but also distant portions of the frontal and parietal cortices of the brain. The degree of a memory deficit is closely related to the size of the lesions in the medial temporal lobe—a result at least partially in agreement with Lashley's earlier conclusions. An excellent review of current views of the relationship between medial temporal lobe regions and function and declarative function can be found in Squire, Stark, and Clark (2004). Suffice it to say, that the problem of this region's role in memory is complex and controversial.

Some other investigators believe that the memory deficits observed are due to the disruption of nerve tracts rather than the cerebral cortical tissue itself. There is also some controversy, according to Squire, Stark, and Clark, concerning the parsing of both function and anatomy into meaningful modules. They ask—do the anatomically defined subregions of the medial temporal cortex have equally distinct functions in the memorization process?

In a recent report Malin and McGaugh (2006) summarized their view of the current theoretical situation by noting that three different brain regions seem to be associated with three different kinds of memory storage. The hippocampus seems to be a major player in the consolidation of memories for tasks that require "learning of contextual cues." The rostral anterior cingulate cortex, on the other hand, seems to play the same role for other kinds of stimuli, specifically those involving "painful stimulation." Portions of the amygdala, Malin and McGaugh further suggest, are responsible for storing memories for emotionally arousing experiences. It is important to reiterate that this trichotomy is only concerned with the process of storing different kinds of memories and not with the location or nature of how the memories are stored.

The bottom neurological line for long-term declarative memory is that, like any other cognitive process we have considered so far, the storage system itself is most probably widely distributed across and within the brain.[12] This does not mean that all of the amnesias have a common source, but rather that different regions of the brain can differentially modulate several different aspects of what is obviously a complex collection of behavioral symptoms. Combined with the multiple dimensions and parameters of the behavioral deficits we call "amnesias," it is not too surprising that we have not yet achieved a complete understanding of how brain dysfunction leads to memory disorders. Many investigators in the field now appreciate that much of the traditional knowledge of localized brain dysfunction in the aphasias is obsolescent. Much is yet to be learned, however, and distributed (as opposed to localized) storage seems to be an increasingly likely alternative.

All of this uncertainty raises very difficult problems in the courtroom for patients who have suffered head injuries and are involved in legislation for damages. First, there is often no specific brain injury that can be uniquely and exclusively associated with a particular form of amnesia. Second, amnesias often spontaneously resolve themselves totally or in part. Third, evidence of organic damage may be elusive and specific damage, in particular, especially elusive. Fourth, claimants may themselves have poor recollection of an accident as well as exhibit generalized confusion at the time of a trial. The resulting inability to serve as a witness for one's self may imperil an otherwise clear cut case for damages. Fifth, given that the "damage" claimed is a behavioral problem, it is possible to simulate memory deficits.

The problem of distinguishing between valid amnesia and malingering has been studied extensively by psychologists. For example, Ferraro, Park, Hage, and Palm (2005) consider how one might distinguish between true memory loss and malingering. They used a priming technique and showed that malingerers were less likely to be influenced by distracting priming than were control groups.

They showed, therefore, that one of the key factors is that many malingerers overstate the memory loss, not appreciating the known limitations of amnesias in general. Ferraro and his colleagues point to the work of Horton, Smith, Barghout, and Connolly (1992) as a source of tests that help to sort malingerers from the true amnesiacs.

4. Apraxia

Apraxias are complex disorders of skilled motor function that cannot be attributed to other causes such as musculo-skeletal lesions. It is usual to distinguish between conceptual errors and production errors in motor skills; that is, between motor dysfunctions due to high level cognitive processes and those due to an actual physical inability to produce the motor movements—the latter being characterized as a paralysis rather than an apraxia. Patients suffering from apraxia may be able to name a tool, report understanding of its function, intend to make the movement, and even make some of the partial responses (such as picking up the tool) in a motor sequence, but finally be unable to carry out the appropriate action with the tool.

The definition of apraxia depends on eliminating alternative explanations of what may at first seem to be bizarre uncoordination or even the complete absence of a particular motor behavioral sequence. Apraxia, in the purest scientific sense, therefore, is as much a disorder of cognitive processing as are any of the sensory or speech disorders previously defined as agnosias or aphasias, respectively. Therefore, these dysfunctions are often exhibited and diagnosed on the basis of the meaningful relationships with objects or tasks, not on the basis of a simple motor incapacity or paralysis.

Because motor behavior requires the integrated interaction of numbers of individual muscles, a simple lack of coordination or a delay in response is not sufficient to make the diagnosis of apraxia nor is a generalized inability to control movements of the limbs or hands. Many other types of motor disorders can occur that are not considered to be apraxias including those due to Parkinson's disease and various kinds of age-related dementias. Instead, the apraxic dysfunction must occur in the presence of otherwise normal motor function. The patient may be perfectly capable of carrying out coordinated tasks such as reaching or stepping, but be incapable of performing a motor task that involves more skilled coordinated movements. Many of the apraxias are highly specific and may involve inabilities such as drawing a picture of an object or even such specific acts as dressing one's self or tying one's shoelaces. Apraxia of eye movement is also known in which the gaze of the patient may be inappropriately directed.

A further complication is that apraxia may be secondary to agnosias of one kind or another; the recognition error of an agnosia may sometimes be confused with a lack of a specific, but relatively complex motor skill. Obviously, under these conditions, the diagnosis of a true cognitive-level apraxia and its assignment to a particular brain region is a difficult and time-consuming medical task. The possibility that sensory and motor deficits and other cognitive processes are simulating motor apraxia must be excluded in making a firm diagnosis. Once such exclusions are made, a diagnosis of apraxia can be considered.

Like any of the other cognitive disorders discussed in this chapter, the possible range of disorders that can be diagnosed as apraxias is very large and very confused. The current typology of apraxias that is now generally accepted is based on a classification system originally proposed by Liepmann (1900). His three categories are presented in the following list.

- Limb-kinetic apraxia: An inability to make skilled movements of the finger, hand, arm, or leg in the absence of any motor paralysis, but with the necessary knowledge of what should be done.
- Ideokinetic apraxia: An inability to make a skilled movement even though the patient reports the intent to do so, especially involving the sequencing of a series of motor actions. A typical symptom would be a failure to imitate a motion performed by another person or to produce a specific motion on command.
- Ideational or conceptual apraxia: An inability to use a tool correctly. May be due to a lack of understanding of the tool's function or an inability to correctly associate the tool with the task.

Other more specific diagnoses must be added to this list.

- Oculomotor apraxia: Inability to appropriately control one's gaze.
- Buccofacial apraxia: An inability to perform organized movements with the lips and tongue seems (for example, whistling).
- Constructional apraxia: The inability to draw or construct and object from a sample in the absence of any physical inability.[13]
- Agraphia: Inability to write.
- Akathisa: Inability to sit still.
- Akinesia: Inability to move.

Although many neurologists assume that apraxias are related to more or less localized brain lesions, the exact brain locations associated with the different kinds of apraxia remain both obscure and controversial. One thing on which most investigators agree is that the cause of an apraxia should not be sought in the primary motor area of the brain. Rather it is generally agreed to be a higher order integrative or associative process mediated by widely distributed brain regions, mainly on the left side of the brain, but less frequently occurring in the right hemisphere and sometimes bilaterally. The regions that have been associated with apraxia include (but are not limited to) the inferior parietal, supplementary motor regions, and, for mysterious and especially poorly understood reasons, the corpus callosum. Other reviewers such as Leiguarda and Marsden (2000) emphasize defects occurring in the interconnections between the parietal and frontal regions. However, they also invoke the temporal, parietal, and frontal lobes as contributing to apraxia.

However, even these general locales do not account for all categories of apraxia. Buccofacial apraxia, for example, has been linked to lesions near Broca's speech region. Zaidikof and Lang (2005) present another theory when they linked the three classic Liepmann syndromes with the following brain areas in their review of the apraxia literature.

- Limb-Kinetic Apraxia: Frontal and parietal lobes or the primary motor cortex.
- Ideomotor Apraxia: Left hemisphere parietal lobes as well as tracts connecting the frontal and parietal lobes. Also involved in some cases are premotor and supplementary motor areas and the basal ganglia and/or the thalamus.
- Ideational Apraxia: This apraxia is associated with damage to many brain regions but may include damage to the interfaces between the parietal and occipital and the parietal and temporal regions as well as the frontal regions.

Other specific factors leading to apraxia or apraxia-like symptoms include Cortico-Basal Degeneration (CBD), a combination of lesions in the cortex and the basal ganglia—a group of nuclei that are heavily connected with both cerebral and brain stem regions. Apraxias of one kind or another can also occur as a symptom in many other diseases that have been associated with specific regions of brain damage. For example, apraxia is a symptom of both Parkinson's and Huntington's diseases, both of which are known to involve basal ganglia degeneration.

Furthermore, it should not be overlooked that although true apraxias are supposed to be associative or cognitive in origin, there are other general neurological lesions that can produce nearly identical symptoms. These may include spinal problems, peripheral motor dysfunctions, damage to underlying tracts, and, arguably, lesions of the primary motor cortex. That an apraxia has a name does not mean that its neurological origins have been established. A search of the literature would undoubtedly show that virtually all regions of the brain have been associated with one or another kind of apraxia.

Finally, it should be noted that although it is rarely mentioned in the literature, apraxias, like the other cognitive deficits being considered in this chapter, could conceivably have a psychogenic origin. The inability to properly use a firearm, for example, could be attributed to the same kind of cognitive post traumatic experience that produced amnesia or agnosia.

Another problem is that some of the apraxias are relatively rare and not all of the observed cases are subject to the postmortem or brain imaging studies necessary to definitely determine where a correlated brain lesion might be located—if it is localized. A further complexity is that some conditions diagnosed as apraxias may actually be due to other cognitive processes; "agnosic" or "amnesic" apraxias are not simple conflations of words but may reflect motor errors that are primarily due to something other than motor-cognitive conditions.

Given that there is often considerable recovery of motor function after injury to the brain, additional uncertainty is inserted into the discussion. Part of this uncertainty may be due to the actual nature of these brain dysfunctions. Rather than being localized or even localizable, they may, in point of empirical fact, be the result of distributed neural mechanisms, some of which are necessary, but not sufficient, and others of which are sufficient to account for these complex symptoms, but not necessary. This opposing point of view suggests that it is possible for a particular behavioral symptom to result from redundant neural causes in ways that cannot be explained in conventional terms.

In addition to the agnosia, amnesias, aphasias, and apraxias, there are a number of other miscellaneous cognitive disorders that seem not to fit into these four categories. These are now listed.

- Dyscalcula: Inability to use mathematics
- Abulia: Inability to make decisions
- Acoria: Inability to feel satiated after eating
- Anosmia: Inability to recognize smells
- Dysmimia: Inability to imitate
- Synethesia: Perception in one domain (e.g., visual color) when stimulated by another (e.g., acoustic stimuli.)
- Time Agnosia: Inability to perceive the passage of time.[14]

Like all of the other cognitive deficits that I have described in this chapter, diagnosis of and the neural pathology associated with such specific and subtle disorders is not a simple or easy judgment. A number of different brain disorders may account for a number of different impairments and different lesions can produce what are virtually indistinguishable diagnoses. Many of the diagnostic decisions are, therefore, somewhat arbitrary, as the ambiguity of the categories used in Liepmann's original tripartite classification scheme suggests.

The result of this confusion of data and associations, of symptoms and lesions, is that, despite the expressed hopes of many researchers in this field, we may not be attacking the problem at the most appropriate level of analysis. The source of the dysfunction might actually be found in the interactions of the relevant microscopic neural networks, a level of analysis not open to us (see Chapter 2). As it stands now, the variability and inconsistency of the data suggest that it may not be a reasonable approach to try to force these ambiguous data onto a theoretical framework based on function of specific regions of the brain.

The main conclusion that is forthcoming from these brief reviews of current thinking concerning these highly specific cognitive deficits is that each of them is the result of the interactive function of a number of different brain regions broadly distributed across the brain. The repeated observation that many different regions of the brain may produce similar behavioral deficits makes it clear that although many areas may be sufficient, none is uniquely necessary. As Hillis (2007) put it in a recent review article:

> ...a given language task depends on a complex set of cognitive processes and representations carried out by an intricate network of neural regions working together. (p. 200)

If this perspective is correct, then we have to acknowledge that little is known about how a dysfunctional brain produces these abnormal mental and behavioral processes. It is certain, therefore, that the inexactness of this science means that its role in the courtroom will always be subject to contentious disagreement. This is not to say that there may be a variety of instances in which the neuroscience will intersect with the law.

The key neuroscientific point here is that these cognitive dysfunctions cannot be used to specify a particular brain lesion just as a particular brain lesion cannot be used to specify a particular behavioral outcome. This is the illogic of "reverse inference" by Poldrack (2006) and others. These are points well-taken and should be a part of the training given to all kinds of neuropsychologists, all too many of which assume that these kinds of inferential leaps are possible.

B. Consciousness and Coma States

There is perhaps no place where the problems generated by the inaccessibility of mind are better illustrated than in the matter of measuring consciousness. The determination of the conscious state of a patient has enormous practical, ethical, and legal implications in today's advanced level of medical care and it regularly becomes a matter of contention in both civil and criminal cases. Indeed, the matter is further complicated by the fact that consciousness is now appreciated not to be a binary state (conscious or unconscious) but to come in degrees and levels. As a result, it is an unfortunate fact that much of the vocabulary used in defining states of consciousness is ambiguous. One of the most difficult to define is the state of unconsciousness we refer to as coma.

Coma states vary from slight disturbances of situational awareness to deeply profound conditions of mental disconnect with the world. We now know that they can be caused by a variety of different insults to the brain. Neonates, by virtue of medical malpractice or due to conditions that were entirely unavoidable, may suffer from birth from an inability to develop normal responsiveness and may appear to be comatose. Illegal as well as legal drug overdoses are another increasingly common cause of coma. Furthermore, automobile accidents take their toll on our consciousness with head injuries resulting in coma more and more often. Medical conditions such as strokes, both hemorrhagic and those due to ischemic occlusion can lead to either highly specific lesions or generalized brain disorders that can produce the comatose state. The swimming pool, a more and more common part of homes especially popular in the southwest, can lead to drowning that even for a short period (approximately 5 minutes) in which oxygen is not getting to the brain can also lead to persistent comas. Aging, unfortunately, accompanied by a general vascular deterioration, can produce coma among our senior citizens.

In this context of brain damage and injury-induced comas that in many cases can be attributed to the negligent or criminal misbehavior of others, the coma has become a major arena of litigation. Because the nature of a comatose state is so difficult to measure, there is ample uncertainty about what might constitute not only causes and effects, but also what would represent appropriate monetary damages. Disputes also can arise over the desirability or necessity of preserving the remnants of life that may be exhibited by a comatose patient. Clearly, the coma state is a highly active area of contention in our courtrooms and it is, therefore, necessary for attorneys to at least understand the basic neuroscientific facts concerning its origins and classifications.

Because we have no way to make direct measures of mental activity, it is necessary to observe a person's motor behavior and neurological signs to gather some indication of their degree of consciousness. The behavioral capacity of a person in a coma may range from an ability to carry out moderately coherent conversation to nothing more than the most automatic of reflexes. However, as I have argued throughout this book, behavior is not always a concomitant or even a satisfactory basis for drawing inferences about consciousness. It is all too easy to mistake an unresponsive person for an unconscious one. For example, the drug curare has been known to act selectively on our musculature (i.e., specifically the neuromuscular junctions) systems of the body since the 1860s (Bernard, 1865). This drug is capable of inducing a profound motor paralysis with only a minimal effect on the sensory systems. Thus, a completely unresponsive patient may be totally aware of incoming visual, auditory, and touch signals. In spite of this knowledge, curare[15] was used early on to control movements during surgery by relaxing muscle activity by at least a few surgeons without any additional anesthetic drugs. Such a procedure was especially reprehensible since the method was considered by some surgeons to be particularly useful in surgery on infants and children.

What terrible pain may have been inflicted on curarized patients was made clear in one of the great personal experiments of medical history. Concerned about the absence of any strong evidence that curare was actually suppressing sensory and mental activities and that it was mistakenly being used from the early 1940s as the sole "anesthesia," a young surgeon—Scott M. Smith—allowed himself to be curarized with no other anesthetic. His personal report (Smith, Brown, Toman, and Goodman, 1947) is extremely important because it was definitive in establishing that mental and sensory experiences continued under total curare-based paralysis. Smith and his colleagues reported the following summary statement after this heroic experiment:

> From the evidence presented, it would appear that curare does not possess central stimulant, depressant, or analgesic properties. In a normal subject not undergoing operation, a dose of d-tubocurarine chloride at least two and a half times that required to cause complete respiratory failure failed to alter the electro-encephalogram or to impair consciousness, memory, or sensorium. (p. 11)

Thus, a person could conceivably be in enormous pain but be unable to communicate in any way the nature of this entirely conscious experience because of the curare-induced paralysis. It is now widely appreciated that curare is solely a muscle relaxant that should be used only in conjunction with a true anesthesia, one that is well documented to also suppress consciousness. Its use alone is totally unacceptable in modern surgical procedures.

Although it is known that some perceptual phenomena are affected by curare, it is now presumed that this is always due to the abnormal condition of feedback signals from the paralyzed motor system (for example, see the classic work by Matin, Picoult, Stevens, Edwards, Young, and MacArthur, 1982, and Matin, Stevens, and Picoult, 1983).[16]

The more general problem confronting the medical and legal systems with regard to coma is that defects in consciousness range from various minor disorientation and momentary failures of memory to conditions that are difficult to distinguish from brain death. Let's begin our analysis by considering some of the problems concerned with the disorders of consciousness we call comas. Unfortunately, a coma is usually defined simply as a prolonged period of unconsciousness, a circular definition that provides little practical help for either the neurological practitioner or the advocate in the courtroom. The problem is a familiar one: having no direct means of measuring consciousness we must use various secondary criteria such as the behavior of patients as well as neurological signs, neither of which are absolute indicators of consciousness.

A continuing problem is that there is no evidence that an unresponsive patient with minimal reflexes may not have some vestige of consciousness. Indeed, some recent research (Owen, Coleman, Boly, Davis, Laureys, and Pickard, 2006)[17] suggests that a patient who was diagnosed as being in a profoundly "vegetative" state[18] produced different fMRI activations when verbally asked to perform two different kinds of activities. When asked to play tennis in her mind, activity in the supplementary motor area was increased. When asked to imagine a tour through her home, on the other hand, activity increased in the parahippocampal gyrus, the posterior parietal and the lateral premotor cortices. If such a report is replicated and a doorway to the "mind" of what otherwise would be a considered a vegetative patient opened, this would be both an astonishing and disturbing development. It would give credence to one of the greatest fears of humans: the fear of being buried alive. In this case, the patient was buried in her own body in what has been referred to as an extreme version of the "locked-in" syndrome. In many cases, the condition permits some access to the patient's consciousness such as eye blinks; in others, such as the study by Owen and his colleagues, the "locked-in" state may be virtually total.[19]

What the "locked-in" state illustrates (if this extreme state actually exists) is the difficulty in associating consciousness with neural or behavioral responsiveness. It seems possible for a person to be conscious and sensing their environment in the throes of the deepest motor paralysis (recall the use of curare). It is only with the most subtle of neurological signals that a person who is profoundly paralyzed can be distinguished from a person who is totally brain dead; and then, as we see shortly, this is also a very difficult decision in many situations.

Table 5.1
The Glasgow Coma Scale

EYE OPENING
None 1 = Even to supra-orbital pressure
To pain 2 = Pain from sternum/limb/supra-orbital pressure
To speech 3 = Non-specific response, not necessarily to command
Spontaneous 4 = Eyes open, not necessarily aware   _____

MOTOR RESPONSE
None 1 = To any pain; limbs remain flaccid
Extension 2 = Shoulder adducted and shoulder and forearm internally rotated
Flexor response 3 = Withdrawal response or assumption of hemiplegic posture
Withdrawal 4 = Arm withdraws to pain, shoulder abducts
Localizes pain 5 = Arm attempts to remove supra-orbital/chest pressure
Obeys commands 6 = Follows simple commands   _____

VERBAL RESPONSE
None 1 = No verbalization of any type
Incomprehensible 2 = Moans/groans, no speech
Inappropriate 3 = Intelligible, no sustained sentences
Confused 4 = Converses but confused, disoriented
Oriented 5 = Converses and oriented   _____

TOTAL (3–15):   _____

Table 5.2
A Simple Coma Scale

1= fully awake
2= conscious but drowsy
3= unconscious but responsive to pain with purposeful movement e.g. flexion/withdrawal
4= unconscious but responding to pain by extension
5= unconscious and unresponsive to pain

For all practical, empirical, and theoretical purposes, there is no way to avoid this limitation on our knowledge of another person's mind. All of our judgments about the degree to which a person's mind is active must depend on inferences from behavior. In the final analysis, not even neurological responses obtained with an EEG or an fMRI are unambiguous. As a result, the criteria for diagnosing levels of coma vary considerably and contentiously. For example, the Glasgow Coma Scale, developed by Teasdale and Jennett (1974), shown in Table 5.1, rates the depth of a patient's coma on a purely behavioral scale that varies in scores from 3 to 15 based on the presence or absence of certain key responses.

Other scales have been proposed and used over the years. Among the most widely used attempts to indicate the depth of a coma is the eight-level Rancho Los Amigos Scale.[20] It is characterized not only by much more specific behavioral tests (for example, "purposeful attempts to remove restraints") but also many more of them.

On the other hand, simple and much less quantitative behavioral scales are also available such as the one shown in Table 5.2.

Neurologists now distinguish between four closely related conditions—coma, persistent vegetative state (PVS), minimally conscious state (MCS), and the "locked-in" syndrome. Although these four conditions are similar in some aspects, they do have quite different prognoses and it is, therefore, useful to distinguish between the various conditions. An important tabulation of the clinical features of each of these four conditions has been presented by Giacino, Ashwal, Childs, Cranford, Jennett, Katz, Kelly, Rosenberg, Whyte, Zafonte, and Zasler (2002). Their behavioral criteria for distinguishing between the four categories are tabulated in Table 5.3.

Clearly, all of the scales and criteria I have discussed here leave a great deal of latitude for the individual neurologist's judgment, latitude that is broadened by the many possible dimensions of the many behavior and neurological signs that can reasonably be used to estimate the depth of a coma. Obviously, these diagnostic scales are subject to overlap and idiosyncratic patterns of response; the fact that numbers are assigned should not distract us from appreciating that they are really quite arbitrary and qualitative. The judgment of the clinician who applies the tests, within wide bounds, may be more important than the actual numbers generated by these diagnostic tests. The arbitrariness involved in the diagnoses and ultimately the treatment of MCS and the other closely related cognitive disorders was summed up by Giacino and his colleagues (2002) when they said:

There were insufficient data to establish evidence-based guidelines for diagnosis, prognosis and management of MCS. Therefore, a consensus-based case definition with behavioral referenced diagnostic criteria was formulated to facilitate future empirical investigations. (p. 349)

Table 5.3

Comparison of clinical features associated with coma, vegetative state, minimally conscious state, and locked-in syndrome. From Giacino et al. (2002).

Condition	Consciousness	Sleep/wake	Motor Function	Auditory Function	Visual Function	Communication	Emotion
Coma	None	Absent	Reflex and postural responses only	None	None	None	None
Vegetative State	None	Present	Postures or withdraws to noxious stimuli	Startle	Startle	None	None
			Occasional nonpurposeful movement	Brief orienting to sound	Brief visual fixation		Reflexive crying or smiling
Minimally conscious state	Partial	Present	Localizes noxious stimuli	Localizes sound location	Sustained visual fixation	Contingent vocalization	Contingent smiling or crying
			Reaches for Objects	Inconsistent command following	Sustained visual pursuit	Inconsistent but intelligible verbalization or gesture	
			Holds or touches objects in a manner that accommodates size and shape				
			Automatic movements (e.g., scratching)				
Locked-in syndrome	Full	Present	Quadriplegic	Preserved	Preserved	Aphonic/ Anarthric	Preserved
						Vertical eye movement and blinking usually intact	

This summary is equally valid for all of the other related conditions. For plaintiffs and their families, the legal complications in the courtroom of the absence of any objective indicators of coma may seem as devastating as the mental damage itself. Because of the vagueness of the diagnoses of coma, it often becomes a matter of dueling opinions and an attorney's advocacy rather than the scientific merits of the patient's condition. Unfortunately, serious brain dysfunction may be totally invisible to any of the instruments used by neurologists. On the other hand, some people do remarkably well with very serious damage to their brains.[21]

A further complication for any legal claim is that a coma may not be permanent; it may vary over time with some cases progressively worsening and others improving. The most salient issue, of course, for lawyers is the determination of damages (which may be very large considering the long periods of care often required) for a person in a coma when it is due to the fault of another.

C. Brain Death

The tangled difficulty of defining coma, minimally conscious, vegetative, and the "locked-in" states merge at the upper end with the even more serious ethical and technical problems of determining whether or not a person is dead. Although the layperson's judgment is that there is a sharp line of demarcation between the living and the dead, modern developments have made the bases of such a determination far less precise. Death has traditionally been defined as the "cessation of all bodily and mental activity." However, all of the organs of the body do not necessarily die at the same time and there may be cryptic signs of biological activity long after other signs have disappeared. Furthermore, some of the biological signals may be maintained even in situations in which a person's body may not be able to do so independently. For example, it is now possible to artificially ventilate a person who cannot breathe on their own—a symptom that had long been considered to be a sign of death.

Another problem is that modern technology can detect some ongoing activities even when some of the more overt and obvious activities such as breathing and heartbeat (the usual religious criteria of death) have ceased. A person may appear to be dead on the basis of behavioral responses and cardiopulmonary activity and yet neurological activities may remain measurable with modern electronic instruments. It is now appreciated, furthermore, that some brain activity may persist below the technical ability of electroencephalographic or MRI devices to measure it.

The issue of defining death has become increasingly clouded as many other even newer technologies have become available to measure brain activity. These new devices include such esoteric methods as "diffusion weighted magnetic resonance," "near infrared spectroscopy," "somatosensory and auditory evoked potentials," and "Doppler ultrasonography," among others. The availability of such devices further complicates our ability to distinguish between a dead person and one in the deepest of comas. Thus, the conceptual and technical situation is clouded with ambiguous clinical meanings of the word "death."

A further complication is that there is now a considerable amount of pressure to ignore some of these persisting signs of life so that organs may be salvaged for transplants from the "near dead." The ethical problems inherent in terminating one "life" to save the lives of others add to the already complex religious and technical definitions of what constitutes death.

To understand the nature of the problem of defining death it is also important to appreciate that this is not a new issue. Laureys (2005) has reviewed the history of the criteria that have been used over the ages to define death. Each stage of history has had its own criteria for death. During classical times, especially in the Aristotelian tradition in which the heart was considered to be the seat of the soul, when the heart ceased functioning, the person was considered to be dead. The absence of breathing had also been widely used as a behavioral signal distinguishing the living for the dead. The whole concept of what constitutes a coma, particularly when unconsciousness seemed to last for more than a few hours, was alien to early scholars and physicians.

Laureys went on to note that only a few scholar-philosophers such Maimonides (1135-1204) the medieval scholar, suggested to the contrary that it was the integrity of the head, if not specifically the brain, that was responsible for perpetuation of life. This idea was consistent with the Platonic idea that the brain was the seat of the soul. Obviously, however, this was an inspired hunch rather than an idea based on any evidence available at Maimonides' time.

The concept of death as determined by the pulse, breathing, or the absence of behavioral responses persisted until recently mainly because the cessation of the cardiac activity led quickly to anoxia of the brain and other organs of the body, and then to their near simultaneous cessation of function. However, as Laureys and many others have pointed out, everything changed in 1952 when the Danish anesthesiologist Bjorn Ibsen invented a mechanical respirator that could keep patients alive despite respiratory failure. During forced respiration, the brain did not die immediately upon the cessation of breathing as it had prior to the invention of this device. Rather, a person's spontaneous pulmonary functions could cease and the brain could continue to function to at least some degree. As we have seen, in a persistent vegetative state, the converse could also be true; cardiopulmonary functions could continue in the absence of any measureable evidence of consciousness.[22] In such situations, death became more and more difficult to determine and the legal and ethical problems proliferated. What had been a simple criterion of death—the absence of breathing and cardiac activity—became a highly arbitrary standard that had to be determined by more and more complicated tests for any residual signs of biological activity.

Settergen (2003) delved deeply into the early nineteenth and twentieth century history of the shift from cardiopulmonary criteria for death to the concept of brain death. As it became possible to measure the physiological signs of brain activity, early investigators realized that various regions of the cerebrum and brain stem, although unable to control the heartbeat and breathing, might still remain active. This created a very serious problem in light of traditional definitions of death. As a result the emphasis began to shift from the absence of heart and lung function to the slight signals from the brain as the specific criteria of death. Perhaps the dividing line between the cardiopulmonary and brain criteria for death occurred in 1959 when two studies (Wertheimer, Jouvet, and Descites, 1959; Mollaret and Goulon, 1959) both argued that death should be defined by the absence of any measurable brain activity. It is somewhat startling to notice how recent these ideas were.

This situation, the increasing acceptance of the idea that the brain was the center of a person's being and the new technological means of measuring residual brain activity, led to a major change in thinking about death. A number of different scholars and organizations led the way for a redefinition of death as a total absence of both brain stem and cortical function. However, the situation did not become simpler. If there was increasing acceptance of the role of brain activity as the criterion for death, controversy grew over *which* parts of the brain were necessary and sufficient and which of the many signs of brain activity were required to support a clinical judgment of death.

Clinical tests thought to reflect brain stem activity include pupillary reflexes to light, the insertion of ice-water in the ear (a stimulus that would lead to eye-movements or nystagmus), and simply moving the head (a stimulus that would lead to what is called the "Doll's eye" phenomenon). Other tests for brain function include reactivity to painful stimuli, gagging, or efforts to breathe when carbon dioxide concentrations were elevated or a respirator was turned off—the so-called apnea test.

The standard EEG was also used as a means of detecting cortical function as were auditory event-related potentials (ERPs). However, many neurologists dislike these tests because they have relative high thresholds and may not detect localized or low-level brain activity. Another widely touted but rarely used test for brain death is a demonstration of the absence of blood flow to the cerebrum.

The next major historical step in the history of defining brain death in the United States was the product of a 1968 meeting among the faculty of Harvard medical school under the direction of H. K. Beecher (1904-1976) specifically organized to deal with this increasingly complex matter. The Harvard committee report (Beecher, Adams, and Banger, 1968) codified specific tests for the cessation of function in the brain as the basis of a clinical definition of death. Their criteria were based upon the absence of behavior and EEG signals that collectively indicated that the whole brain, both the cerebrum and the brain stem, was no longer functional. They also required the exclusion of conditions that might simulate whole brain death such as drugs and hypothermia. Their criteria included:

- Irreversible coma
- Unreceptivity and unresponsivity: No evidence of any sensitivity to or response to stimuli
- No movements or breathing
- No reflexes
- Flat EEG

Unfortunately, the criteria suggested by the Harvard committee are no longer considered to be adequate and have been severely criticized and subsequently expanded over the years since their publication. As discussed when I considered the nature of coma, irreversibility is sometimes a judgment call rather than a hard decision based on evidence. Furthermore, the concepts of "unreceptivity" cannot be validly tested if the patient is extremely paralyzed as is the case in the "locked-in" syndrome.

We have also seen how the requirement of EEG activity is a flawed measure of brain death because of a potential lack of sensitivity. Finally, movements may occur and breathing may be maintained in even the deepest of vegetative states, a condition in which the person is presumed to have no semblance of consciousness or self-awareness. Some patients may breathe, have a pulse, exhibit sleep and wakeful cycles, and even respond with some reflexive motions when stimulated. Such a responsive "body," however, may show absolutely no indication of any residual cerebral activity with an fMRI or the most sensitive EEG.

The debate continues over what constitutes brain death—cerebral inactivity, brain stem inactivity, or both. Mohandas and Chou (1974) argued for a criterion of brain stem death under the assumption that if that region was dead, none of the functions of the cerebral cortex would be possible since no signals would be able to move from the periphery to the sensory and associative regions of the brain. However, this criterion is also open to dispute. In 1975 Veatch argued that it was only necessary to show cerebral death for a person to be declared to be clinically dead. This was a view also held by Koppelman (2003).

The situation was further complicated when the federal government issued a report (Anonymous, 1981) attempting to define death in a uniform way for all of the states. Like so many other government reports, it had to accommodate a diversity of views and its concluding criteria were somewhat ambiguous. As noted earlier, most traditional religions have deep-seated definitions of death as the cessation of the heartbeat and of breathing. Apparently, these nonscientific considerations were taken into account in the deliberations that led to the 1981 report. In so doing, the members of that committee backed off from what had recently become a medical consensus that total brain death should be the unique criteria of death. In its place, the 1981 report adopted the dual criteria of "*either* the irreversible cessation of circulatory and respiratory functions *or* the irreversible cessation of all functions of the entire brain including the brain stem." This ambiguous definition was consistent with an earlier statement—the Model Brain Death Act—that had been agreed to by the American Medical Association, the American Bar Association, and the National Conference of Commissioners on Uniform State Laws that had been presented in 1979. It was, however, in sharp contrast to the emerging scientific consensus that the functional integrity of the whole brain was the criterion dividing line between life and death because of the cardiovascular option.

In 1995, the American Academy of Neurology offered up a much more complete set of criteria for determining brain death in adults based on an extensive review of the literature. Rather than permitting the criterion of cardiopulmonary dysfunction to be used as a sign of death, they returned to the cessation of activity in the brainstem as the essential criterion for death. After excluding drugs and metabolic disturbances, and hypothermia, they suggested that the three main findings for death are:

1. Coma as indicated by unresponsiveness as well as a definable reason for the coma.
2. Absence of all brain stem reflexes including pupillary and eye movement reflexes including facial responses or grimacing.
3. An extensive apnea test, including the measurement of blood levels of oxygen and carbon dioxide, and then a controlled increase in blood carbon dioxide. If no respiratory motions (gasping or gagging) are observed and these three tests are repeated in six hours, the person may be declared dead.

Perhaps the most complete current statement of what should constitute death was published in the form of a checklist by Van Norman (1999) as an appendix to a comprehensive review article on the current criteria for death. This checklist is reproduced in Table 5.4 because it spells out the most complete and explicit diagnostic statement of death now available. It is a far cry from the simple cardiopulmonary tests that had dominated medical and religious thinking for millennia.

Table 5.4
Checklist for Brain Death (Adapted from Van Norman, 1999)

1. The source of coma must be determined.

2. Preclinical tests (all must be checked to confirm diagnosis)?
_____ Absence of sedation
_____ Absence of shock (systolic BP 90 mmHg, or within 10% of patient's baseline)
_____ Absence of neuromuscular blocking agents, confirmed by nerve stimulator
_____ Absence of hypothermia (core temp 32.3 deg C in all cases, higher in some institutions)
Absence of the following metabolic or endocrine disorders:
_____ hypo- or hyperglycemia
_____ Ketoacidosis
_____ Uremia
_____ Hepatic failure
_____ Hyponatremia
_____ Hypercalcemia
_____ In cases of coma of unknown etiology, documented absence of other possible sources of coma.

3. Clinical examination (all must be checked to confirm diagnosis):
_____ No spontaneous movement
_____ No movement in response to pain,* including supraorbital ridge pressure
_____ No seizures or decerebrate, decorticate, or dyskinetic movements or posturing
* Movements due to spinal reflexes are acceptable. Such movement should be local, minor flexion only in response to locally applied painful stimulus—for example, painful stimulus to an upper extremity should elicit no movement or only minor flexion of the extremity to which the stimulus is applied. Other types of movement, spinal automatism (Lazarus sign) requires further confirmatory testing to establish the diagnosis of brain death.
Brain stem reflexes (all must be checked to confirm diagnosis):
_____ Absence of pupillary response to light

continued on next page

Table 5.4 (continued)
Checklist for Brain Death (Adapted from Van Norman, 1999)

_____ Absence of corneal reflexes
_____ Absence of caloric response
_____ Absence of pharyngeal reflexes
_____ Absence of cough with suctioning

4. Time between clinical assessments (note that in some cases of obvious irreparable brain damage, two tests may not be required):
_____ At least 6 h in adults
_____ At least 24 h in infants between 2 months and 1 yr of age
_____ At least 48 h in infants younger than 2 months of age

5. Apnea test: No movements, gasping, coughing, or respiratory effort of any kind.

6. Confirmatory tests (medically optional if physical exam and apnea test confirm brain death, but may be required if the clinical picture is confusing or if institutional policy dictates).
_____ The EEG should be isoelectric, i.e., flatlined. (This test is not sufficient by itself as a confirmatory test. The presence of electrical activity on EEG testing may indicate a need for further confirmatory tests.)
_____ Cerebral blood flow study by nuclear, radiographic or Doppler technique demonstrates no cerebral blood flow, including no blood flow to the posterior fossa (sufficient by itself to confirm brain death).
_____ Brain stem evoked responses show no brain stem activity. (This test is not sufficient by itself to confirm brain death.)

It might be of interest to note that Van Norman's checklist includes tests for both cerebral and brain stem activity as well as supplementary tests in ambiguous cases. It is unlikely, however, that all of these tests are carried out as routinely as this strict checklist requires.

At present in the United States, it is the absence of function in the whole brain, including both the brain stem and the cerebrum that is now generally considered to be the necessary neurological sign of death. Although acknowledged by such neurologists as Bernat (2006) as being imperfect, he still argued that:

> …despite its shortcomings, the whole brain formulation remain coherent
> on the grounds of the critical functions of the organism as a whole…The
> whole-brain death formulation comprises a concept and a public policy
> that makes intuitive and practical sense and have been well accepted by
> the public throughout many societies. (p. 41)

By no means, however, is it to be inferred that there is complete agreement nowadays concerning the determination of death or when a body may be
removed from artificial ventilation or feeding tubes. The case of Terri Schiavo,
which attracted so much public attention, was beset by conflicting criteria concerning her neurological state and the social and psychological needs of her family. Her symptoms were those of someone in a profoundly vegetative state and
the postmortem neurological examination showed that her brain was, to the best
of modern medical opinion, incapable of perception or cognition. Nevertheless,
religious and emotional issues clouded what were highly controversial decisions
pertaining to her state of consciousness, life, and death. It is likely that such
extrascientific issues will always conflict with what is increasingly the widely
accepted medical consensus requiring total brain inactivity.

Currently, the problem of defining death has been raised anew with regard
to the problem of harvesting human organs for transplants? Uncertainties about
what constitutes death in one person may expose other people to death or pain.
When is it appropriate to "harvest" organs? The consensus is that the conditions
specified by the protocol suggested by Van Norman (1999) represent the best that
modern medical science has to offer. The problem is that such complete examinations are rarely carried out and, therefore, there are continued openings for debate and controversy about individual cases. The entire issue of the controversies
that now pervade the determination of death was discussed in much greater detail
in a book edited by Younger, Arnold, and Schapiro (1999).

5.4 When "Neuroscience" is not Neuroscience

Neuroscience is not omnipotent, a fact that should be well appreciated by my
readers at this point. Indeed, the challenges faced by modern neuroscience are
often so overwhelming that I have argued that many of them may be intractable.
Relating the mind to the brain is going to remain one of the most difficult intellectual challenges to face mankind for the foreseeable future. Although there is
no question that many of the behavioral problems faced by human beings are due
to some malfunction of the nervous system, many of these problems remain unaffected and unreconciled even by the rapidly accumulating scientific database.
Some human activities that in a philosophical sense are the result of brain states
remain totally unexplained in terms of the language and concepts of those brain

states. Despite the continuing calls to formulate such complex "ethical" or "altruistic" social behaviors in the language of neurosciences, there is still no acceptable neuroscience of such high level cognitive processes. Instead, other forms of holistic description and analysis have evolved to handle controversies involving behavioral and ethical dysfunctions. Almost universally, our legal, medical, and psychological institutions deal with behavior at a global level and rarely has any specifically neuroscientific evidence been able to add anything to the adjudication process in the courtroom. The search for neuroscientific answers to some of the most serious questions of human existence, therefore, are not likely to be found in the neuroscientific laboratory.

In recent years in particular there has been a rush of reports that imply that a neuroscientific explanation is at hand for certain important social and behavioral problems including mental illness, behavior disorders, and impaired intelligence. However, a review of the scientific literature (as well as the popular claims) indicates that these imaginative, if not pseudoscientific, explanations are running far ahead of the scientific knowledge.

In this section of this chapter I will deal with a number of these social and behavioral issues for which I believe we have no definitive neuroscientific explanations. Before I start, I must reiterate the main point of this discussion—*there is no question that all mental and behavioral states are the results of neurological activity.* This statement is an ontological one that expresses the fundamental belief of modern neuroscientists and provides the intellectual foundation for the science. The problem we face in dealing with mental problems, however, is not the ontological one of mind-brain identity. Rather, it is a result of the fact that whatever brain states account for these discrepancies in thought or behavior are so complex that cognitive neuroscience has not been able to explain or understand them. Our challenge, therefore, is to determine the limits of knowledge—the epistemological issue—concerning what we can know. That we will ever be able to explain mind in terms of neurophysiology is, or course, controversial. However, the suggestion based on what we know about complexity and combinatorics is that we will always have to deal with these phenomena in a more holistic than a reductionist manner.

How great the epistemological or scientific barriers are can best be illustrated by considering some of the mind-brain relationships that are now attracting considerable public attention.

A. Mental Illness

The problems intrinsic to explaining the abnormal behavior we call mental illness has long been a source of consternation and confusion in legal proceedings. Prior to recent years it has always been handled at the behavioral level and dealt with as an extenuating condition that might in some cases be used to relieve a person of responsibility for some misconduct. Only recently have neurological or other biological signs been questionably used to diagnose someone as mentally ill.

Therein lays the rub! The definition and diagnosis of an abnormal mental state is for the many reasons I have already discussed in this book a highly arbitrary process. Unlike other categorical and taxonomic schemes, there are no objective scales that can be used to distinguish a marginally disturbed person from a seriously disturbed one. The closest approximation to such a diagnostic scheme is the DSMV-IV (Anonymous, 2000), the current edition of the Diagnostic and Statistical Manual of Mental Disorder, an effort to classify and organize the mass of what are generally agreed to be arbitrary psychiatric and psychological diagnostics. I have already mentioned earlier the fragility of this classification system and its curious history (Spiegel, 2005). It is important to reiterate the point that the definition of medical illnesses is in the same unresolved and controversial state it has been for many years.

In the place of an objective science of mental health has arisen a sequence of legal definitions of what constitutes mental illness. These are social constructions that have varied over the years as interpretations have waxed and waned. Robinson's (1996) history of the ancient world's ideas about mental illness and their relation to legal proceedings is a comprehensive look at the most ancient legal and quasi-legal concepts about exculpatory "insanity." Only a few interesting highpoints might be useful in understanding the current situation.

In medieval times, those behaving irresponsibly (or just differently) were simply classed as bewitched or possessed. The penalties for antisocial behaviors mediated by what we would now call mental illnesses were the same as those motivated by greed, gain, or revenge. The idea of exculpatory conditions due to mental disorders was a relatively modern development. One point made by all scholars in this field, however, should not go unmentioned; namely that what is considered to be inappropriate behavior that would fall under the rubric of insanity is a dynamic, social decision that changes from one society and time to another. The deranged behavior of a witch doctor, an oracle, or a prophet might be quite acceptable at some points in history and totally rejected in another just as is the adjustable admonition—"thou shalt not kill." In one situation, it may be a crime; in another it may be a duty. Any attempt to define mental illness must be considered in this social and historical context.

In recent years, a legal theory has evolved asserting that there is a class of criminals who simply do not know that their acts are wrong. This has led to the idea that such persons, although behaviorally guilty of a crime, may not be "responsible" in a socio-legal sense for their actions. The criterion term used in this context was "insanity," an idea that many have noted is not a scientific term, but rather a legal one. The traditional definition of insanity is:

"A deranged state of the mind or lack of understanding."

Or:

"A mental state that deviates from cultural norms."

Or:

"A psychiatric condition affecting legal circumstances. Legal incompetence or irresponsibility that results from a psychiatric disorder."

These are obviously not quantitative- or criterion-based judgments; much is left to the arbitrary decision making and evaluation by whichever adjudicator assumes the difficult task of distinguishing between normal and abnormal behavior. Indeed, the very biological reality of the word has been challenged. Szasz (1960), for example, referred to insanity (he uses the term "mental illness") as a disembodied and mythical concept. He considered mental illness to be a social construct that describes the behavior of people who have difficulty in accommodating themselves to society's norms. They exhibit, according to Szasz, deviations from the norms that are greater than acceptable by the community at large. These deviations are then medicalized and become subject to the type of "medical" treatments despite the fact that the symptoms of mental illness are defined in terms of nonmedical (i.e., social or behavioral) conditions. Szasz believed this is an "absurd" situation that challenges the concept of mental illness. He went on to point out that:

While I have argued that mental illnesses do not exist, I obviously did not imply that the social and psychological occurrences to which this label is currently being attached also do not exist. Like the personal and social troubles which people had in the Middle Ages, they are real enough. It is the labels we give them that concerns us and, having labeled them, what we do about them. (p. 117)

Although there were a number of early cases that dealt with the so-called "insanity" defense (summed up in Ray, 1838), the modern history of determining responsibility for a person who may exhibit socially unacceptable behavior yet have no sense of right and wrong begins with the 1843 trial of Daniel McNaughton.[23] McNaughton was an English radical who attempted to assassinate the then prime minister Robert Peel but mistakenly killed his secretary instead. As a result of the trial (he was acquitted by virtue of being "insane") an effort was made to codify what was meant by insanity. This resulted in what came to be known as the McNaughton rule:

> It must be proven that at the time of committing the act, the accused was laboring under such a defect of reason, from disease of the mind, as not to know the nature and quality of the act he was doing or, if he did know it, that he did not know what he was doing was wrong.

The key concept that characterizes the McNaughton rule is an inability to distinguish right from wrong. Although it is widely accepted in the United States, almost from the beginning it was challenged as being too vague and repeated attempts have been made to refine it. One relatively modern alteration is referred to as the Durham Rule, named after a relatively minor 1953 case. It simply stated:

> An accused is not criminally responsible if his unlawful act was the product of mental disease or mental defect.

The Durham Rule has since been considered to be inadequate as it deviated from the "right or wrong" criterion and invoked "illnesses" whose diagnoses could depend on the misbehavior itself, a circular definition by any means. As a result, a further modification in 1972 of the responsibility rule came to be known as the Brawner rule:

> A person is not responsible for criminal content, if at the time of such conduct, as a result of mental disease or mental defect he lacks substantial capacity to either appreciate the wrongfulness of his conduct or to conform his conduct to the requirements of the law.

Following the attempted assassination of President Reagan in 1981, the U.S. federal government attempted to improve on these insanity "rules" by proposing the following:

> At the time of the commission of the acts constituting the offense, the defendant, as a result of severe mental disease or defect, was unable to appreciate the nature and quality or the wrongfulness of his acts.

It is difficult to distinguish between the intended meanings and foundation premises of any of these various formulations. Most open the door to an interpretation of exculpation based on an accused's capacity or ability to distinguish right or wrong and then circularly define mental illness as an inability to make that distinction. Like many other legal and social conventions, the scientific foundation for these judgments is confused and incomplete.

Since the 1981 modification, there have been a number of further attempts to modify these rules. However, most jurisdictions seem to have reverted back to some version of the McNaughton rule with its simple, if not simplistic, emphasis on the accused's appreciation of right or wrong. The important property they all share is that they all depend on a subjective judgment by an expert to evaluate the intellectual and judgmental capacity of the accused from the observed behavior. These rules are, therefore, not only legal statements but behavioral ones and none of them directly involve any biological or neuroscience assertions about the causes of mental illness.

A main reason for this lacuna is that mental illness remains a great unknown from the neuroscientific point of view. None of the "diseases" of the mind have been understood in terms of the actual abnormal neural states that must underlay them. Whereas, misbehavior[24] must be a result of dysfunctional neural network processes at a microscopic level in principle, we are constrained to macroscopic explanations based on chunks of the brain or chemical shortages or surpluses. Therefore, the tendency has been to describe the behavior, consider the social conditions under which they emerge, and apply in a totally atheoretical manner, drugs and therapies that seem to alleviate the problem. What brain states constitute the neural underpinnings of specific mental disorders such as bipolar or schizophrenic conditions remain unknown. Diagnoses are varied, redundant, and nonexclusive; chemical treatments are mostly ad hoc; wild excursions into such therapies as psychosurgery and electro-shock therapy are periodically introduced and then rejected, all of which results in treatment effectiveness that is wildly inconsistent from patient to patient for all kinds of therapy.

Mental illness is, as a result, still looked upon as a result of an ensemble of factors including social, hereditary, environmental, chemical, neurological, and psychological factors of uncertain origins and of even less certain combination. All of this does not deny the basic fact that mental illnesses, like all other mental processes, are the end products of what are still incomprehensibly complex, subtle, and largely unknown neural mechanisms influenced by an aggregate of factors.

The argument that mental illness is not subject to the same kind of neuroscientific explanation as is, for example, the study of degenerative neurological diseases, seems correct. Years of research searching for hypothesized differences that may occur between the brains or brain chemistry of schizophrenics and normal persons have been fruitless. There is no measuring instrument or test that has consistently shown any universal differences between the brain structures or functions of normals and people with most kinds of mental disorders. What has

been shown by the most modern fMRI images are widespread and highly variable differences that may or may not be related to the behavioral outcomes. For
example, Shenton, Dickey, Frumin, and McCarley (2001), in an extensive review
of this literature on schizophrenia found many studies in which one or another
brain region seemed to be involved but most of the observed relationships were
"small and subtle." The 193 articles they reviewed did not provide even the slim-
mest support for any neurological theory of the source of this disease nor, for that
matter, did they highlight a common locale of brain dysfunctions that could be
associated with it. Shenton and his colleagues concluded that "After more than
a hundred years of research the neuropathology of schizophrenia remains unknown..." (p. 1). This a widely held view by most current experts in the field.

Given that the gross morphology of the brain was not indicative of a unified
cause of schizophrenia, we might well inquire further into whatever other causal
factors might be involved. Valenstein (1998), in his book *Blaming the Brain*,
argues strongly that there has not yet been any other explanation of this devastating illness, only a few weak correlations. He pointed out that after a period
of time in which the social factors were emphasized (and "talk" psychotherapy
heavily depended on) there has been a resurgence of research attention to the
other biological factors such as deviations in normal amounts of neurotransmitters, fluctuations in normal "biological rhythms," birth trauma, immune systems
interactions, and chemical imbalances, among many others. Valenstein summed
up the enormous, but still unfulfilled, body of scientific literature as follows:

> There is some supporting data to back up each of these biological theo-
> ries, and in our present state of ignorance about the causes of mental
> disorder, there is no alternative but to cast a wide net in our research ef-
> forts. However, it is troubling that there are so few replications of any of
> the brain findings reported to date and so many brain abnormalities have
> been proposed to be the cause of the same mental disorder. (p. 143)

It seems to me that the main impact of what Valenstein and others are saying (beyond the basic statement that we do not have a neuroreductive theory
of mental illness) is that although neuroscientific tools are being applied to the
study of such illnesses as schizophrenia, there is still no consensus of empirical
or theoretical opinion and, therefore, no neuroscience of mental illness worthy
of admissibility into our courtroom proceedings. The best we can do is concentrate on fallible indicators of past, present, and future behavior and treatments
thereof.

Similarly, the other major mental illness—bipolar disorder—also remains
largely outside of the realm of neuroscientific knowledge. Equally poorly de-

fined, it too has been the target of a substantial amount of research without avail. Like schizophrenia, bipolar disorder (as well as its companion disturbance, unipolar depression) has also been attributed to a very large number of different chemical, social, psychological, and brain dysfunctions. None of these theories have attracted a consensus of researchers working in the field. Indeed, one recent review (Callicott and Weinberger, 1999), although very hopeful about the future applications of brain imaging to the study of mental illness, pointed out that the progress so far has been slow and uncertain; they stated:

> …functional neuroimaging has not generated any pathognomic findings in mental illness, has not established a clear link between neurophysiology and observable behavior, and has not resolved the potential confounds of medication. (p. 95)

It is common throughout the literature to find other such relatively modest judgments about the progress that has been made in associating gross brain anomalies with mental illnesses. Current knowledge is considered by most to be "speculative." Bearden, Hoffman, and Cannon (2001), as another example, assert that:

> The etiology of the structural brain abnormalities commonly seen in bipolar illnesses, and their corresponding functional deficits remains unknown. (p. 106)

A very current review article by Belmaker and Agam (2008) on depression reflects exactly this same conclusion for monopolar depression:

> Depression is a heterogeneous disorder with a highly variable course, an inconsistent response to treatment, and no established mechanism. (p. 55)

Furthermore, the fact that some drugs tend to help individuals to overcome these debilitating illnesses and that they are also known to affect certain synaptic neurotransmitter mechanisms does not detract from the fact that our knowledge of the specific action of these drugs on behavior is often unknown. There are many speculative and hypothetical theories of how a particular drug works on a specific synaptic transmitter substance. Depression, for example, is often attributed both to a surplus of a putative transmitter as well as its deficiency. A variety of synaptic transmitter chemicals including dopamine and serotonin have been targeted over the years. Direct, cause and effect relationships, however, have rarely been demonstrated. The fact that the neurological systems using a common transmitter substance are widely dispersed throughout the brain makes the problem even more difficult to solve.

Very often, the use of a particular psychoactive drug to affect mental illness is based on nothing other than accidental or fortuitous observations of their utility, often in instances in which they were used for some other purpose. Lithium, for example is the best known and, many psychiatrists agree, the most effective therapy for bipolar disorder (it treats both mania and depression). Yet, nothing is known of how it affects the brain at the level that most likely accounts for moods. It was originally used for the treatment of gout. Another frequently used drug for bipolar disorder is sodium valpronate; it was discovered to have psychotherapeutic effects when it was originally used as an anticonvulsant.

It is also difficult to assign specific behavioral effects to drugs of one kind or another. A common defense in a criminal case is that an accused committed a crime under the influence of some psychoactive drug, legal or prescribed. For example, psychotic states have been blamed on antidepressants inducing the resulting criminal behavior. Marijuana, alcohol, and methamphetamines have also been associated with criminal behavior. However, no widely accepted neuroscientific explanations of how such chemicals work on the mind-brain are available. Whatever creditability drugs might have as causative agents is based on dosage-behavior relationships. The intervening neurological mechanisms—the basis of any future neuroscientific explanation—are just not known. It is possible that the criminal activity associated with the drugs is probably epiphenomenal, reflecting a need for money to buy the drugs rather than the effects of the drugs themselves.

There is also ample evidence that psychiatry and neuropsychology are beset by an extraordinary amount of bias in their respective research enterprises. A compelling argument that this is the case for a dozen different antidepressants has been made by Turner, Matthews, Linardatos, Tell and Rosenthal (2008). They compared the publication rate for clinical trials that produced positive results with those that produced negative results. Their results indicated a positive result led to publication 12 times more often than those that reported a negative result. This is obviously a source of bias that could lead to misapplication of this kind of drug. Furthermore, it should not go without mention that in a two alternative outcome state—the drug works or it does not—50% is a random outcome. Thus, a newly developed drug would have a high probability of being placed on the market despite the fact that it was totally ineffective.

Not only are there systematic biases in our research publication protocols, but there are many interested parties who strive to profit by making behavioral anomalies into drug-treatable biological illnesses. Furthermore, there is increasing evidence that those who are likely to make a profit from the sale of these drugs—the drug companies—or those whose professional careers may be affected—the researchers—may be further biasing the scientific evidence.

A not unusual example of the perfidy of large drug companies was reported in the *Journal of the American Medical Association* (JAMA). The company Merck was subpoenaed to provide some documents in one of the many cases involving Rofecoxib, a nonsteroidal, anti-inflammatory pain-controlling drug marketed under the trade name Vioxx. Upon examination of these documents, Ross, Hill, Egilman, and Krumholz (2008) discovered that a number of what were supposedly research reports authored by independent academic researchers were actually ghostwritten by Merck representatives. This raised serious questions about the credibility of not only these documents but also much of the rest of research conducted or supported by drug companies according to Ross and his colleagues.

More serious was the discovery by Psaty and Kronmal (2008) that the company-sponsored, ghostwritten reports were reporting to the FDA only modest fatality differences between Vioxx-treated groups and control groups. Quite to the contrary, internal reports showed three times as many deaths in the Vioxx treated group than in a placebo-treated group. These data were not submitted to the FDA.

Just how widespread the influence of drug and medical device industries has been on medical science was summed up in an adjoining editorial in the *Journal of the American Medical Association* (DeAngelis and Fontanarosa, 2008). They pointed out that this influence pervades clinical, educational, and research aspects of modern medicine. In situations in which the "illnesses" are difficult to define and treatment effects marginal, the attempts to mislead physicians and patients alike open the door to unwarranted influence by those that have a vested financial interest in "proving" their efficacy.

None of this uncertainty, corruption, and misleading research should be surprising given that the details of our mental life are actually a function of the microscopic arrangement of the inaccessible neural networks of the brain. Nor should the variability of mental illness data on cures and explanations be unexpected. All of the traditional problems of defining stimuli, measuring responses, and interpreting data are exacerbated in this field. Diagnostic tests of mental illness are subject to all of the problems that psychologists and psychiatrists face when they undertake to measure mental processes. Since the symptoms of mental illness are mainly a matter of subjective introspection and self-reporting or behavioral dysfunction (remember there is no direct accessibility to the mental states, normal or otherwise) the possibility of false results in experiments that are not adequately "double blind" is always present.

Therefore, we must conclude that mental illness is best understood these days as abnormal behavior and there are few legally admissible neuroscientific explanations of any of the many currently psychotic states. This generalization holds true even for those mental diseases for which there is a triggering condition. Thus, although there is no question that mental illness is the end result of brain processes, at the present stage of our knowledge, there is no widely accepted neuroscientific theory of the specific dysfunctional behavior.

B. Other Behavioral Mysteries Lacking a Neuroscientific Foundation

Although it is clear that the organ of all aspects of the mind is the brain, it is equally clear that there are a host of other abnormal behavioral symptoms for which we have only the most speculative answers concerning their underlying mechanisms. The problem is, to reiterate a central point of this book, that all of our mental functions are instantiated by neural mechanisms of extreme and, quite possibly, intractable complexity. The result is that the etiology of many of the abnormal behaviors that are inflicted on so many human beings is barely known. It is a situation in which weak correlation, variable empirical findings, and uncertain diagnoses lead to theories that are often just descriptions or proliferating neologisms. More and more dysfunctional behaviors are assigned to medical categories of mental illnesses that were unknown only a few years ago. It is, for example, still a matter of debate if the increasing numbers of such behavior disorders as autism are due to an increase in this "disease" or to a lowered threshold for what society will accept as normal behavior.

Whatever the causes of the behavior disorders I am about to discuss, it is important to appreciate that unlike most of the disorders dealt with in previous sections of this chapter, there is absolutely no neuroscientific explanation of any of them. For many of these disorders, the only therapies that have been shown to alleviate them are behavioral. They are in the purest sense of the word "psychological" phenomena bereft of any but the most preliminary hypothetical neural explanations. The list of the conditions to which I refer is long. However, a brief sampling of a few of them may help to clarify the point I am making here.

1. Autism

Autism is an increasing problem in society. It is observed in boys more than girls and may be evident in children as young as two years. It was defined in terms of a constellation of factors by Kanner (1943) that include:

- Inadequate social awareness and development
- Inadequate use of language and verbal behavior
- Abnormally repetitive behavior

Autism is now considered to be an extreme version of a cluster of similar behavioral disturbances that include Asperger's Syndrome, Pervasive Development Disorder, Pervasive Development Disorder (Not Otherwise Specified), and Rett Syndrome, among others. Collectively, these behavioral dysfunctions are referred to as the Autism Spectrum Disorders. It is likely that they all represent different points on a continuum and it is not clear where one fades into the next. Obviously this proliferation of diagnostic states suggests that the encountered behavioral symptoms are very variable from child to child. It is possible that these multiple diagnoses may represent nothing more than the various stages of a single disorder, each separated from the other more by the interests of the investigator than by the nature of the condition.

The most important principle in the present context concerning this spectrum of behavior disorders is that there is no known or even plausible specific neurological cause of any of them. Beyond the nearly worthless truism that they are due to errors in (unobserved and perhaps, unobservable) brain development and may be genetic, there is no known neural mechanism to which these disorders have been strongly associated. As with many other behavioral or mental problems, many researchers have sought to find a brain correlate of autism with the new brain imaging devices. None has yet shown a robust correlation between any region of the brain and a particular kind of behavioral dysfunction. Most researchers now agree that these disorders are mediated by unknown dysfunctions at the microscopic neural net level. There are no drugs or any other kind of intervention, other than behavioral therapies, that have been shown to have a significant effect on autism.

Autism, therefore, is almost unique in that the only known therapy for it is behavioral training and, amazingly enough, this kind of therapy works completely for many children (Thompson, 2005; 2007). What we are learning is that the earlier the training the better. Like so many other psychotherapeutic practices, there is no evidence according to Thompson (2005) that any particular behavioral therapy, procedure, or method works better than any other.

2. Attention Deficit Hyperactivity disorder

Another mental "disease" which shares some properties with autism is known as Attention Deficit Hyperactivity Disorder (ADHD). ADHD is also diagnosed purely on the basis of abnormal behavior. However, rather than being characterized by a disconnection between the child and the external environment as are the various kinds of autism, it is characterized by a persistent inability to maintain attention, hyperactivity, and a diminished control over impulsive behavior. It also includes, to various degrees, short-term memory problems, procrastination, and a general reluctance to carry out responsibilities. Like autism, it is more common in boys than in girls. However, unlike autism which is considered to be mainly a childhood complaint, some authorities suggest that ADHD can also occur later in adult life.

The first public indication of the presence of this abnormal behavior pattern was, curiously enough, described in a poem by Heinrich Hoffman entitled "The Story of Fidgety Phillip" about 1845. ADHD was first formally described by Still (1902) wherein he referred to it as a "morbid defect of moral control." It has been repeatedly renamed over the years (for example, as "Hyperkinetic Reaction"). The diagnosis has become more and more frequent in recent years. It was not until 1980 that the National Institute of Mental Health defined ADHD as a medical entity.

The diagnosis of ADHD is based on purely behavioral symptoms. Individually each item on the checklist shown in Table 5.5 represents a version or extension of more or less normal behavior. It is when a sufficient number of these symptoms aggregate that the abnormal "medical" condition we call ADHD is said to exist.

There is considerable controversy concerning the diagnostic nature of the symptoms, many of them bordering on the behavior of otherwise normal children or being of a temporary nature. The DSMV-IV has standardized the ADHD checklist in a way that leads to three different categories of this condition. The diagnosis requires that the misbehavior persist for an extended period of time (six months). The checklist is presented in Table 5.5.

Most germane to the present discussion is the fact that there is no physiological test included in this diagnostic checklist. Like most other such behaviorally defined conditions, there is enormous leeway in what would constitute an acceptable diagnosis of ADHD. For this reason there has been a substantial amount of controversy on whether or not the increasing number of children diagnosed with ADHD represents an increased awareness of what had previously been considered to be relatively normal nuisance activities on the part of bored children. Alternative hypotheses suggest that the increasing epidemic of ADHD is due to genetic or social factors.

If there has been controversy concerning the diagnostic situation, disagreement reached a crescendo with the introduction of a new therapeutic approach — the application of stimulant drugs such as Ritalin to the treatment of ADHD. The first use of drugs as treatment for this behavior disorder was by Bradley (1937). He suggested that the stimulant drug Benzedrine (an amphetamine) could temper the behavior of ADHD-afflicted children. The children, according to Bradley, were paradoxically calmed down from their hyperactivity but did not appear to be sedated. In recent years a number of other drugs have been used with some effect to treat ADHD. These include stimulants like Benzedrine such as Concerta, Methylin, and, most often, Ritalin. However new nonstimulant drugs, for example, Strattera, have recently attracted some attention as has the use of antidepressants such as Pamelor, the latter reserved for extremely difficult cases. Why, how, and if these drugs work remains some of the great mysteries of medical science.

Table 5.5
DSM-IV Criteria for ADHD (From Anonymous, 2000)

I. Either A or B:

A. Six or more of the following symptoms of inattention have been present for at least six months to a point that is disruptive and inappropriate for developmental level:

Inattention

1. Often does not give close attention to details or makes careless mistakes in schoolwork, work, or other activities.
2. Often has trouble keeping attention on tasks or play activities.
3. Often does not seem to listen when spoken to directly.
4. Often does not follow instructions and fails to finish schoolwork, chores, or duties in the workplace (not due to oppositional behavior or failure to understand instructions).
5. Often has trouble organizing activities.
6. Often avoids, dislikes, or doesn't want to do things that take a lot of mental effort for a long period of time (such as schoolwork or homework).
7. Often loses things needed for tasks and activities (e.g. toys, school assignments, pencils, books, or tools).
8. Is often easily distracted.
9. Is often forgetful in daily activities.

B. Six or more of the following symptoms of hyperactivity-impulsivity have been present for at least six months to an extent that is disruptive and inappropriate for developmental level:

Hyperactivity

1. Often fidgets with hands or feet or squirms in seat.
2. Often gets up from seat when remaining in seat is expected.
3. Often runs about or climbs when and where it is not appropriate (adolescents or adults may feel very restless).
4. Often has trouble playing or enjoying leisure activities quietly.
5. Is often "on the go" or often acts as if "driven by a motor."
6. Often talks excessively.

Impulsivity

1. Often blurts out answers before questions have been finished.
2. Often has trouble waiting one's turn.

3. Often interrupts or intrudes on others (e.g., butts into conversations or games).
II. Some symptoms that cause impairment were present before age 7 years.
III. Some impairment from the symptoms is present in two or more settings (e.g. at school/work and at home).
IV. There must be clear evidence of significant impairment in social, school, or work functioning.
V. The symptoms do not happen only during the course of a Pervasive Developmental Disorder, Schizophrenia, or other Psychotic Disorder. The symptoms are not better accounted for by another mental disorder (e.g. Mood Disorder, Anxiety Disorder, Dissociative Disorder, or a Personality Disorder).

Based on these criteria, three types of ADHD are identified:

1. **ADHD, *Combined Type*: if both criteria 1A and 1B are met for the past six months**
2. **ADHD, *Predominantly Inattentive Type*: if criterion 1A is met but criterion 1B is not met for the past six months**
3. **ADHD, *Predominantly Hyperactive-Impulsive Type*: if Criterion 1B is met but Criterion 1A is not met for the past six months.**

As a result of the uncertainty of diagnosis and the lack of knowledge of how or even if such drugs work, there has been substantial controversy concerning the "drugging" of children to control hyperactivity. ADHD is often declared not to be a neurological "illness" or disease, but merely an elaboration of normal behavior. Proponents of this side of the argument argue that its medicalization and the attendant use of drugs are unwarranted. They argue that it is used more as a control or sedating device than a therapeutic one since the overall effect is a calming one. It has been further suggested that the diagnosis was added to the DSM-IV in recent years mainly to open up additional employment opportunities for nurses, psychiatrists, and psychologists. There is, furthermore, a substantial vested interest on the part of drug companies to emphasize drug therapy and schools are always happy to moderate the behavior of unruly or disruptive children. The most extreme criticism is that a number of deaths have been attributed over the years to Ritalin—a fact vigorously challenged by the other side of the argument.

On the other side of the controversy are those who believe that the cluster of symptoms indicate a real neurological problem and point to the efficacy of drugs to change behavior as evidence that it is a treatable as well as a biologically based illness.[25] Unfortunately, even those drugs that have been shown to have some palliative effect are not without their side effects. In situations like this, devoid of a solid scientific foundation, the opportunity for litigation is always present.

3. Post Traumatic Stress Disorder

Another emerging psychological condition[26] that may have increasing presence in our courtrooms is what has come to be called Post Traumatic Stress Disorder (PTSD). PTSD is especially frustrating to deal with in neuroscientific terms since it is defined in the vaguest of possible behavioral and situational terms. The national Institute of Mental Health defines PTSD as:

> ...an anxiety disorder that can develop after exposure to a terrifying event or ordeal in which grave physical harm occurred or was threatened. Traumatic events that may trigger PTSD include violent personal assaults, natural or human-caused disasters, accidents of military combat. People with PTSD have persistent frightening thoughts and memories of their ordeal and feel emotionally numb, especially with people they were once close to. They may experience sleep problems, feel detached or numb, or be easily startled.

A report from the National Academy of Sciences (2006) tabulated the essential characteristics of PTSD as:

- Re-experiencing: Intrusive recollections of a traumatic event, often through flashback or nightmares,
- Avoidance or numbing: Efforts to avoid anything associated with the trauma and numbing of emotions,
- Hyperarousal: Often manifested by difficulty in sleeping and concentrating and by irritability.

Alternatively, a brief definition is that PTSD is an "overly strong emotional response."

All of these definitions require that the PTSD syndrome is not to be diagnosed until after a dormant period that may be as short as a month or as long as many years. Another critical factor is that there must be some specifiable triggering event, not just a general anxiety arising from an otherwise dangerous situation. Without a specific triggering event some investigators have suggested that PTSD would not definable as a disease. Rosen and Taylor (2007), for example, stated that:

[In those cases in which there was not a defined traumatic event,] would PTSD stand on the merits of its symptom criteria? There are reasons to think not. First, PTSD does not represent a discrete disorder with a distinctive etiology....Other behavioral genetic studies raise the possibility that PTSD, like other anxiety and mood disorders, arises from a combination of non-specific genetic and environmental factors (influencing many disorders) along with comparatively small contributions from disorder specific factors....Posttraumatic stress symptoms also overlap with other diagnostic constructs that may just as well account for the symptom criteria of PTSD (e.g., depression, panic disorder, and specific phobia). (p. 206)

In this context, it is not at all clear that PTSD is a medical problem in the sense of a "disease." Indeed, there has been a considerable amount of criticism arguing that PTSD is little more than an intense and, considering the horrific situations in which it is triggered, a reasonable if not normal elaboration of what in many contexts would be considered to be normal psychological responses. A diagnosis of PTSD is also complicated by the fact that it can be simulated leading to the introduction of new diagnostic versions called pseudo-PTSD or simple malingering (Rosen and Taylor, 2007).

The problem posed by the designation of severe anxiety disorders like PTSD is that the terminology is arbitrary and the symptoms are exceedingly variable. For example, like many other behaviorally defined mental and behavioral difficulties, a diagnosis of PTSD is only made if the problems persist for more than a month. If the problems are transient and last for less than a month, another "disease"—Acute Stress Disorder, or ASD—is to be diagnosed.[27] It is, therefore, arbitrary as to what the nomenclature to describe these extreme anxiety states should be. Furthermore, it is now appreciated that individuals with other psychological problems are more likely to concurrently suffer from PTSD. PTSD is also correlated with future psychological problems (Lange, Lange, and Cabaltica, 2000). This arbitrariness in diagnostic criteria is a difficulty faced by all psychiatric conditions because the specific manifestations of mental disease are always so idiosyncratic.

Interest in PTSD has been accelerated by the social and political events beginning with the Vietnam War, although it is quite clear that many previous wars and catastrophes produced similar mental disorders. Despite this arbitrariness and the confounding of social and political issues, there is no question that PTSD may be treatable by psychotherapeutic techniques and some drugs. Indeed, it now appears (from a recent meta-review of the efficacy of psychotherapy by Bradley, Green, Russ, Dutra, and Westen, 2005) that psychotherapy can be very effective in the treatment of PTSD ("the majority of patients treated with psycho-therapy for PTSD in randomized trials recover or improve"—p. 214). Unfortu-nately, there is no neuroscience that presents even the beginnings of a biological explanation of this debilitating condition. No specific neurological or biochemi-cal abnormality has been definitively associated with this elusive anxiety disor-der and there is no explanation for the therapeutic effects of any drug.

5.5 Interim Conclusions

This chapter examines the relationships drawn between the brain and a group of cognitive dysfunctions. The most universal thing we can say about all of the mental difficulties is that they are real and pose major problems for society and the individual. That is, although it is also clear that we do not have good neuro-scientific explanations of these disorders, their existence as deviations from the cognitive norm is undeniable. All types of mental pathologies and the altered mental states involved with the various stages of coma reflect real problems for which therapeutic or palliative solutions are actively sought and desperately needed. No matter that some of them represent exaggerations of normal behav-ior, our science and our social standards tend to mark off boundaries between the normal and the abnormal and seek solutions to the problems designated as ab-normal. From a practical point of view, no matter how inadequate our theoretical knowledge of the mind-brain relationship, nothing should inhibit our search for even the least understood therapies for these illnesses. A serendipitously discov-ered therapy is better than no therapy.

Unfortunately, despite the fact that all of these mental and behavioral aberra-tions are appreciated to be manifestations of the nervous system, the gap between the mind and the brain remains as unbridged in this context as it is for the topics discussed in previous chapters. There is little or no neuroscientific foundation that could unequivocally stand as compelling evidence in the courtroom. Never-theless, the complexities of our society demand that issues of legal significance be resolved sometimes on the basis of ideas that are more mythical than factual. For example, as I write this material there is a class action courtroom battle go-ing on over the liability of the government in which it is charged that a mercury-based preservative—thimerosal—earlier used in some vaccines is a triggering factor, if not a cause, of autism. The scientific findings are hardly controversial; most reputable studies reject any association between autism and thimerosal. However, at the present time, these uncertainties in the scientific situation are corrupted by emotional, social, and political issues that transcend the scientific.

The point is that even though there is little support for the merits of cases like the autism-thimerosal dispute, legal disputes rage on. This case is typical; it represents a misplacement of what is a questionable scientific controversy into the courtroom. Virtually every other one of the topics discussed in this section are likely to become or have already been placed in the same situation. The need is great; the science is either inadequate or contrary to what is being claimed; the desire for recompense is powerful; and, therefore, we throw the issue into what is obviously an arena in which the judges and juries are asked to overcome the inadequacy of the science.

The basic reason that this type of case persists is that we still do not have and may never have an unequivocal and compelling explanation of how mental (and behavioral) processes are instantiated in the brain. This chapter has attempted to make this point clear for a cluster of mental and behavioral disorders. The coverage of this chapter is obviously incomplete but perhaps, by example, it can make the point that neuroscientific findings are still inadequate to unequivocally support claims made about the causes and sources of these dysfunctions. In the remainder of this section, I draw some interim conclusions from the discussions of these topics.

1. Cognitive neuroscience is in a far more primitive state than is generally appreciated. Although strong claims have been made by scientists operating in this field, there are relatively few robust associations between dysfunctional brain activity and abnormal mental or behavioral states. The science is not one in which strong relationships are established with a high degree of certainty. Even the best of research in this field is primarily correlative. That is, the associations between brain lesions and behavior are more probabilistic than determinative. It is only rarely, if ever, that a particular lesion inexorably leads to a particular behavioral dysfunction. For example, Broca's area does not always lead to Broca's aphasia and Broca's aphasia is not always associated with damage to Broca's area. The modest correlations might be useful heuristics to theory development but they certainly should not be used as evidence in a courtroom.

2. The empirical findings in this domain are highly variable. This is one of the most important reasons why inductive statistical methods are used in cognitive neuroscience (as in most other psychological and biological research activities) rather than the deductive methods that characterize physical science. Because of this substantial variability it is not possible to predict or control future behavior. Indeed, the low levels of correlation (typically 0.33) obtained in mind-brain studies would be unacceptable in many other sciences as well as in the courtroom with its doctrine of reasonable doubt.

3. Because of the correlative nature of this science, it is open to a particularly high degree of bias of one kind or another. Some of this bias

emerges because of the theoretical proclivities of the individual researcher. Often, researchers operate under the influence of assumptions of which they are only dimly aware but which, nevertheless, can have potent effects on their thinking and even their results. Systematic biases can also be engendered by the publications system with its tendency to not publish negative reports. More serious bias, however, emerges from commercial interests, sometimes involving huge amounts of profit for a possibly ineffective psychotropic drug.

4. None of these cognitive dysfunctions have a unique biological marker; i.e., none are designated by a definitive physiological or anatomical signature event or condition. Nor is any one of them likely to be so associated in the foreseeable future. Therefore, any attempt to show that a particular lesion or chemical anomaly is diagnostic of a cognitive aberration is fallacious a priori.

5. The uncertainty about the mind-brain relationships opens the door to pseudoscientific interpretations, fads, and fantasies. The likelihood of anyone giving a definitive neuroscientific explanation of a particular mental dysfunction is nil. Unfortunately, this does not prevent anyone from inventing a pseudoscientific or mythical hypothetical explanation.

6. Many of the cognitive dysfunctions discussed in this chapter are only vaguely defined. Many of the clinical diagnoses are overlapping and redundant and inadequately distinguish between very similar abnormalities. The reason for this is obvious; it is very hard to define mental terms and behavioral indicators are only weakly connected to the underlying mental states. Furthermore, many dysfunctions have multiple causes. Aggravating this uncertainty is that a number of these psychological disorders can be simulated by a clever patient.

7. A considerable number of the "reasonable and plausible" hypotheses concerning brain states and behavior are actually premature and unsubstantiated. A particular example is the idea that juvenile misbehavior is to be explained in terms of an underdeveloped nervous system. Such a suggestion has not been empirically established and is, at best, a highly speculative hypothesis. It certainly does not withstand the *Daubert* challenge for scientific credibility at the present time. Indeed, it is hard to imagine what kind of experiment might support this suggestion. Furthermore, it is not entirely clear what such an association would mean in the courtroom in the unlikely event that it could rise from conjecture to fact.

8. A converging view of the origins of mental dysfunction is that they are the result of a constellation of factors—some experiential, some social,

some genetic, and some environmental. The notion of single causes and effect is diminished by such an emerging perspective. No matter how compelling a link may be established between one factor and one behavioral or mental response, no single factor is likely to account for all of the variance in the human condition. The conflict between nature and nurture that has characterized science for millennia is unlikely to be resolved by showing that a modest amount of the explanatory variance is accounted for by any single factor.

9. There is a profound difference in the basic assumptions used in cognitive neuroscience and those used by the legal system. As a result, it is unlikely that even the best established mind-brain theory would change the course of legal adjudication. The court has shown that it is unwilling to admit evidence from polygraphs and is equally unlikely to accept brain images as determinative evidence.

10. The most general and universal conclusion to be drawn from the review of the empirical literature is that there remains a great gulf between our mental and behavioral worlds and the neurological one. None of the dysfunctional conditions described in this chapter can be unequivocally attributed to specific brain abnormalities. Even with the availability of the best modern equipment, it is uncertain whether or not one is dealing with some vestige of consciousness in a comatose patient.

11. Finally, one undeniable theoretical fact is emerging from what knowledge we have gleaned over the years. That is that the idea of modular psychological components represented in sharply defined regions of the brain must change as more and more widely dispersed parts of the brain are shown to be involved in even the simplest cognitive process. If there is any more important theoretical principle to be learned, it is hard to identify.

Endnotes

1. A good discussion of the unfulfilled search for the neuroscientific basis of morality and ethics can found in an article by Miller (2008). Some of the provocative answers asked in this article reveal the complexities and uncertainties of what remains mysterious in this field. The confusion between the axiomatic fact that all mental processes are encoded by brain processes, on the one hand, and the hypothesis that such a subtlety as morality can be found in a particular place in the brain, on the other, is clearly evident in this article.

2. The excitement of the many developments in cognitive neuroscience over-shadows the fact that there are still many scientists and scholars who do not believe the mind-brain problem is solvable in any general sense. See Uttal (2005) for a complete discussion of this topic.

3. The potential impact of this question is enormous because it is entirely pos-sible that antisocial behavior may be not only adaptive but be the result of perfectly "normal" and "logical" brain processes. The point is that abnormal behavior does not by itself indicate abnormal brain function; it may be a reasonable solution to a societal problem. Otherwise we might well con-sider any criminal misbehavior to be prima facie evidence of a neurological disorder. An equally incorrect assumption would be that a brain lesion in a particular place always leads to the same kind of abnormal behavior.

4. However, see the comments by Greene and Cohen (2004) that this is a truism since most modern neuroscientists agree that everything mental is associ-ated with a brain process. The question is—can we link irrational behavior with some specific measurable aspect of youthful brain development in a way that would provide exculpation for juvenile offenders. At present, this is both an unsupported scientific hypothesis and, in general, an inadmissible legal concept.

5. It should not be overlooked that although Damasio and his colleagues may have been the first to attribute prosopagnosia to these regions, the behavioral dysfunctions had been known for many years.

6. The confusion in terminology is exemplified by the similarity in symptoms of the two central terms—auditory agnosia and aphasia. Which diagnosis is used is somewhat arbitrary.

7. The word aphasia is often used to denote any difficulty with speech, either its production or its understanding. I prefer to use the word "aphasia" for the inability to produce coherent speech and the term "auditory agnosia" for the inability to understand speech.

8. It should not be overlooked, however, that the involvement of the right hemi-sphere in the recovery of speech has long been known. The variability of its in-volvement was discussed as far back as Nielsen (1946) in considerable detail.

9. I must repeat here that our thoughts are brain processes. However, we know so little of how they are encoded that the separate languages of psychology and neuroscience must be used. By no means am I proposing some kind of a crypto-dualism. Instead, this comment is made is the spirit of E. L. Thorn-dike (1991) who said:

These objections to be significant should frankly assert that between physical facts and mental facts, between bodies and minds, between any and all of the animal's movements and its states of consciousness, there is an im-passable gap, a real discontinuity, found nowhere else in science; and that by making psychology responsible for territory on both sides of the gap, one makes psychology include two totally disparate group of facts, things and thoughts, requiring totally different methods of study. (p. 6)

10. It is no impediment to the amount of research carried out by experimental psychologists, however. Studies of memory have been a part of this profession's research activities for many years and tens of thousands of studies on learning and memory are published every year.

11. Lashley's (1950) work was an important milestone in the debate over localized and distributed memories. He argued that memories could be stored every place in the brain (the principle of equipotentiality) and that the amount of memory loss was correlated with the amount of brain tissue removed in his experiments on rats. Equipotentiality is not popular these days, but we have no other current satisfactory theory of where or how memories are stored. The compromise theory now gaining credibility is that many regions of the brain are involved in the storage information.

12. Other kinds of memories seem to be instantiated in other parts of the brain. Thompson (1990), for example, has shown classical conditioning is at least partially modulated by the cerebellum. Similarly, extensive medial temporal lobe lesions do not affect short-term memory to the same degree as long-term memories are affected.

13. A more complete discussion of the various kinds of apraxias can be found in a review article by Leiguarda and Marsden (2000).

14. All of the diagnostic tables presented in this section have been abstracted from Nielsen (1936), Dubin (2008) and various sections in the Wikipedia online encyclopedia.

15. Curare is the best known of large numbers of different chemicals, many of which are synthesized, that are known to work on neuromuscular junctions to paralyze the musculature. Other more modern versions of such drugs include Flaxodil, Tubocurarine (an extract of curare), succinylcholine, and a number of other similar drugs that go by various proprietary names. They all work by either depolarizing (increasing the membrane potential) of the muscle fibers or by blocking the neuromuscular transmitter substance ace-

tylcholine itself, thus making it more difficult for neuromuscular transmission to take place.

16. In this case, the volunteer was the eminent vision psychologist Leonard Matin. Although Matin did not go as deeply in the curare-induced paralysis, his courage was as notable as that of Smith.

17. Although this article received a great deal of attention when it was published in 2006, it contents had been essentially anticipated by earlier work. For example, Kuebler, Kotchoubey, Salzmann, Ghanayim, Perelmouter, Homberg, and Birbaumer (1998) had previously reported self-regulation of slow cortical potentials in two patients who were reported to be "extremely paralyzed" or "locked in" displaying only minimal eye and facial muscle movements. The procedures used in the two experiments were different—Kuebler and his colleagues used a biofeedback training procedure and Owen and his colleagues used a verbal command. However, the comatose patients in both experiments did learn what some investigators have assumed to be conscious control of their brain activity.

18. Although there have been many efforts to precisely define what constitutes a vegetative state, the term is still one based on a relative judgment. The term is applied to patients who are assumed to be unconscious but exhibit some reflexes, some indication of sleep and waking cycles, but no indication of appropriate responses to queries that might suggest some residual consciousness. There is no general agreement on what neurological signs determine whether or not a person is in a vegetative state. The situation is further complicated by the fact that it has now been suggested that there are various degrees of vegetative states, some of which are temporary and some of which are "persistent." In the final analysis it is a name given to an arbitrary cluster of symptoms that leads one to judge that a patient is totally unconscious. The fact that it is a judgment call opens the door to controversy and uncertainty.

19. To the extent that the most extreme version of the "locked-in" state exists, it is usually associated with damage to the brain stem and particularly with lesions in the ascending reticular system. It may also be temporarily simulated by hypothermia or drug effects.

20. The Rancho Los Amigos Scale has been attributed to C. Hagen, D. Malkmus, and P. Durham of the Communication Disorders Service of Rancho Los Amigos Hospital in 1972. However, I have not been able to find any formal publication of their work.

21. It is well established that damage as severe as a surgically required hemi-spherectomy may not reduce intellectual capacity or consciousness to any great degree. Such drastic operations are done in extreme cases to control continuous epileptic attacks. Furthermore, some patients have been shown to have advanced cases of hydrocephalous in which the cavities of the brain swell up squeezing the brain tissue into a thin rind on the inside of the skull with virtually no effects on academic success. This is both possible and plau-sible because the topology of the brain's three-dimensional neural network is preserved despite being compressed.

22. It is also possible to maintain a degraded form of "life" by artificially feed-ing a "body" that may have no other signs of life beyond respiration and a pulse.

23. McNaughton has been spelled in numerous different ways as the years have gone by. At present, this is the accepted U.S. spelling.

24. Whether we define the neural network as dysfunctional assumes that the mis-behavior is outside of the bounds of normal or acceptable conduct. It is per-fectly plausible for someone to violate a social constraint and have totally normal and rational brain processes.

25. Valenstein (1998) pointed out, however, that there is no reason to assume that responsiveness to a drug is proof that a behavior pattern is due to a particular neurobiological disorder. The possibility that some other part of the system is able to counteract a particular behavior pattern is always present. For ex-ample, one theory is that activation of the frontal lobes by stimulants such as Ritalin or Benzedrine may moderate hyperactivity. This model is often used as an explanation of the paradoxical calming effects of stimulants.

26. The concept of PTSD as a mental disease entity was first introduced in 1980 into the DSMV by a committee.

27. The distinction in nomenclature may have profound effects. Recent press reports suggest that U.S. military mental health service providers are being pressured to use ASD rather than PTSD as a diagnosis to get personnel back into action at a faster rate.

Chapter 6

Some Concluding and Summarizing Comments

Synopsis
6.1 Introduction
6.2 What is the Current State of Cognitive Neuroscience Theory?
6.3 Ethics

MYTH: The major ethical problem in cognitive neuroscience's application in the courtroom is that authenticated findings and theories will be misused in adjudication and will violate our privacy rights.
TRUTH: The major ethical problem in cognitive neuroscience's application in the courtroom is that fallacious, premature, and pseudoscientific findings and theories will be misused in adjudication and will violate our privacy rights.

6.1 Introduction

It is obvious that new developments in cognitive neuroscience—the study of the relationships between the mind and the brain—are going to be of continuing interest to many other portions of our society. Most notably, among this dispersion of interests from what had been an arcane field of inquiry to the most relevant of our social contexts, is the role that it may play in the legal system. Already, the admissibility of neuroscientific evidence has been tested in our courts. Judges, attorneys, and lay jurors are being asked to make judgments about some of the potentially exciting and novel scientific, but extremely complex, developments concerning the brain's role in controlling our behavior and instantiating our thoughts.

An extended discussion of a number of ways in which neuroscience may impact on legal issues can be found in Moriarty (2008). Moriarty tabulates what she believes is going to be an increasing number of problematic situations as neuroscience evidence is offered as evidence in courtroom deliberations. Her list includes:

- Whether neuroimaging evidence should be admissible as proof of competency, insanity, mental illness, and other forms of mental impairment in both the civil and criminal context.
- Whether neuroimaging should be used in interrogations of suspected criminals and terror suspects. If so, should these results be admissible in trials or tribunals?
- Can neuroimaging reliably prove when individuals are lying or when they have knowledge of a disputed matter? If so, what considerations should govern their use in trials?
- Should neuroimaging be available and admissible for defendants who claim they were wrongfully convicted and allege neuroimaging can prove their innocence?
- Should neuroimaging be admissible in trials in which a party claims neurological harm due to trauma, toxins, intoxicants, or vaccines?
- How important should neuroimaging be in judicial decisions about end of life matters? (p. 30)

Many of these initial steps towards the goal of objectifying that which is all too subjective are based on a philosophical principle that is widely accepted in scientific fields but certainly disputed in philosophical circles. That principle—materialistic monism—on which all applications of cognitive neuroscience research are based—is that all mental activity is, in principle, fully explained by the action of the material brain. This, of course, is not the view held by many outside the neuroscientific world—mind-brain dualism. Nevertheless, the transition from the laboratory to the courtroom is based on this monistic premise. To de-link the mind and the brain would make meaningless any neuroscientific evidence that might be submitted for consideration and make irrelevant its application in the courtroom.

The problem then arising is that, even as we accept the monistic premise, is the scientific evidence sufficiently strong to meet the *Daubert* and *Frye* standards for admissibility. The general answer to which this book leads us is that, in general, it is not. Cognitive neuroscience is a very young field in its most modern incarnation and the problems that it has chosen to pursue are the most complex and challenging any science has ever undertaken. However, in its present state, most of the important and fundamental questions remain unanswered and many scientists suspect that some of the most profound may be unanswerable. To sum it up as succinctly as possible, we do not know how the brain makes the mind, consciousness, awareness, or any other word that one uses to describe the wonderful cognitive powers of humans. This unsolved problem is the basis of the confusion, conflict, and contentiousness of both our empirical findings and the speculative theories that have been proposed by cognitive scientists.

There are many reasons for the prevailing inability of cognitive neuroscience to provide compelling legal evidence or exculpatory explanations of misbehavior that have been made evident throughout the preceding chapters. They include some that are fundamental, some that are methodological, and some that are simply empirical. Among the most salient are:

1. All of our hopes aside that we will ultimately be able determine what a person is thinking, in point of empirical fact, the mind is not directly accessible and cannot be inferred from behavioral and introspective reports. Unfortunately, as we have seen, neither of these two windows into the mind is open in a way that permits us to know another's thoughts.

2. Furthermore, classical research techniques such as brain stimulation and surgical extirpation do not provide straightforward, unequivocal answers to the relationship between the brain and the mind.

3. Even the most modern techniques that measure brain activity are not adequately correlated with thoughts to permit us the luxury of using one as a measure of the other.

4. Because of the recalcitrance of the mind-brain problem, many theoretical approaches that have substantial face validity but little uniqueness now dominate theory in cognitive neuroscience. This is the curse of the underdeterminativeness of behavioral evidence.

5. The idea that the mind can be broken up into modular cognitive processes and that these modules are represented or encoded in localized regions of the brain has widespread acceptance. As a matter of procedural fact, however, cognitive processes are poorly defined and may represent phantoms that are linguistic or experimental conveniences rather than real functional entities. Furthermore, most of the brain seems to be involved in most cognitive processes. Thus, it now seems that mental processes may not be reducible to cognitive or neuroscientific primitives; the whole mind-brain system seems to be much more widely distributed than it was believed only a few years ago.

6. Whatever the actual arrangement of the parts at various levels of the brain, there is no question that the problem faced in explaining mental processes by brain mechanism is enormously complicated. In fact, there is good reason to believe that it may represent an intractable scientific problem that may never be solved.

7. The practical problems of studying the mind-brain problem are further exacerbated by the fact that empirical data is enormously variable. There is always a distribution of possible responses that keeps us from

absolute answers of the type that would be desired in the courtroom. Data from one experiment conflict with those from another leading to a wide range of controversies between weakly supported hypotheses of the relationships between brain and mind. So far, cognitive neuroscience has not produced a unified theory of the mind. Many theories, each with its own failing, contend for attention without resolution.

8. When meta-reviews are carried out almost anyplace in this cognitive neuroscience field, the general result is wide distribution of the results from many experiments. Localization of function is found only in specific places such as the sensory or motor areas and perhaps those regions associated with emotional reactions. The powerful new approach of meta-reviewing data has raised more questions than it answers. One thing that has become clear is that attention to single maximum peak activations in brain images is ill advised.

9. There is an unfortunate tendency for very preliminary results to be popularized among both the lay public and the scientific community. Almost anything associated with the brain is grist for the popular media. Novel and unsubstantiated results are often published with little consideration for how tentative such findings may be. Among the many premature popularizations that are supposed to deal with the brain are:

- "Direct" brain-machine interconnection
- Hemispheric specialization
- Neuroeconomics
- Neuroethics
- Neuromarketing
- Brain enhancement by machines and drugs
- EEG (Alpha) enhancement
- New age brain tuners
- Graphology
- Meditation

along with a number of other marginal mind-brain pseudosciences. For readers who would like to delve more deeply into these fringe scientific activities, there is probably no better nor more interesting source than the work of the late Barry Beyerstein (1999).

These general handicaps to solving the mind-brain problem in a sufficiently robust manner to be useful in the courtrooms are paralleled by the inadequate state of knowledge in the specific fields that I have surveyed in this book. Most disappointing has been the perennial desire to find an objective measure of lying. Over the centuries an objective test of deception has been long sought. The autonomic indicators recorded by the standard polygraph have been shown to be near useless over the past few decades. The persistence of this device in our society, however, is a clear indication of how powerful is the impulse to accept something from the fringes of pseudoscience. Fortunately, our courtrooms have almost universally refused to admit evidence from this classic kind of lie detector.

Nowadays, with the advent of brain imaging devices, the hope for a machine that can read the mind and discriminate between truth and falsehood has arisen again in a refreshed form. Companies have been formed and attempts to introduce fMRI and other signals from the brain as evidence in judicial proceedings have flourished. Unfortunately, for such speculative enterprises, the findings from the several laboratories involved in this kind of work have proven to be unreliable, unreplicated, and thoroughly confusing. Despite the commercial efforts, there is no satisfactory scientific foundation for admitting these newer methods into judicial proceedings any more than there was for the polygraph.

The situation is much the same in any other effort to apply neuroscientific data to other forms of human misbehavior. Among the most important from a legal point of view is the study of aggression. Aggression of one form or another is at the heart of an immense portion of the crime in the world. The hope in applying cognitive neuroscientific knowledge is based on several considerations. It would be wonderful if we could surgically correct some tendency to commit violent crime. Barring that, it has been suggested that if we could find a brain region or dysfunction that was responsible for some misbehavior, it could be used as an argument for the mitigation of the penalties for a perpetrator's violent misbehavior. This is a new twist on the McNaughton defense and will probably continue to share the same conceptual and legal difficulties as does the insanity offense.

Unfortunately, the neuroscientific roots of human violence are complex and still not well understood. Social, genetic, familial, environmental, as well as brain dysfunctions, have all been shown to contribute to violence and aggression. After years of study of the several neural correlates of violence and aggression, there is still no unique or determinative neural cause. Research has repeatedly shown that there are many parts of the brain involved in this destructive kind of misbehavior. Animal studies have led to a contemporary theory of system of highly interactive brain regions that seem to be involved in aggression but nothing that would have a high degree of probity as an explanatory cause has ever been identified. Human studies have produced even more erratic findings than animal studies; damage to many different areas producing essentially the same kind of behavior and damage to one area producing widely variable kinds of behavior in different circumstances. Our understanding is further impeded by the fact that much of the research is based on individual studies that vary from case to case in surprising and inconstant ways. The difficulty in justifying human research except in the case of already dysfunctional people also adds difficulties to the development of a coherent theory of the brain mechanisms of aggression.

Beyond the fields in which there is a modicum of empirical biological findings are a group of behavioral problems for which we have no biological markers of any kind. These include new diagnostic categories that have probably been with us for a long time but unrecognized (e.g., autism and ADHD) and some traditional disorders (metal illnesses) for which the hope of finding a biological cause has been ever present but never fulfilled.

Despite the preliminary and incomplete nature of our understanding of the neuroscientific basis of abnormal human behavior and misbehavior, there is no question that abnormal cognitive and emotional states represent an immense set of societal and personal problems. It is also true that despite the absence of solid theoretical explanations of behavioral dysfunctions, it is possible to treat and sometimes cure them. It is clear, however, that many of the most useful therapies are ad hoc solutions to these serious problems. Drugs, electrical stimuli, as well as psychotherapies of many different kinds are known to work. However, the reasons they work almost always remain unknown. All workers in this field seem to agree that "we do not yet know what causes mental illness."

6.2 What is the Current State of Cognitive Neuroscience Theory?

This brings us to the next important general issue—the role of these psychological dysfunctions in the determination of a coherent cognitive neuroscience theory of mind-brain relationships. Currently two main assumptions guide theory development in this domain. First, the mind is conceptualized as a collection of quasi-independent cognitive modules that can be independently controlled. Second, it is widely but not universally assumed that these cognitive modules are narrowly localized in particular regions of the brain. These two assumptions have been referred to as the "new phrenology" (Uttal, 2000).

Given the current prevalence among cognitive neuroscientists of these two assumptions, it is not surprising that there is a widespread, if ill-advised, acceptance of the concept that diagnosable cognitive deficits can be interpreted as evidence of specific brain lesions. Because of all of the uncertainties and the variability of both the psychological and anatomical data, it is possible, however, to conceive of a completely different interpretation of how brain regions may be associated with these cognitive dysfunctions. That alternative is that the aphasias and their kindred dysfunctions are actually the result not of localized damage, but of disruptions of very complex and distributed systems of neural activity. This is referred to as the distributed neural network hypothesis.

One reason that this alternative theory has remained dormant is that it is terribly difficult to carry out and even conceptualize experiments on such distributed neural systems. Nevertheless, there appears to be sufficient evidence to suggest that any notion of sharply demarcated functional regions in the brain is incorrect and that these cognitive dysfunctions are the result of distributed rather than localized activity.

Another reason that argues against wide acceptance of the distribution hypothesis is that the idea of localized functional units represents a conceptual and pragmatic convenience. Conceptually, it is very easy, as discussed throughout this book, to deal with a system of separable parts as opposed to an inseparable whole. It is clear that the disruption of the function of any component of a distributed system may seriously degrade the entire system performance and, therefore, lead to cognitive deficit whose origins cannot be determined. Localization, at least, offers a promise of progress. Distribution, on the other hand, suggests that the system may not be analyzable and the problem may be intractable—an unacceptable but undeniable outcome for those of us who seek answers and explanations.

A third reason that the distributed neural system's point of view is difficult to conceptualize and harder to study is that the observed data are likely to lead to redundant and multiple explanations that cannot be distinguished, verified, or rejected. That is, if damage to any one of several regions can each produce the same cognitive deficit, then none may be necessary and any may be sufficient. This inevitably leads to an atheoretical mess in which all alternative theories are plausible.

A fourth reason is that the ability of the brain to recover functions that may have been lost (such as the ability to move a limb or to regain speech competency after a stroke) over long periods of time tends to disassociate particular regions from specific abilities. This argues that no single region has the unique capacity to embody a cognitive process.

6.3 Ethics

My goal in this book is to deal mainly with the technical matters concerning how the brain and our behavior are related, particularly in the context of how this cognitive neuroscientific data may be applied, if at all, in the courtroom. I have not dealt directly, beyond a few mentions, with the ethical problems that are generated when this body of knowledge comes into contact, as it will, with our judicial system. I leave it to others far more qualified than I in this context to deal with these important issues. Two important collections (Garland, 2004; Goodenough and Zeki, 2006) have appeared in recent years to which my readers are directed for consideration of the many ethical issues raised by cognitive neuroscience. An increasing number of scholarly articles are also being published. New professional groups such as the Neuroethics Society have been organized "to promote the development and responsible application of neuroscience through better understanding of its capabilities and consequences."

Some of the ethical issues now being raised are perennial and some are new, emerging as the potential of cognitive neuroscience to play a role in our courtrooms becoming evident in the past decade or two. Thus, traditional legal problems such as privacy and personal responsibility have taken on new significance when, for example, even the remote possibility of reading a person's thoughts with a brain imaging device is raised. Even more serious ethical issues would arise with the development of mind-altering procedures including the insertion of physical devices or drugs that would alter the cognitive processes and personality of a person. How far, one must ask, would society go in changing the personality of a felon or even, in the most extreme version, of the general public?

The list of potential ethical issues is long. Although some are based on realistic interpretations of what we know about the brain and the mind, much of it is based on flimsy speculation about how the brain can either be manipulated or can manipulate our behavior. "New age" techniques for improving our "brain power" by exercises or food supplements must contend with problems associated with employment discrimination based on the fallacious claim that we can infer personality types from brain images. The age old philosophical issue of whether or not people have free will and can make choices, and thus have responsibility, about their behavior has now been further confused with the possibility that people might be forced to take antipsychotic drugs to make them competent for a trial for which they would otherwise be considered incompetent.

The problems involved in judging future behavior on the basis of psychological tests has been with us for many years. Nowadays many of the same ethical problems previously created by testing have to be framed in the modern neuroscientific context of predicting behavior based on brain lesions or dysfunctions. More complex matters arise with forthcoming proposals that morality itself may be the outcome of the function of an identifiable brain region.

Clearly, the ethics of how and where we apply the knowledge gleaned by cognitive neuroscience is going to be a major issue as the field develops and its legal implications become clearer. If I were to summarize it all, I would argue that the major battle ground is going to be between "brain responsibility" and "behavioral responsibility." This is a fair social and judicial arena in which to wage the ethical battles that are sure to come. However, a major caveat must be made clear—many of the neuroscientific "facts" that are introduced into our judicial proceedings are less than robust; much of what is currently being introduced into the courtroom is a wild extrapolation from what scientists in this field really know. The issues of variability and replicability, discussed throughout this book, make most attempts to seek mitigation from responsibility based on knowledge of the brain premature, at best.

Perhaps the most serious problem is whether or not this knowledge should be offered in the courtroom at all. Since I have concluded that the both theoretical and empirical knowledge in this field is woefully incomplete, it seems that a reasonable argument may be made that it is not yet appropriate to attempt to use these data as legal arguments. Because of the great variability of the data and the incompleteness of our knowledge, these findings do not meet the usual standards for admissibility. The ethical arguments for and against using only that neuroscientific knowledge that may be reliable and valid are formidable enough. The argument against the use of ill-founded and controversial findings, however, is even stronger. Unfortunately, the state of this field of science is not one that yet offers compelling probative power and potency to a legal argument. Much more often, the neuroscience is used as window dressing or to generate an emotional context in which it is hoped that some responsibility can be shifted from the individual to an organic condition.

Given this state of affairs, it seems much more appropriate to argue that the behavioral mode of adjudication that has characterized courts for many years should remain the gold standard. However compelling the philosophical and theoretical argument may be that, in principle, every behavior and cognitive response is underlain by a neural state, in the final analysis it should be the behavior, not some cryptic and doubtful neural state, that should determine the outcome of a trial.

Bibliography

Abe, N., M. Suzuki, T. Tsukiura, E. Mori, K. Yamaguchi, M. Itoh, and T. Fujii. "Dissociable Roles of Prefrontal and Anterior Cingulate Cortices in Deception." *Cerebral Cortex* 16 (2006): 192-99.

Adams, D. B. "Brain Mechanisms of Aggressive Behavior: An Updated Review." *Neuroscience and Biobehavioral Reviews* 30 (2006): 304-18.

Adler, K. "A Social History of Untruth: Lie Detection and Trust in Twentieth Century America." *Representations*, no. 80 (2002): 1-33.

— — —. *The Lie Detectors: A History of an American Deception.* New York: Free Press, 2007.

Anonymous. "President's Commission for the Study of Ethical Problems in Medicine and Biomedical and Biobehavioral Research. Defining Death: A Report of the Medical, Legal, and Ethical Issues in the Determination of Death." 1-66. Washington DC: US Government Printing Office, 1981.

— — —. "Scientific Validity of Polygraph Testing: A Research Review and Evaluation." Washington DC: Office of Technology Assessment (OTA-TM-H-15), 1983.

— — —. "The Quality Standards Subcommittee of the American Academy of Neurology. Practice Parameters for Determining Brain Death in Adults (Summary Statement)." *Neurology* 45 (1995): 1012–14.

— — —. *Diagnostic and Statistical Manual of Mental Disorders DSMV-IV-TR.* Washington DC: American Psychiatric Association, 2000.

Aron, A. R., M. A Gluck, and R. A. Poldrack. "Long-Term Test-Retest Reliability of Functional MRI in a Classification Learning Task." *Neuroimage* 29 (2006): 1000-06.

257

Avidan, G, U. Hasson, R. Malach, and M. Behrmann. "Detailed Exploration of Face Related Processing in Congenital Prosopagnosia: 2 . Functional Neuro-imaging Findings." *Journal of Cognitive Neuroscience* 17 (2005): 1150-67.

Bandler jr., R. "Predatory Aggression: Midbrain-Pontine Junction Rather Than Hypothalamus as Critical Structure." *Aggressive Behavior* 1 (2006): 261-66.

Bard, P .A. "Diencephalic Mechanisms for the Expression of Rage with Special Reference to the Sympathetic Nervous System." *American Journal of Physiology* 84 (1828): 490-515.

Beecher, H. K. , R. D. Adams, and A. C. Banger. "A Definition of Irreversible Coma. Report of the Ad Hoc Committee of the Harvard Medical School to Examine the Definition of Brain Death." *Journal of the American Medical Association* 205 (1968): 337-40.

Behrmann, M., and G. Avidan. "Congenital Prosopagnosia: Face-Blind from Birth." *Trends in Cognitive Science* 9 (2005): 180-87.

Belmaker, R. H., and G. Agam. "Major Depressive Disorder." *The New England Journal of Medicine* 358 (2008): 55-68.

Bender, L. *A Visual Motor Gestalt Test and Its Clinical Use.* New York: American Orthopsychiatric Association, 1938.

Bentin, S., J. M. DeGutis, M D'Esposito, and L. C. Robertson. "Too Many Trees to See the Forest: Performance, Event-Related Potentials, and Functional Magnetic Resonance Imaging Manifestations of Integrative Congenital Prosopagnosia." *Journal of Cognitive Neuroscience* 19 (2007): 132-46.

Bergerbest, D., D. G. Ghahremani, and F. D. E. Gabrieli. "Neural Correlates of Auditory Repetition Priming: Reduce fMRI Activation in the Auditory Cortex." *Journal of Cognitive Neuroscience* 16 (2004): 966-77.

Bernard, C. "Note Sur La Curarine Et Ses Effects Physiologique." *Bulletin General of Therapie* 69 (1865): 23.

Bernat, J. L. "The Whole-Brain Concept of Death Remains Optimum Public Policy." *Journal of Law, Medicine and Ethics* 34 (2006): 35-43.

Beyerstein, B. L. "Pseudoscience and the Brain: Tuners and Tonics for Aspiring Superhumans." In *Mind-Myths: Exploring Everyday Mysteries of the Mind and Brain*, edited by S. Della Sala. New York: John Wiley and Sons, 1999.

Bitterman, M. E., and F. L. Marcuse. "Xcv Cardiovascular Responses of Innocent Persons to Criminal Interrogation." *American Journal of Psychology* LX (1947): 407-12.

Bookheimer, S. "Functional MRI of Language: New Approaches to Understanding the Cortical Organization of Semantic Processing." *Annual Review of Neuroscience* 25 (2002): 151-88.

Bradley, C. "The Behavior of Children Receiving Benzedrine." *American Journal of Psychiatry* 94 (1937): 577-85.

Bradley, R., J. Greene, E. Russ, L. Dutra, and D. Westen. "A Multidimensional Meta-Analysis of Psychotherapy for Ptsd." *American Journal of Psychiatry* 162 (2005): 214-27.

Brindley, G. S. *Physiology of the Retina and the Visual Pathway*. London: Edward Arnold, 1960.

Broca, P. P. "Loss of Speech, Chronic Softening and Partial Destruction of the Anterior Left Lobe of the Brain." *Bulletin de la Société Anthropologique* 2 (1861): 235-38.

Broca, P. "Nouvelle Observation Aphémie Produite Par Un Lesion De La Moite Posterieure Des Deuxieme Et Troisieme Circonvolutions Frontales." *Bulletins de la Société Anatomique de Paris* 6 (1861): 398–407.

Brodmann, K. *Brodmann's Localization in the Cerebral Cortex*. London: Imperial College Press, 1909/1999.

Brower, M. C., and B. H. Price. "Neuropsychiatry of Frontal Lobe Dysfunction in Violent and Criminal Behavior: A Critical Review." *Journal of Neurology, Neurosurgery, and Psychiatry* 71 (2001): 720-26.

Brutus, M., M. B. Shaikh, A. Siegel, and H. E. Siegel. "An Analysis of the Mechanisms Underlying Septal Control of Hypothalamically Elicited Aggression in the Cat." *Brain Research* 310 (1984): 235-48.

Bufkin, J. L., and V. R. Luttrell. "Neuroimaging Studies of Aggressive and Violent Behavior." *Trauma, Violence, and Abuse* 6 (2005): 176-91.

Cabeza, R., and L. Nyberg. " Imaging Cognition II: An Empirical Review of 275 Pet and fMRI Studies." *Journal of Cognitive Neuroscience* 12 (2000): 1-47.

Callicott, J.H., and D. R. Weinberger. "Neuropsychiatric Dynamics: The Study of Mental Illness Using Functional Magnetic Resonance Imaging." *European Journal of Radiology* 30 (1999): 95-104.

Cao, Y., E. M. Vikingstad, K. Paige-George, A. F. Johnson, and K. M. A. Welch. "Cortical Language Activation in Stroke Patients Recovering from Aphasia with Functional MRI." *Stroke* 30 (1999): 2331-40.

Chance, B., S. Nioka, and y. Chen. "Shining New Light on Brain Function." *OE magazine* 3 (2003): 16-20.

Chaytor, N., and M. Schmitter-Edgecombe. "The Ecological Validity of Neuropsychological Tests: A Review of the Literature in Everyday Cognitive Skills." *Neuropsychology Review* 13 (2003): 181-97.

— — —. "The Ecological Validity of Neuropsychological Tests: A Review of the Literature on Everyday Cognitive Skills." *Neuropsychology Review* 13 (2003): 181-97.

Clark, D. L., N. N. Boutros, and M. F. Mendez. *The Brain and Behavior: An Introduction to Behavioral Neuroanatomy.* New York: Cambridge University Press, 2005.

Coltheart, M. "Assumptions and Methods in Cognitive Neuropsychology." In *The Handbook of Cognitive Neuropsychology: What Deficits Reveal About the Human Mind*, edited by B. Rapp. Philadelphia: The Psychology Press, 2000.

Cormack, A. M. *Journal of Applied Physics* 34 (1963): 2722.

— — —. *Journal of Applied Physics* 35 (1964): 2908.

Damadian, R. "Tumor Detection by Nuclear Magnetic Resonance." *Science* 171 (1971): 1151-53.

Damasio, A. R., H. Damasio, and G. W. Van Hoesen. "Prosopagnosia: Anatomic Basis and Behavioral Mechanisms." *Neurology* 32 (1982): 331-41.

Damasio, H. "Neuroanatomical Correlates of the Aphasias." In *Acquired Apahasia*, edited by M. T. Sarno. New York: Academic Press, 1991.

Damasio, H., T. Grabowski, R. Frank, A. M. Galaburda, and A. R. Damasio. "The Return of Phineas Gage: Clues About the Brain from the Skull of a Famous Patient." *Science* 264 (1994): 1102-05.

Darby, D. *Neuropsychology, 5th Edition*. New York: Churchill Livingstone, 2004.

Davatzikos, C., K. Ruparel, Y. Fan, D. Shen, M. Acharyya, J. W. Loughhead, R. C. Gur, and D. D. Langleben. "Classifying Spatial Patterns of Brain Activity with Machine Methods: Application to Lie Detection." *Center for Cognitive Science of University of Pittsburgh Neuroethics Publications* (2005).

Dax, M. "Lesions De La Moitie De L'encephale Coincident Avec L'oubli Des Signes De La Pensee." Paper presented at the Congress Meridonal tenu a Montpellier 1836.

DeAngelis, C. D., and P.B. Fontanarosa. "Impugning the Integrity of Medical Science: The Adverse Effects of Industry Influence." *Journal of the American Medical Association* 299 (2008): 1833-35.

Delgado, J. M. R. "Aggressive Behavior Evoked by Radio Stimulation in Monkey Colonies." *American Zoologist* 6 (1966): 669-81.

———. "Social Rank and Radio-Stimulated Aggressiveness in Monkeys." *Journal of Nervous ad Mental Diseases* 144 (1967): 383-90.

Descartes, R. *A Discourse of a Method for the Well-Guiding of Reason and the Discovery of Truth in the Sciences (English Translation)*. London: Thomas Newcombe, 1649.

Dubin, M. *Agnosia, Aphasia, Apraxia and Related Terms for Cognitive, Behavioral, and Neurological Disorders* University of Colorado, 2008 [cited March 10, 2008. Available from http://spot.colorado.edu/~dubin/talks/agnosia.html.

Duhem, P. M. M. *The Aim and Structure of Physical Theory*. Translated by L. de Broglie. New York: Atheneum, 1906/1962.

Efron, R. *The Decline and Fall of Hemispheric Specialization*. Hillsdale NJ: Erlbaum, 1990.

Elliott, F. A. "Biological Roots of Violence." *Proceedings of the American Philosophical Society* 127 (1983): 84-94.

Ellison, G. D., and J. P. Flynn. "Organized Aggressive Behavior in Cats after Surgical Isolation of the Hypothalamus." *Archives italiennes de biologie* 106 (1968): 1-20.

Emery, N. J., J. P. Capitanio, W. A. Mason, C. J. Machado, S. P. Mendoza, and D. G. Amaral. "The Effects of Bilateral Lesions of the Amygdala on Dyadic Social Interactions in Rhesus Monkeys (Macaca Mulatta)." *Behavioral Neuroscience* 115 (2001): 515-44.

Engelien, A., E. Stern, and D. Silbersweig. "Functional Neuroimaging of Human Central Auditory Processing in Normal Subjects and Patients with Neurological and Neuropsychiatric Disorders." *Journal of Clinical and Experimental Neuropsychology* 23 (2001): 94-120.

Farwell, L. A., and E. Donchin. "The Truth Will Out: Interrogative Polygraphy ("Lie Detection") with Event-Related Brain Potentials." *Psychophysiology* 28 (1991): 531-47.

Farwell, L. A., and S. S. Smith. "Using Brain Mermer Testing to Detect Knowledge Despite Efforts to Conceal." *Journal of Forensic Science* 46 (2001): 135-43.

Fernandez, B., D. Cardebat, J-F. Demonet, P. A. Joseph, J-M. Mazaux, M. Barat, and M. Allard. "Functional MRI Follow-up Study of Language Processes in Heathy Subjects and During Recovery in a Case of Aphasia." *Stroke* 35 (2004): 2171-76.

Ferraro, R. F., R. V. Park, H. Hage, and S. Palm. "Inhibiting Irrelevant Information in Malingered Amnesia." *The Psychological Record* 55 (2005): 125-34.

Ferrero, G. L. *The Criminal Man (Second Edition)*. Montclair NJ: Patterson Smith, 1911/1972.

Finkelstein, I., and N. A. Silberman. *The Bible Unearthed: Archeology's New Vision of Ancient Israel and the Origin of Its Sacred Texts*. New York: Simon and Schuster, 2001.

Fisher, G. "The Jury's Rise as Lie Detector." *Yale Law Journal* 107 (1997): 575-713.

Fodor, J. A. *The Modularity of Mind*. Cambridge MA: MIT Press, 1983.

Fridriksson, J., and L. Morrow. "Cortical Activation Associated with Language Task Difficulty in Aphasia." *Aphasiology* 19 (2005): 239-50.

Ganis, S. M. Kosslyn, S. Stose, W. L. Thompson, and D. A. Yugelun-Todd. "Neural Correlates of Different Types of Deception: An fMRI Investigation." *Cerebral Cortex* 13 (2003): 830-36.

Garland, B., and P. W. Glimcher. "Cognitive Neuroscience and the Law." *Current Opinion in Neurobiology* 16 (2006): 130-34.

Giacino, J. T., S. Ashwal, N. Childs, R. Cranford, B. Jennett, D. I. Katz, J. P. Kelly, J. H. Rosenberg, J. Whyte, R. D. Zafonte, and N. D. Zasler. "The Minimally Conscious State: Definition and Diagnostic Criteria." *Neurology* 58 (2002): 349-53.

Goltz, F. "Der Hund Ohne Grosshirn. Siebente Abhandlung Uber Die Verrichtungen Des Grosshirn." *Pfluegers Archives ges. Physiologie* 51 (1892): 570-614.

Goodenough, O. R., and S. Zeki, eds. *Law and the Brain*. Oxford: Oxford University, 2006.

Goodson, J. L., R. Eibach, J. Sakata, and E. Adkins-Regan. "Effect of Septal Lesions on Male Song and Aggression in the Colonial Zebra Finch (Taeniopygia Guttata) and the Territorial Field Sparrow (Spizella Pusilla)." *Behavioural Brain Research* 101 (1999): 167-80.

Gödel, K. "Uber Formal Unentscheidbare Satz Der Principia Mathematica Undverwandter Systeme I. (on Formally Undecidable Propositions in Principia Mathematica and Related Systems.)." *Monatshefte fur Mathematik und Physik* 38 (1931): 173-98.

Grafman, J., K. Schwab, D. Warden, A. Pridgen, H. R. Brown, and A. M. Salazar. "Frontal Lobe Injuries, Violence , and Aggression." *Neurology* 46 (1996): 1231-38.

Graham, J., and R. W. Gerard. "Membrane Potential and Excitation of Impaled Single Muscle Fibers." *Journal of Cellular and Comparative Physiology* 28 (1946): 99-117.

Graziano, M. S. A. "A System of Multimodal Areas in the Primate Brain." *Neuron* 29 (2001): 4-6.

Greene, J., and J. Cohen. "For the Law, Neuroscience Changes Nothing and Everything." *Proceedings of the Transactions of the Royal Society of London B.* 359 (2004): 1775-85.

Gregg, T. R., and A. Siegel. "Brain Structures and Neurotransmitters Regulating Aggression in Cats: Implications for Human Aggression." *Progress in Neuropsychopharmacology and Biological Psychiatry* 25 (2001): 91-140.

Grezes, J., S. Berthoz, and R. E. Passingham. "Amygdala Activation When One Is the Target of Deceit: Did He Lie to You or to Someone Else?" *NeuroImage* 30 (2006): 601-08.

Grubin, D., and L. Madsen. "Lie Detection and the Polygraph: A Historical Review." *Journal of Forensic Psychiatry and Psychology* 16 (2005): 357-69.

Hadjikhani, N, and B. de Gelder. "Neural Basis of Prosopagnosia: An fMRI Study." *Human Brain Mapping* 16 (2002): 176-82.

Hale, S. *The Man Who Lost His Language: A Case of Aphasia*. London: Jessica Kingsley Publishers, 2007.

Harley, T. A. "Does Cognitive Neuropsychology Have a Future?" *Cognitive Neuropsychology* 21 (2004): 3-16.

Harlow, J.M. "Recovery from a Passage of an Iron Bar through the Head." *Publications of the Massachusetts Medical Society* 2 (1868): 327-47.

Hawkins, F. H. *Human Factors in Flight (2nd Ed.) Orlady, H. W. (Ed)*. Hants England: Avebury Aviation, 1993.

Hawkins, K. A., and K. K. Trobst. "Frontal Lobe Dysfunction and Aggression: Conceptual Issues and Research Findings." *Aggression and Violent Behavior* 5 (2000): 147-57.

Healy, E. W., D. C. Moser, K. L. Morrow-Odom, D. A. Hall, and J. Fridiksson. "Speech Perception in MRI Scanner Noise by Persons with Aphasia." *Journal of Speech, Language, and Hearing Research* 50 (2007): 323-34.

Heimburger, R. F., C. C. Whitlock, and J. E. Kalsbeck. "Stereotaxic Amygdalotomy for Epilepsy with Aggressive Behavior." *Journal of the American Medical Association* 198 (1966): 741-45.

Henkin, L. "Systems, Formal, and Models of Formal Systems." In *The Encyclopedia of Philosophy (Vol. 8)*, edited by P. Edwards. New York: Macmillan and the Free Press, 1967.

Hilgetag, C. C., M. A. O'Neil, and M. P. Young. "Indeterminate Organization of the Visual System." *Science* 271 (1996): 776-77.

Hillis, A. E. "Aphasia: Progress in the Last Quarter of a Century." *Neurology* 69 (2007): 200-13.

Hodgkin, A. L., and A. L. Huxley. "Action Potentials Recorded from inside a Nerve Fiber." *Nature* 144 (1939): 710.

Horton, K. D., S. A. Smith, N. K. Barghout, and D. A. Connolly. "The Use of Indirect Memory Tests to Assess Malingered Amnesia." *Journal of Experimental Psychology: General* 121 (1992): 326-51.

Hunsley, J., C. M. Lee, and J. M. Wood. "Controversial and Questionable Assessment Techniques." In *Science and Pseudoscience in Clinical Psychology*, edited by S. O. Lilienfeld, S. J. Lynn and J. M. Lohr, 39-76. New York: The Guilford Press, 2003.

Iacono, W. G. "Oral Statement Regarding Polygraph Screening of Federal Employees and Job Applicants." *http://www.antipolygraph.org/hearings/senate-judiciary-2001/iacono-statement.shtml* (2001).

James, W. *The Principles of Psychology*. New York: Holt, 1890.

James, T. W., J. Culham, G. K. Humphrey, A. D. Milner, and M. A. Goodale. "Ventral Occipital Lesions Impair Object Recognition but Not Object-Directed Grasping: An fMRI Study." *Brain* 126 (2003): 2463-75.

Kaas, J. H., R.J. Nelson, M. Sur, and M.M. Merzenich. "Organization of the Somatosensory Cortex in Primates." In *The Organization of the Cerebral Cortex: Proceedings of a Neuroscience Research Program Colloquium*, edited by F. O. Schmitt, Worden F. G., G. Adelman and S. G. Dennis. Cambridge MA: MIT Press, 1981.

Kandel, E., and D. Freed. "Frontal-Lobe Dysfunction and Antisocial Behavior: A Review." *Journal of Clinical Psychology* 45 (1989): 404-13.

Kanner, L. "Autistic Disturbances of Effective Control." *Nervous Child* 2 (1943): 217-50.

Kanwisher, N., J. McDermott, and M. M. Chun. "The Fusiform Face Area: A Module in Human Extrastriate Cortex Specialized for Face Perception." *Journal of Neuroscience* 17 (1997): 4302-11.

Kaufer, D., M. Nuwer, and D. F. Benson. "Two Cases of Generalized Auditory Agnosia: Electrophysiological Distinction and Neurobehavioral Correlates." *Electroencephalography and Clinical Neurophysiology* 95 (1995): 21P.

Keeler, L. "A Method for Deception Detection." *American Journal of Police Science* 1 (1930): 38-51.

—— —. "Debunking the Lie Detector." *Journal of Criminal Law and Criminology* 25 (1934): 153-59.

Kelly, A. H., L. E. Beaton, and H. W. Magoun. "A Midbrain Mechanism for Facio-Vocal Activity." *Journal of Neurophysiology* 9 (1946): 181-89.

Kennedy, J. L. " A Possible Artifact in Electroencephalography." *Psychological Review,* 66 (1959): 347-52.

Klein, D. B. *A History of Scientific Psychology: Its Origins and Philosophical Backgrounds.* New York: Basic Books, 1970.

Kluver, H., and P. C. Bucy. "Preliminary Analysis of Functions of the Temporal Lobes in Monkeys." *Archives of Neurology and Psychiatry* 42 (1939): 979-1000.

Konorski, J. *Integrative Activity of the Brain: An Interdisciplinary Approach.* Chicago: University of Chicago Press, 1967.

Koppelman, E. R. "The Dead Donor Rule and the Concept of Death: Severing the Ties That Bind Them." *The American Journal of Bioethics* 3 (2003): 1-9.

Kozel, F. A., L. J. Revell, J. P. Lorberbaum, A. Shastri, J. D. Elhai, M. D. Horner, A. Smith, Z. Nahas, Bohning. D. E., and M. S. George. "A Pilot Study of Functional Magnetic Resonance Correlates of Deception in Healthy Young Men." *Journal of Psychiatry and Clinical Neuroscience* 16 (2004(a)): 295-305.

Kozel, F. A., T. M. Padgett, and M. S. George. "A Replication Study of Neural Correlates of Perception." *Behavioral Neuroscience* 118 (2004(b)): 852-56.

Kozel, F. A., K. A. Johnson, Q. Mu, E. L. Grenesko, S. J. Laken, and M. S. George. "Detecting Deception Using Functional Magnetic Resonance Imaging." *Biological Psychiatry* 58 (2005): 605-13.

Kriegeskorte, N., E. Formisano, B. Sorger, and R. Goebel. "Individual Faces Elicit Distinct Response Patterns in Human Anterior Temporal Cortex." *Proceedings of the National Academy of Sciences of the United States of America* 104 (2007): 20600-05.

Kruk, M. R., A. M. Van der Poel, W. Meelis, J. Hermans, P. G. Mostert, J. Mos, and A. H. Lohman. "Discriminant Analysis of the Localization of Aggression-Inducing Electrode Placements in the Hypothalamus of Male Rats." *Brain Research* 260 (1983): 61-79.

Kruk, M. R., K. G. C. Westphal, A. M. M. Van Erp, J. Van Asperen, J. Cave, B. J. Slater, J. de Koning, and J. Haller. "The Hypothalamus: Cross-Roads of Endocrine and Behavioural Regulation in Grooming and Aggression." *Neuroscience and Biobehavioral Reviews* 23, no. 163-177 (1998).

Kuebler, A., B. Kotchoubey, H. -P. Salzmann, N. Ghanayim, J. Perelmouter, V. Homberg, and N. Birbaumer. "Self-Regulation of Slow Cortical Potentials in Completely Paralyzed Human Patients." *Neuroscience Newsletters* 252 (1998): 171-74.

Kuhn, T. S. *The Essential Tension: Selected Studies in Scientific Tradition and Change.* Chicago: University of Chicago Press, 1977.

Lange, J. T., C. L. Lange, and R. B. G. Cabaltica. "Primary Care Treatment of Post-Traumatic Stress Disorder." *American Family Physician* 62 (2000).

Langleben, D. D., L. Schroeder, J. A. Maldjian, R. C. Gur, S. McDonald, J. D. Ragland, C. P. O'Brien, and A. R. Childress. "Brain Activity During Simulated Deception: An Event-Related Functional Magnetic Resonance Study." *NeuroImage* 15 (2002): 727-32.

Langleben, D. D., J. W. Loughhead, W. B. Bilker, K. Ruparel, A. R. Childress, S. I. Busch, and R. C. Gur. "Telling Truth from Lie in Individual Subjects with Fast Event-Related fMRI." *Human Brain Mapping* 26 (2005): 262-72.

Larson, J. A. "Modification of the Marston Deception Test." *Journal of Criminal Law and Criminology* 12 (1921): 390-99.

Lashley, K. S. 1950. , 4, . "In Search of the Engram." In *Symposia of the Society for Experimental Biology*, 454-82, 1950.

Leahey, T. H. *A History of Psychology: Main Currents in Psychological Thought.* Upper Saddle River NJ: Prentice Hall, 1997.

Lee, T. M. C., H-L. Liu, L-H Tan, C. C. H. Chan, S. Mahankali, C-M. Feng, J. Hou, P. T. Fox, and J-H. Gao. "Lie Detection by Functional Magnetic Resonance Imaging." *Human Brain Mapping* 15 (2002): 157-64.

Lee, T. M. C., H-L. Liu, C. C. H. Chan, Y-B. Ng, P. T. Fox, and J-H. Gao. "Neural Correlates of Feigned Memory Impairment." *NeuroImage* 28 (2005): 305-13.

Lehar, S. *Harmonic Resonance Theory: An Alternative to the "Neuron Doctrine" Paradigm of Neurocomputation to Address Gestalt Properties of Perception. [Internet].* [cited October 1, 2003]. Available from http://cns-alumni. bu.edu/~slehar/webstuff/hr1.html.

Leiguarda, R. C., and C. D. Marsden. "Limb Apraxias: Higher-Order Disorders of Sensorimotor Integration." *Brain* 123 (2000): 860-79.

Lennenberg, E. H. "Language and Brain: Developmental Aspects." *Neurosciences Research Program Bulletin* 12 (1974): 511-656.

Leyton, A. S. F., and C. S. Sherrington. "Observations of the Excitable Cortex of the Chimpanzee, Orang-Utan, and Gorilla." *Quarterly Journal of Experimental Physiology* 11 (1917): 135-222.

Liepmann, H. "Das Krankheitsbild Der Aphasia (Motorische Asymbolie)." *Monatsschrift für Psychiatrie und Neurologie* 8 (1900).

Lissauer, H. "A Case of Visual Agnosia with a Contribution to Theory (Translated by M. Jackson)." *Cognitive Neuropsychology* 5 (1890/1988): 157-92.

Lombroso, C. *L'homme Criminel Paris, Alcan.* Paris: Alcan, 1895.

Luria, A. R. *The Man with a Shattered World: The History of a Brain Wound (Translated by L. Solotaroff).* Cambridge MA: Harvard University Press, 1972/2004.

Lykken, D. T. *A Tremor in the Blood: Uses and Abuses of the Lie Detector (2nd Edition)*: Plenum Press, 1998.

MacCorquodale, K., and P. E. Meehl. "On a Distinction between Hypothetical Constructs and Intervening Variables." *Psychological Review* 55 (1948): 95-107.

MacLean, P. D., and J. M. R. Delgado. "Electrical and Chemical Stimulation of Fronto-Temporal Portions of Limbic System in Waking Animals." *Electroencephalography and Clinical Neurophysiology* 5 (1953): 91-100.

MacLean, P. D. *The Triune Brain in Evolution: Role in Paleocerebral Functions.* New York: Plenum Press, 1990.

Malcolm, C. *Who Made the First Computer?* 2001 |cited 10-7-2007. Available from www.dai.ed.ac.uk/homes/cam/fcomp.shtml.

Malin, E. L., and McGaugh J. L. "Differential Involvement of the Hippocampus, Anterior, Cingulate Cortex, and Basolateral Amygdala in Memory for Context and Foot Shock." *Proceedings of the National Academy of Science* 103 (2006): 1959-63.

Marchant, G. "Brain Scanning in the Courts: The Story So Far." Paper presented at the The Law and Ethics of Brain Scanning, Phoenix AZ, April 13, 2007.

Marcuse, F. L., and M. E. Bitterman. "Minimal Cues in the Peak-of-Tension Procedure for Determining Guilt." *American Journal of Psychology* LIX (1946): 144-46.

Marsh, E. B., and A. E. Hillis. "Recovery from Aphasia Following Brain Injury: The Role of Reorganization." *Progress in Brain Research* 157 (2006): 143-56.

Marx, M. H., and W. A. Hillix. *Systems and Theories in Psychology.* New York: McGraw-Hill, 1973.

Maschke, G. W., and G. J. Scalabrini. *The Lie Behind the Lie Detector* AntiPolygraph.org, 2003 |cited. Available from http://www.antipolygraph.org/pubs.shtml.

Matin, L., E. Picoult, J. K. Stevens, M. W. Edwards, D. Young, and R. MacArthur. "Oculoparalytic Illusion: Visual-Field Dependent Spatial Mislocalizations by Humans Partially Paralyzed with Curare." *Science* 216 (1982): 198-201.

Matin, L., J. K. Stevens, and E. Picoult. "Perceptual Consequences of Extra-ocular Muscle Paralysis." In *Oriented Behavior*, edited by A. Hein and M. Jeannerod, 243-62. New York: Springer-Verlag, 1983.

Mattson, J., and M/ Simon. *The Pioneers of Nmr and Magnetic Resonance in Medicine: The Story of MRI.* Jericho, NY: Dean Books Co., 1996.

McCabe, D. P., and A. D. Castel. "Seeing Is Believing: The Effect of Brain Images on Judgments of Scientific Reasoning." *Cognition* (2007): 343-352.

McEllistrem, J. E. "Affective and Predatory Violence: A Bimodal Classification System of Human Aggression and Violence." *Aggression and Violent Behavior* 10 (2004): 1-30.

McKay, C., J. E. Casey, J. Wertheimer, and N. L. Fichtenberg. "Reliability and Validity of the Rbans in a Traumatic Brain Injury Sample." *Archives of Clinical Neuropsychology* 22 (2007): 91-98.

Michell, J. *Measurement in Psychology: Critical History of a Methodological Concept*. Cambridge: Cambridge University Press, 1999.

Miller, G. "The Roots of Morality." *Science* 320 (2008): 734-37.

Mohamed, F. B., S. H. Faro, N.J. Gordon, S. M. Platek, H. Ahmad, and Williams J. M. "Brain Mapping of Deception and Truth Telling About an Ecological Valid Situation: Functional Mr and Polygraph Investigation--Initial Experience." *Radiology* 238 (2006): 679-88.

Mohandas, A. , and S.N. Chou. "Brain Death: A Clinical and Pathological Study." *Neurosurgery* 35 (1974): 211-18.

Mollaret, P., and M. Goulon. "Le Coma Depasse. Memoire Preliminaire." *Revue Neurologie* 101 (1959): 3-15.

Mollenhoff, C. R. *Atanasoff: Forgotten Father of the Computer*. Ames: Iowa State University Press, 1988.

Moore, E. F. "Gedanken-Experiments on Sequential Machines." In *Automata Studies*, edited by C. E. Shannon and J. McCarthy, 129-53. Princeton NJ: Princeton University Press, 1956.

Morgan, C. T., and E. Stellar. *Physiological Psychology (Second Edition)*. New York: McGraw Hill, 1950.

Moriarty, J. C. "Flickering Admissibility: Neuroimaging Evidence in the U. S. Courts." *Behavioral Sciences and the Law* 26 (2008): 29-49.

Morse, S. J. "New Neuroscience, Old Problems." In *Neuroscience and the Law*, edited by B. Garland and M. S. Frankel, 157-98. New York: Dana Press, 2004.

Moyer, K. E. "Kinds of Aggression and Their Physiological Basis." *Communications in Behavioral Biology* 2A (1968): 65-87.

NAS. *The Polygraph and Lie Detection:A Report by the Committee to Review the Scientific Evidence on the Polygraph; National Research Council of the Us*. Washington DC.: National Academies Press, 2003.

Neumann, J., J. Derfuss, G Lohmann, and D. Y. von Cramon. "The Meta-Analysis of Functional Imaging Data Using Replicator Dynamics." *Human Brain Mapping* 25 (2005): 165-73.

Newman, S. "The Medial Extended Amygdala in Male Reproductive Behavior." *Annals of the New York Academy of Sciences* 877 (1999): 242-57.

Nielsen, J. M. *Agnosia, Apraxia, Aphasia Their Vale in Cerebral Localization.* New York: Paul B. Hoeber, 1936.

Nunez, J. M., B. J. Casey, T. Egner, T. Hare, and J. Hirsch. "Intentional False Responding Shares Neural Substrate with Response Conflict and Cognitive Control." *NeuroImage* 25 (2005): 267-77.

Ogawa, S., T. M. Lee, A. R. Kay, and D. W. Tank. "Brain Magnetic Resonance Imaging with Contrast Dependent on Blood Oxygenation." *Proceedings. National . Academies . Science. (USA)* 87: 9868-72.

Ogden, J. A. *Fractured Minds: A Case-Study Approach to Clinical Neuropsychology.* New York: Oxford University Press,, 1996.

Olson, P. L., and E. Farber. *Forensic Aspects of Driver Perception and Response, 2nd Ed.* Tucson: Lawyers and Judges Publishing Company, 2003.

Owen, A. M., M. R. Coleman, M. Boly, M. H. Davis, S. Laureys, and J. D. Pickard. "Detecting Awareness in the Vegetative State." *Science* 313 (2006): 1402.

Papez, J. W. " A Proposed Mechanism of Emotion." *Journal of Neuropsychiatry and Clinical Neuroscience* 7 (1937): 103-12.

Penfield, W., and H. H. Jasper. *Epilepsy and the Functional Anatomy of the Human Brain.* Boston: Little, Brown, 1954.

Penfield, W., and L. Roberts. *Speech and Brain Mechanisms.* Princeton: Princeton University Press, 1959.

Pevsner, J. "Leonardo Da Vinci: Neuroscientist." *Scientific American*, no. April (2005).

Phan, K. L., A. Magalhaes, T. J. Ziemlewicz, D. A. Fitzgerald, C. Green, and W. Smith. "Neural Correlates of Telling Lies: A Functional Magnetic Resonance Imaging Study at 4 Tesla." *Academic Radiology* 12 (2005): 164-72.

Phelps, M. E., E. J. Hoffman, N. A. Mullni, and M. M. Ter-Pergossian. "Application of Annihilation Coincidence Detection to Transaxial Reconstruction Tomography." *Journal of Nuclear Medicine* 16 (1975): 210-24.

Pillmann, F., A. Rohde, S. Ullrich, S. Draba, U. Sannemuller, and A. Marneros. "Violence, Criminal Behavior, and the Eeg: Significance of the Left Hemispheric Focal Abnormalities." *Journal of Neuropsychiatry and Clinical Neurosciences* 11 (1999): 454-57.

Pinel, J.P. J. *Biopsychology*. Needham Heights MA: Allyn and Bacon, 1993.

Poldrack, R. A. "Can Cognitive Processes Be Inferred from Neuroimaging Data." *Trends in Cognitive Science* 10 (2006): 59-63.

Popper, K. R. *The Logic of Scientific Discovery*. Translated by K. R. Popper, J. Freed and L. Freed. New York: Basic Books, 1959.

Premack, D. G., and G. Woodruff. "Does the Chimpanzee Have a Theory of Mind?" *Behavioral and Brain Sciences* 1 (1978): 615-36.

Psaty, B. M., and R. A. Kronmal. "Reporting Mortality Findings in Trials of Rofecoxib for Alzheimer Disease or Cognitive Impairment." *Journal of the American Medical Association* 299 (2008): 1813-17.

Rabi, I. I., J. R. Zacharias, S. Millman, and P. Kusch. " A New Method for Measuring Nuclear Magnetic Moments." *Physical Review* 53 (1937): 318.

Raine, A. "Biosocial Studies of Antisocial and Violent Behavior in Children and Adults: A Review." *Journal of Abnormal Child Psychology* 30 (2002): 311-26.

Ramirez, J. M., and J. M. Andreu. "Aggression, and Some Related Psychological Constructs (Anger, Hostility, and Impulsivity) Some Comments from a Research Project." *Neuroscience and Biobehavioral Reviews* 30, no. 276-291 (2006).

Rapp, B. *The Handbook of Cognitive Neuropsychology*. Philadelphia PA: Psychology Press, 2001.

Ray, I. *A Treatise on Medical Jurisprudence*. Boston: Little Brown, 1838.

Raz, A., B. Lieber, F. Soliman, J. Buhle, J. Posner, B. S. Peterson, and M. I. Posner. "Ecological Nuances in Functional Magnetic Resonance Imaging (fMRI): Psychological Stressors, Posture, and Hydrostatics." *Neuroimage* 25 (2005): 1-7.

Reitan, R. M., and D. Wolfson. *The Halstead-Reitan Neuropsychological Test Battery: Theory and Clinical Interpretation.* Tucson: Neuropsychology Press, 1985.

Robinson, D. N. *Wild Beasts and Idle Humours: The Insanity Defense from Antiquity to the Present.* Cambridge MA: Harvard University Press, 1996.

Robinson, D. *The Mind.* Oxford: Oxford University Press, 1998.

Rose, A. M. *Theory and Method in the Social Sciences.* Minneapolis: The University of Minnesota Press, 1954.

Rosen, G. M., and S. Taylor. "Pseudo-Ptsd." *Journal of Anxiety Disorders* 21 (2007): 201-10.

Rosenfeld, J. P. "Brain Fingerprinting: A Critical Analysis." *The Scientific Review of Mental Health Practice* 4 (2005): 20-37.

Roskies, A. L. "Neuroimaging and Inferential Distance." *Neuroethics* 1 (2008): 19-30.

Ross, J S., K. P. Hill, D. S. Egilman, and H. M. Krumholz. "Guest Authorship and Ghostwriting in Publications Related to Rofecoxib." *Journal of the American Medical Association* 299 (2008): 1800-10.

Rossion, B., R. Caldara, M. Seghier, A-M. Schuller, F. Lazeyras, and E. Mayer. "A Network of Occipital-Temporal Face-Sensitive Areas Besides the Right Middle Fusiform Gyrus Is Necessary for Normal Face Processing." *Brain* 126 (2003): 2381-95.

Sacks, O. *The Man Who Mistook His Wife for a Hat: And Other Clinical Tales (5th Ed.).* New York: Touchstone, 1985/1998.

Saks, M. J., and J. J. Koehler. "The Coming Paradigm Shift in Forensic Identification Science." *Science* 309 (2005): 892-95.

Sanders, M. S., and E. J. McCormick. *Human Factors in Engineering and Design.* New York: McGraw Hill, 1993.

Saunders, K. W. "A Disconnect between Law and Neuroscience: Modern Brain Science, Media Influences, and Juvenile Justice." *Utah Law Review* 2005 (2005): 695-741.

Seagrave, K. *Lie Detectors: A Social History.* Jefferson NC: McFarland & Company, 2003.

Searle, J. R. *The Rediscovery of the Mind.* Cambridge MA: MIT Press, 1992.

Semon, R. *The Mneme.* London: George Allen and Unwin, 1921.

Settergen, G. "Brain Death: An Important Paradigm Shift in the 20th Century." *Acta Anaesthesiologica Scandinavica* 47 (2003): 1053-58.

Shallice, T. *From Neuropsychology to Mental Structure.* Cambridge: Cambridge University Press, 1988.

Shenton, M. E., C.C. Dickey, M. Frumin, and R. W. McCarkey. "A Review of MRI Findings in Schizophrenia." *Schizophrenia Research* 49 (2001): 1-52.

Shorter, J. M. "Other Minds." In *The Encyclopedia of Philosophy (Volume 6),* edited by P. Edwards, 7-13. New York: Macmillan, 1967.

Siegel, A., and J. P. Flynn. "Differential Effects of Electrical Stimulation and Lesions of the Hippocampus and Adjacent Regions Upon Attack Behavior in Cats." *Brain Research* 7 (1968): 252-67.

Siegel, A. *The Neurobiology of Aggression and Rage.* Boca Raton: CRC Press, 2005.

Smith, S. M., H. O. Brown, J. E. P. Toman, and L. S. Goodman. "The Lack of Cerebral Effects of D-Tubocurarine." *Anesthesiology* 8 (1947): 1-14.

Spence, S. A., T. F. D. Farrow, A. E. Herford, I. D. Wilkinson, Y. Zheng, and P. W. R. Woodruff. "Behavioral and Functional Anatomical Correlations of Deception in Humans." *Brain Imaging* 12 (2001): 2849-53.

Spence, S. A., M. D. Hunter, T. F. D. Farrow, R. D. Green , D. H. Leung, C. J. Hughes, and V. Ganesan. "A Cognitive Neurobiological Account of Deception: Evidence from Functional Neuroimaging." *Philosophical Transactions of the Royal Society of London (B)* 359 (2004): 1755-62.

Spiegel, A. "The Dictionary of Disorder: How One Man Revolutionized Psychiatry." *New Yorker, January 3, 2005* (2005): 56-63.

Squire, L. R., C. E. L. Stark, and R. E. Clark. "The Medial Temporal Lobe." *Annual Review of Neuroscience* 27 (2004): 279-306.

Steeves, J. K. E., G. K. Humphrey, J. C. Culham, R. S. Menon, and M. A. Goodale. "Scene Classification and Parahippocampal Place Area Activation in an Individual with Visual Form Agnosia [Abstract]." *Journal of Vision* 2 (2002): 495.

Steinberg, L., and E Scott, S. "Less Guilty by Reason of Adolescence: Developmental Immaturity, Diminished Responsibility, and the Juvenile Death Penalty." *American Psychologist* 58 (2003): 1009-18.

Still, G. F. "Some Abnormal Psychical Conditions in Children: The Goulstonian Lectures." *Lancet* 1 (1902): 1008-12.

Strawson, P. F. "Critical Notice of Wittgenstein's Philosophical Investigations." *Mind* 63 (1954): 70-99.

Swiercinsky, D. P. *Tests Commonly Used in a Neuropsychological Examination* 2001 [cited November 15, 2007. Available from http://brainsource.com/nptests.htm.

Szasz, T. S. "The Myth of Mental Illness." *American Psychologist* 15 (1960): 113-18.

Talairach, J., and P. Tournoux. *Co-Planar Stereotaxic Atlas of the Human Brain: An Approach to Cerebral Imaging.* Translated by M. Rayport. New York: Thieme Medical Publishers, 1988.

Talbot, M. "Duped: Can Brain Scans Uncover Lies." *The New Yorker*, July 2 2007, 52-61.

Tateno, A., R. E. Jorge, and R. G. Robinson. "Clinical Correlates of Aggressive Behavior after Traumatic Brain Injury." *Journal of Neuropsychiatry and Clinical Neuroscience* 15 (2003): 155-60.

Teasdale, G., and B. Jennett. "Assessment of Coma and Impaired Consciousness." *The Lancet* 304 (1974): 81-84.

Ter-Pogossian, M. M., M. E Phelps, E. J. Hoffman, and N. A. Mullani. "A Positron-Emission Transaxial Tomograph for Nuclear Imaging (Pett)" *Radiology* 114 (1975): 114: 89.

Thierry, G., and C. J. Price. "Dissociating Verbal and Non Verbal Conceptual Processing in the Human Brain." *Journal of Cognitive Neuroscience* 18 (2006): 1018-28.

Thompson, R. E. "Neural Mechanisms of Classical Conditioning in Mammals." *Philosophical Transactions of the Royal Society of London* 329 (1990): 161-70.

Thompson, T. "Paul E. Meehl and B. F. Skinner: Autitaxia, Autitypy, and Autism." *Behavior and Philosophy* 33 (2005): 101-31.

— — —. *Making Sense of Autism*. Baltimore: Paul H. Brookes Publishing Co., 2007.

Thorndike, E. L. *Animal Intelligence*. New York: Macmillan, 1911.

Thornton, K. "The Anatomy of the Lie: A Qeeg Investigation into Lie Detection." *Journal of Offender Rehabilitation* 22 (1995): 179-210.

Tootell, R. B., M. S. Silverman, E. Switkes, and R. L. deValois. "Deoxyglucose Analysis of Retinotopic Organization in Primate Striate Cortex." *Science* 218 (1982): 902-04.

Trovillo, P. V. "A History of Lie Detection." *Journal of Criminal Law and Criminology* 29 (1939a): 848-81.

— — —. "A History of Lie Detection (Continued from the Previous Issue)." *Journal of Criminal Law and Criminology* 30 (1939b): 104-19.

Tsang, P. S., and M. A. Vidulich. *Principles and Practice of Aviation Psychology*. Mahwh NJ: Erlbaum, 2003.

Tulving, E. "Episodic and Semantic Memory." In *Organization of Memory*, edited by E. Tulving and W. Donaldson, 381-403. New York: Academic Press, 1072.

Turing, A. "Computing Machinery and Intelligence." *Mind* 59 (1950): 433-60.

Turkeltaub, P. E., G. F. Eden, K. M. Jones, and T. A. Zeffiro. "Meta-Analysis of the Functional Neuroanatomy of Single Word Reading; Methodology and Validation." *Neuroimage* 16 (2002): 765-80.

Turkeltaub, P. E., G. F. Eden, K. M. Jones, and T. A. Zeffiro. "Meta-Analysis of the Functional Neuroanatomy of Single-Word Reading: Method and Validation." *Neuroimage* 16 (2002): 765-80.

Turner, E. H., A.M. Matthews, E. Linardatos, R. A. Tell, and R. Rosenthal. "Selective Publication of Antidepressant Trials and Its Influence on Apparent Efficacy." *The New England Journal of Medicine* 358 (2008): 252-60.

Uttal, W. R. *The Psychobiology of Mind*. Hillsdale NJ: Erlbaum, 1978.

— — —. *The New Phrenology: Limitations on the Localization of Cognitive Processes in the Brain*. Cambridge MA: MIT Press, 2001.

— — —. *Dualism: The Original Sin of Cognitivism.* Mahwah NJ: Erlbaum, 2004.

— — —. *Neural Theories of Mind: Why the Mind-Brain Problem May Never Be Solved.* Mahwah, NJ: Erlbaum, 2005.

— — —. *Human Factors in the Courtroom: Mythology Versus Science.* Tucson: Lawyers and Judges Publishing, 2006.

— — —. *The Immeasurable Mind: The Real Science of Psychology.* Amherst NY: Prometheus Books, 2007.

— — —. *Time and Space in Physics and Psychology.* Cornwall-on-Hudson NY: Sloan Publishing, 2008.

Valenstine, E. S. *Great and Desperate Cures: The Rise and Decline of Psychosurgery and Other Radical Treatments for Mental Illness.* New York: Basic Books, 1986.

— — —. *Blaming the Brain: The Truth About Drugs and Mental Health.* New York: The Free Press, 1998.

Van Norman, G. A. "A Matter of Life and Death: What Every Anesthesiologist Should Know About the Medical, Legal, and Ethical Aspects of Declaring Brain Death." *Anesthesiology* 91 (1999): 275-87.

Van Orden, G. C., B. F. Pennington, and G. O. Stone. " What Do Double Dissociations Prove? Modularity Yields a Degenerating Research Program." *Cognitive Science* 25 (2001): 111-72.

Veatch, R. M. "The Whole-Brain-Oriented Concept of Death: An Outmoded Philosophical Formulation." *Journal of Thanatology* 3 (1975): 13-30.

Vittelo, B., and D. M. Stoff. "Subtypes of Aggression and Their Relevance to Child Psychiatry." *Journal of the American Academy of Child and Adolescent Psychiatry* 36 (1997): 307-15.

Vogt, B. A., D. M. Finch, and C.R. Olson. "Functional Heterogeneity in Cingulate Cortex: The Anterior Executive and the Posterior Evaluative Regions." *Cerebral Cortex* 2 (1992): 435-43.

Wagner, H. N. "A Brief History of Positron Emission Tomography (Pet)." *Seminars in Nuclear Medicine* 28 (1998): 213-20.

Wegner, D. M., D. J. Schneider, S. R. Carter III, and T. L. White. "Paradoxical Effects of Thought Suppression." *Journal of Personality and Social Psychology* 53 (1987): 5-13.

Weizenbaum, J. "Eliza - a Computer Program for the Study of Natural Language Communication between Man and Machine." *Communications of the Association for Computing Machinery* 9 (1966): 36-45.

Wernicke, C. *Der Apasische Symptomencomplex.* Breslau: Cohn and Weigert., 1874.

Wertheimer, P., M. Jouvet, and J. Descites. "Appropos Due Diagnostic De La Mort Du Systeme Dans Les Coma Avec Arret Repiratoire Traites Par Respiration Artficelle." *Press Med* 67 (1959): 87-88.

Wickens, C. D., S. E. Gordon, and Y. Liu. *An Introduction to Human Factors Engineering.* New York: Longman, 1998.

Wisdom, J. *Other Minds.* Oxford: Oxford University Press, 1956.

Wise, R. J. S. "Language Systems in Normal and Aphasic Human Subjects: Functional Imaging Studies and Inferences from Animal Studies." *British Medical Bulletin* 65 (2003): 95-119.

Wittgenstein, L. *Philosophical Investigations.* Translated by G. E. M. Anscombe. New York: Macmillan, 1953.

Younger, S. J., R. M. Arnold, and R. Schapiro, eds. *The Definition of Death Contemporary Controversies.* Baltimore: Johns Hopkins University Press, 1999.

Yule, G. U. "Why Do We Sometimes Get Nonsense-Correlations between Time Series? A Study in Sampling and the Nature of Time Series." *Journal of the Royal Statistical Society* 89 (1926): 1-64.

Zadikoff, C., and A. E. Lang. "Apraxia in Movement Disorders: A Review." *Brain* 128 (2005): 1480-97.

About the Author

William R. Uttal is Professor Emeritus of Psychology at the University of Michigan and Professor Emeritus of Engineering at Arizona State University. Uttal has been concerned with the way in which cognitive neuroscience has been applied to various fields for the last couple of decades. His critical analysis of the applications of this new field in the age-old venue of the courtroom was stimulated by his role as an expert witness. He is also the author of *Human Factors in the Courtroom* and 25 other books on various topics in philosophy, psychology, and engineering. Uttal has worked at the IBM Watson Research Center, The University of Michigan, The Naval Ocean System Center, and Arizona State University in addition to a number of visiting appointments at U.S. and Foreign Universities. He is married and has three daughters all of whom are professional scientists.

Index

A

Acute Stress Disorder (ASD), 238
adaptability, 21
aggression, 121-122, 126, 141-146, 148-170, 178-179, 183, 251-252
agnosia, 175-176, 178, 186-189, 191-197, 201, 204, 207
altruism, 176, 223
amnesia, 175, 186-189, 191, 198-204, 207
amygdala, 85, 92, 148, 153-154, 164, 166, 168, 203
analogy, 2, 4-5, 22, 113, 125
anterograde amnesia, 200
anti-social personality disorders, 144-145
aphasia, 186, 188-192, 196-198, 240
apnea, 217, 219, 221
apraxia, 188-189, 191, 193, 204-207
Aristotelian trichotomy, 142
Attention Deficit Hyperactivity Disorder (ADHD), 132, 178, 185, 233-236, 252
auditory agnosia, 186, 194-196
autism, 154, 178, 185, 232-233, 239, 252
autonomic responses, 68, 70-71, 73-75, 105-106, 109
averaged data, 103, 111

B

behavioral responsibility, 254
behaviorism, 13, 15
Bender Visual Motor Gestalt Test, 134
Benzedrine, 234
bipolar, 227-230
Blood Oxygen Level Dependence (BOLD), 47
brain death, 175, 178, 211, 215, 217-221
Brain Electrical Activity Mapping (BEAM), 122, 171
brain enhancement, 178, 250
brain field theories, 34-35

281

brain fingerprinting, 74, 123, 171, 179
brain region theories, 34, 38
brain responsibility, 254
brain stem, 29, 148, 165, 206, 217-221
Brawner rule, 226
Broca's aphasia, 33, 131-132, 186, 189-190, 192-193, 195-198, 206, 240
Brodmann System, 79-81, 100

C

case studies, 121, 131-133, 169, 191
causation, 160, 185
cerebral blood flow, 73, 221
cerebrum, 29, 148-149, 153, 157, 160, 217-218, 221
Christianity, 9-10
cingulate cortex, 91-92, 162-163, 203
Class B observation, 17
cognitivism, 13
coma, 175, 178, 208-209, 211-216, 218-220, 239, 242
Computer Aided Tomography (CAT), 40, 123
confabulation, 199
Confessions (Augustine), 9-10
consciousness, 2, 4, 6, 8, 10, 12, 14, 29, 65, 75, 175-176, 178, 208-211, 214, 216,
    218, 222, 242, 244, 248
construct validity, 140
content validity, 139
Control Question Test (CQT), 72
cooperativeness, 104, 111-112
cosmological principle, 18
countermeasures, 103, 109, 114
culpability, 175, 179-180
curare, 210-211

D

Daubert rule, 64, 71, 109, 116, 124, 175, 241, 248
De Anima (Aristotle), 9, 14
death, 6, 8-10, 14, 28, 66, 118, 175, 178, 211, 215-222
deception, 5, 16, 33, 51, 60, 63-68, 70-75, 77-79, 81-83, 85, 87, 93, 95, 97, 100,
    102-105, 107-109, 111, 113-115, 117-118, 134, 251
declarative memory, 201, 203
depression, 229-230, 238
depth electrodes, 133
description, 1, 20, 23, 31, 196, 223

Diagnostic and Statistical Manual of Mental Disorder (DSM-IV), 129, 224, 234-236
Diffusion Tensor Imaging (DTI), 47
digital computer, 13, 37
Directed Lying Test (DLT), 72, 81-82
discriminant validity, 140
distributed activity, 53, 97
Distributed Neural Systems Theory (DNST), 60
doll's eye, 217
dopamine, 164, 229
double blind, 104, 113, 231
double dissociation, 50
Du Humani Corporis Fabrica (Vesalius), 30
dualism, 6, 8-12, 14-15, 248
Durham rule, 226

E
ecological validity, 139
Egyptian writing, 8
electroencephalogram (EEG), 35, 40, 51, 73-74, 105-106, 122, 151, 171, 179, 213, 217-218, 221, 250
emotion, 19, 60, 102, 105, 107-108, 141, 153-155, 164, 214
endocrine system, 148
engram, 202
episodic memory, 201
epistemology, 24
equipotentiality, 32
Essay Concerning Human Understanding (Locke), 12
ethical issues, 77, 110-111, 115, 122, 124, 165, 168-169, 176-178, 180-181, 208, 215-216, 223, 242, 247, 253-255
Event Related Potential (ERP), 73-74, 122, 171, 179
exculpatory defense, 122
explanatory gap, 184

F
face validity, 49, 51, 105, 108, 140, 181, 249
false positives, 103, 109-110
forensic neuropsychology, 124, 134, 141, 146, 150, 169
free-will, 10, 176, 181, 184, 254
frontal cortex, 158, 161, 163
Frye rule, 71, 77, 124, 248
Fusiform Face Area (FFA), 191-192, 194

G

Glasgow Coma Scale (GCS), 212-213
glucose, 42, 106
Guilty Knowledge Test (GKT), 71-72, 82, 89, 101, 107, 171

H

Halstead-Reitan Neuropsychological Battery, 134
Hammurabi, 66-67, 118
harmonic theory, 51
Hebrews, 9, 67
hierarchical order, 39
hippocampus, 93, 148, 154, 163, 166, 202-203
holists, 20, 32, 184, 223
homologies, 22
homunculus, 33
human aggression, 121, 144, 165
humoral substance, 29
hydraulic theories, 30-31
hypothalamus, 148-150, 153-157, 163-164

I

ideational apraxia, 206
ideokinetic apraxia, 205
illusion of inferential proximity, 49
inaccessibility, 1, 16, 18-19, 138, 170, 208
incremental validity, 140
insanity, 123, 224-226, 248, 251
intelligence, 6, 24, 141, 223
introspection, 9, 13, 15, 17-18, 231
irreducibility, 1, 19

K

Korsakoff syndrome, 200

L

Larmor equation, 45-46
lie detection, 63-72, 74-78, 84-85, 88, 93, 96, 99, 102-103, 105, 107-109, 111, 114-117, 177-178, 251
limbic system, 121, 148, 152-155, 158, 161-164, 169
limb-kinetic apraxia, 205-206
linguistic confusions, 175, 184
localized brain regions, 126

locked-in, 211, 213-215, 218
lost wax techniques, 30

M
magnetic field, 45-47
magnetic moment, 45
magnetic resonance, 27, 38, 41, 44, 215
materialism, 11
mathematics, 12, 21-22, 24, 181-182, 207
maximum activation peaks, 95-96
Mayo Clinic, 133
McNaughton rule, 226-227
memory, 10, 17, 56-58, 64-65, 82, 89, 101, 107, 134, 141, 153-154, 188-189, 199-204, 210-211, 233
mental illness, 147, 154, 175-176, 178, 180, 223-232, 248, 252
mental modules, 15, 66
mental states, 3, 5-6, 16-17, 19, 24, 32, 47, 49-52, 64-65, 70-72, 102, 105, 108, 113, 146, 224-225, 231, 239, 241
mentalism, 13, 15
meta-studies, 28, 33, 39, 55-56, 58
microelectrodes, 36-37, 40
midbrain, 148, 154, 156-157
midbrain periaqueductal gray matter, 156-157
Minimal Brain Dysfunction (MBD), 125-126, 185, 190
minimally conscious state, 213-214
modularity, 1, 3, 19, 49, 93, 105, 130, 140
modules, 3, 14-15, 19-20, 28, 31, 50, 66, 93, 116, 125, 130, 143, 197-198, 202, 249, 252
monism, 248
multifactorial, 20, 160, 175, 182-183
mutual annihilation, 43
Myer-Briggs Type Indicator, 137

N
National Academy of Sciences (NAS), 72, 76, 114-115, 237
natural theology, 10
necessity, 11, 49, 131, 149, 156, 209
neophrenological, 39
neural network theories, 34, 37-40
neurological determinism, 181
neurologist, 121, 124-126, 129-130, 133, 205, 213, 215, 217, 221
neuropsychology, 33, 39, 108, 121, 124-142, 146, 150, 165, 169-171, 201-202, 208, 230

nominalism, 11
nonlinear system, 3
nystagmus, 217

O
Ockham's razor, 6, 11
Office of Technology Assessment (OTA), 75-76
Old Testament, 66-67, 118
one to many, 18, 185
ontology, 24
oxygen, 42-43, 47-48, 51-52, 106, 209, 219

P
Papez circuit, 121, 152, 163-164, 169
parahippocampal cortex, 163
Parkinson's disease, 204
peak activation, 54-55
personality disorder, 167, 236
Phaedo (Plato), 9
Phineas Gage, 147, 150, 158
pineal gland, 30-31
pneuma, 29
polygraph, 63, 68, 70-79, 103, 105-106, 109, 112, 114-115, 117, 181, 242, 251
pontifical neurons, 36
Positron Emission Tomography (PET), 27, 38, 41-42, 44, 122-123
Post Traumatic Stress Disorder (PTSD), 176, 178, 237-239
precession, 45-46
priming, 195, 201, 203
procedural memory, 201
projective tests, 137
protons, 42, 45-46
pseudoneurologizing, 185
pseudo-PTSD, 238
pseudoscience, 61, 77-78, 114, 117, 250-251
psychiatrist, 121, 126, 128-129, 147, 169, 230-231, 236
psychologist's fallacy, 4-5
psychoneural equivalent, 22, 105
psychotherapy, 127, 228, 238-239

Q
QEEG (or quantitative EEG), 123

R

radio frequency, 45-47
radioisotopes, 40
reasonable doubt, 182, 240
recall, 10, 188, 199-201
recognition, 49, 87-89, 186, 188, 191, 194-195, 201, 204
reconstruction, 41, 202
recovery of function, 143, 191, 193, 198
redundancy, 6
reliability, 27, 55, 58, 79, 97, 101-103, 114-115, 117, 121, 134, 136-139, 141
Renaissance, 10-11, 14, 29-30, 141
respirator, 216-217
response variability, 21
retrograde amnesia, 200
reverse inference, 208
rice chewing, 68
right from wrong, 183, 226
Ritalin, 234, 236
Roman Empire, 29
Rorschach Ink Blot Test, 137

S

schizophrenia, 167, 227-229, 236
self-awareness, 3, 7, 73, 218
sensus communis, 30-31, 33
septal nuclei, 154, 163
serotonin, 148, 165, 229
Signal Detection Theory (SDT), 110
simple coma scale, 212
single neuron theories, 34-35, 37
single word reading, 56-57
squid, 35
statistical anomalies, 103, 111
statistics, 21-22, 101, 111, 138, 181
stochastic nature of mind, 1, 20
stochastic thinking, 182
Stroop effect, 58-59
subtraction, 50, 52-53, 81, 104, 112-113
sufficiency, 39, 149, 156
Sumerian writing, 8
Summa Theologiae (Aquinas), 10
supernatural, 4, 8-9, 11-12, 14
synaptic transmitter, 27, 229

T

test-retest, 51, 137
thalamus, 78, 90, 93, 98, 100, 149, 157-158, 163, 167-168, 195, 206
Thematic Apperception Test, 137
theory of mind, 5, 13, 15
thimerosal, 239
torture, 69
transplants, 216, 222
triune brain, 148
Turing test, 24

U

underdetermination, 135, 177
unipolar, 229
unreasonable search, 115

V

vegetative state, 176, 213-214, 216, 222
Venn type diagram, 54
ventricles, 11, 29-30, 156
violence, 121-122, 141, 144-146, 151-155, 158-162, 164, 167-170, 178, 183, 251
Vioxx, 231
visual agnosia, 191, 194
voxel, 94, 97, 101

W

Wernicke's aphasia, 196
whole brain, 186, 218-219, 221-222
working memory, 56, 58

X

x-rays, 40-41, 44